Switching Theory

Volume I:
Combinational Circuits

Switching Theory.

Volume I:

Combinational Circuits

Raymond E. Miller

IBM Thomas J. Watson Research Center
Yorktown Heights, New York

John Wiley & Sons, Inc., New York · London · Sydney

Preface

Switching theory includes mathematical models and techniques for handling problems associated with networks of elements which are capable of exhibiting only a finite number of signal values. Examples of such "digital circuits" are digital computers, communication switching systems, and digital control systems. In *Switching Theory*, which appears in two volumes, my purpose is to present a unified treatment of the subject, with emphasis on those aspects related to the synthesis and analysis of switching circuits. Although I have made no attempt to describe every technique which has been developed for switching circuit design, each of the selected subjects is treated in detail. In addition, the approach is aimed at both describing certain techniques not covered in previous books and giving a broad introduction to the various disciplines in switching theory. The separation of material into two volumes provides, I believe, greater flexibility in their use. The underlying theory, rather than detailed cookbook procedures for designing special circuits, is stressed. These concepts and mathematical techniques are fundamental to the methods of analysis and design of switching circuits; they also form the basis for future developments in switching theory itself. Much of the material is of very recent origin and, consequently, has not appeared previously in a book. This is to be expected, since the subject is rapidly expanding, and very often current texts are badly outdated.

I have written both volumes primarily for advanced undergraduate and graduate study in electrical engineering, computer sciences, and related courses, although each volume can also serve as a reference book. To meet this double purpose, I have included a considerable number of exercises, extensive references to original papers and other works, and a short discussion of references at the end of each chapter. This material should prove valuable to those students and people interested in doing further research on particular topics. Each volume contains sufficient material for a one-semester course, and combined can be used for a one-year course.

A word about the selection of subject matter is appropriate. To provide some background for Volume I, an introductory description of digital computers and some other digital systems is given in Chapter 1. Chapter 2 is concerned with an extensive development of Boolean algebra, its basic connections with switching circuits of various types, and its relationship to other mathematical structures. Special types of functions and functional forms of importance to switching theory are also discussed. Chapter 3 treats the most common type of circuit minimization problem—that of two-level circuits. For the first time in a book the formulation is presented in terms of the cubical representation, rather than in the more commonly used chart or functional forms. Both geometric visualization and algebraic formalism of the cubical representation are given. Because connections with functional forms and chart forms are discussed and these techniques are readily available in many references, I feel that the use of cubical representation will give the reader a broader understanding of this classical problem of switching theory. Chapter 4 discusses two methods for treating multiple output circuits as well as the theory of functional decomposition and its application to gate-type circuit design, an important concept which has not been treated in previous texts. Some standard approaches to bilateral switching (relay-type) networks and an application to cryogenic circuits appear in Chapter 5.

Volume II consists of Chapters 6 through 10. Chapter 6 introduces various models for sequential circuits and machines and discusses the relationship between them. To my knowledge one of these models, the formal language of regular expressions, has never been discussed in a text on switching circuit theory. State minimization of sequential machines is treated for general incompletely specified machines, and state minimization for completely specified machines is developed as a special case in Chapter 7. Chapter 8 discusses various approaches to state assignment for synchronous sequential machines, including the theory of partitions for reduced dependence. In Chapter 9 and 10 an extensive theoretical treatment of asynchronous circuits and speed independent circuits is given.

I am indebted to many people for their direct and indirect aid in making it possible to write this book. The references and reference notations at the end of each chapter indicate my indebtedness to the many researchers in the field who are cited in the literature. I particularly want to thank Professor G. D. McCann for inviting me to the California Institute of Technology, during 1962 and 1963, for it was during this year of teaching a course on switching theory that the first draft of this book was written and many improvements were suggested by the students. Initial drafts of several chapters were also written for a course at the University of Illinois during the fall semester of 1960; and I am grateful to Professors D. E. Muller and A. H. Taub for inviting me to visit the Digital Computer Laboratory and teach this course. In connection with this teaching I wish to acknowledge the assistance of IBM Corporation, and thank Dr. H. H. Goldstine and Dr. C. C. Elgot for enabling me to accept these invitations and providing continued encouragement and support. Finally, I thank Mrs. M. A. Kenny for her patient and expert typing of the final manuscript, the editors of John Wiley and Sons for their immeasurable help in all phases of the preparation, and my wife Marilyn for her patience and continued encouragement.

December 1964   R. E. MILLER

Contents

CHAPTER 3   COMBINATIONAL SWITCHING CIRCUITS:
            NORMAL FORM CIRCUIT DESIGN   **134**

CHAPTER 4   MULTIPLE OUTPUT AND MULTILEVEL
            COMBINATIONAL CIRCUITS   **197**

Contents for Volume Two

1

Digital Systems

1.1 INTRODUCTION

In the study of switching theory we consider various models and techniques for handling problems associated with networks, or systems, of elements which can be assumed to exhibit only discrete, finitely valued signals. Such systems are called *digital systems*, many varieties of which are known: digital computers, communication switching systems, and digital control systems, to name a few. Many of the interesting topics in switching theory are concerned with analysis, synthesis, interconnection, and related problems of digital systems, or relatively small portions of digital systems. Thus the theory includes appropriate models and analytical techniques for attacking these problems.

Before developing some of these models and techniques of switching theory, however, we shall describe briefly in this chapter several types of digital systems. As we shall see later, a basic understanding of digital systems will enable us to obtain a deeper insight into some of the theoretical problems considered in switching theory and will also provide a source for many examples and exercises.

Early contributions to switching theory arose from engineering problems in the analysis and design of relay switching networks such as telephone switching systems. One of the greatest influences on recent work in switching theory has been the rapid development of electronic digital computers. Thus much of this chapter is devoted to a basic description of digital computer organization and the types of circuit elements used in such machines.

The theory of automata, which is quite closely related to switching theory, is also concerned with digital systems. In automata theory we are primarily interested in describing and coming to a fuller understanding of the terminal behavior and capability of digital systems. Automata theory has stemmed from some rather pure mathematical questions of computability, as illustrated by the work of Turing [23]*. However, it is

* The numbers enclosed in square brackets refer to references which appear at the end of each chapter.

natural to expect that as a deeper understanding of such systems is gained through automata theory, resultant advances in treating the switching theory problems of analysis and synthesis may also become apparent. Similarly, switching theory results may bring about further understanding in the behavior of digital systems, and thus affect automata theory. Because of this close relation between automata and switching theory, some references to, and techniques of, automata theory are discussed in this book.

1.2 BASIC FUNCTIONAL UNITS OF A COMPUTER

Electronic digital computers perform arithmetic operations such as addition, subtraction, multiplication, and division on numbers at speeds of thousands of operations per second. Some of the very fast computers being built will attain several millions of operations per second. Obviously, it is not practical to use a human operator to control which operation is to be performed next and to supply the numbers to the computer for each arithmetic operation, since the operator would require several seconds to perform these tasks. Rather, a control system is used which sequences the operations in the computer; and fast input and output devices and internal storage are used to supply the computer with the numbers for the calculation.

The basic operations required in a computer can be conveniently broken down into four different functional units:

1. A *memory unit* used to store the information for calculating and for the control of the machine.

2. An *input-output unit* used to read information into the machine and also to remove results from the machine.

3. An *arithmetic unit* to perform the calculations.

4. A *control unit* to sequence the operations in a manner which is flexible enough to allow the sequences to be dependent on some of the previous results in the calculation.

In many machines each of these functional units can be easily distinguished from the other units since the components are different for each different function. It is common practice to show a block diagram of these units, such as Figure 1.2.1, which indicates the basic interconnection of these units. The solid arrows indicate the possible lines of flow for information being processed in the computer, and the dotted arrows indicate the control signals which control the computer operation.

The block diagram is not intended to mislead us into assuming that the computer must have a structure which is readily partitioned into these four functional units, such that each unit performs exclusively its own function. In fact, some arithmetic may be done in any of the other three units, some of the control functions may be decentralized to units other than the control unit, and some storage may be done in the control, arithmetic unit, and input-output units. This decentralization has been found to be advantageous in many computers, and newer computer designs are tending toward much further decentralization, as well as the use of additional functional units and interconnections, to create a more efficient use of each unit and to increase the speed of the computer.

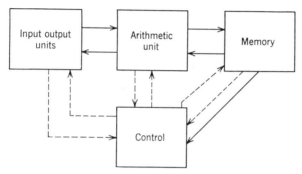

Figure 1.2.1   Block diagram for a digital computer.

Comparing the use of each functional unit of a computer with the typical operation of a desk calculator may provide further insight into their functions. The desk calculator itself, when supplied with numbers, is capable of performing certain basic arithmetic operations such as addition, subtraction, multiplication, and division. Thus the desk calculator corresponds to the arithmetic unit of the computer. The operator supplies numbers to the desk calculator by punching numerical data into the keys of the calculator. This corresponds to the input of data which is one function of the input-output unit of the computer. The output function of the input-output unit is also carried out by the operator of the desk calculator when he reads the desired resultant numbers off the indicator dials of the calculator and records these results on a sheet of paper. Some results obtained during a calculation are only of an intermediate or temporary nature, not being the desired resultants of the calculation but simply being required at some later point in the calculation. The desk calculator operator would normally write such intermediate results on a sheet of paper for further reference. In the computer these intermediate results are recorded in the memory unit. Finally, the desk calculator operator determines the arithmetic operation to be performed by depressing an appropriate key on the desk calculator; this task is performed by the control unit of the computer. The high-speed operation of the computer is thus seen to be attained not only by performing the arithmetic operations at high speeds but also by a balanced speed for performing the control, memory, and input-output functions.

1.3 REPRESENTATION OF NUMBERS

For a computer to perform the various arithmetic operations it is necessary to have some representation for numbers in the machine. From our earliest training we have become familiar with the decimal number system, the symbols used to represent these numbers, and arithmetic operations on these numbers. One of the important facets of the decimal number system is the *positional notation* which is used; for example, 738 is interpreted as $7 \times 10^2 + 3 \times 10^1 + 8 \times 10^0$*. More generally, if N_{10} is a positive decimal integer written as

$$N_{10} = n_p n_{p-1} \cdots n_1 n_0,$$

where
$$0 \le n_i \le 9,$$

we interpret N_{10} as

$$N_{10} = n_p \cdot 10^p + n_{p-1} \cdot 10^{p-1} + \cdots + n_1 \cdot 10^1 + n_0 \cdot 10^0.$$

This positional notation is readily extended to decimal fractions. For example, 0.625 is easily seen to be

$$0.625 = 6 \times 10^{-1} + 2 \times 10^{-2} + 5 \times 10^{-3},$$

and, more generally, a fraction $F_{10} = 0.n_{-1} n_{-2} \cdots n_{-f}$,

where
$$0 \le n_{-i} \le 9,$$

is a positional notation for

$$F_{10} = n_{-1} \cdot 10^{-1} + n_{-2} \cdot 10^{-2} + \cdots + n_{-f} \cdot 10^{-f}.$$

In the decimal number system 10 is called the *base* or *radix* of the number system, that is, 10 different symbols or digits can occur in any given position of a number in the decimal system. Note that N_{10} and F_{10}

---

* Although we take this positional notation for granted, it is interesting to read accounts of the many different methods of representing large numbers which man has devised over the ages [21].

use the subscript 10 to denote the radix of the number. Since we have ten fingers, it is natural that a number system using a base 10 evolved which is convenient for us to use. This should not imply, however, that the decimal number system is necessarily the most convenient system for machine use, and we should consider other possible representations.

Generalizing from the decimal number system, we let r be a finite positive integer representing the radix of the number systems. Then an integer in the r-base system $N_r = n_p n_{p-1} \cdots n_1 n_0$ would have $0 \leq n_i \leq r - 1$ and would be interpreted as

$$N_r = n_p \cdot r^p + n_{p-1} \cdot r^{p-1} + \cdots + n_1 \cdot r^1 + n_0 \cdot r^0.$$

Similarly, r-base fractions would be represented as

$$F_r = 0.n_{-1} n_{-2} \cdots n_{-f},$$

where

$$0 \leq n_{-i} \leq r - 1$$

and

$$F_r = n_{-1} r^{-1} + n_{-2} r^{-2} + \cdots + n_{-f} r^{-f}.$$

Thus a mixed number, an integer plus a fraction, can be interpreted as

$$N_r + F_r = \sum_{i=-f}^{p} n_i r^i,$$

and by using the positional notation would be written as

$$N_r + F_r = n_p n_{p-1} \cdots n_1 n_0 n_{-1} n_{-2} \cdots n_{-f}.$$

An additional factor in number representation which adds considerable flexibility to the systems is using the radix to some positive or negative power to indicate the position of the decimal or radix point. For example, we can express 0.625 as 625×10^{-3} and 738,000,000 as 738×10^6. When numbers are represented in a computer if powers are not used, the representation is called a *fixed-point representation*. In some problems it is extremely helpful to use the representation, called *floating-point*, which uses the radix to powers to indicate the position of the radix point. This is easily seen, for example, when we consider multiplication of two numbers. In this case, the radix point of the resultant is placed automatically by a simple addition of the powers of the operands.

We can illustrate some of the differences between fixed- and floating-point representations by several simple examples. Suppose a computer uses a fixed-point representation where all numbers are represented as fractions. Then if two numbers, say 0.625 and 0.400, are to be multiplied, the resultant product is 0.250, which is easily represented in the fractional form of the computer. If the two numbers are added together, however, we obtain 1.025, which is no longer a fraction. Thus, if the computer can represent only fractional numbers, this sum could not be properly represented in the computer. This problem can be combated in a fixed-point computer by *scaling* all numbers so that all results remain in fractional form. For example, in this case we could have first scaled or divided each number by 10, giving 0.0625 and 0.0400, and then the addition gives the fraction 0.1025, which is a fraction and can be handled by the computer. With the scaling, of course, we must keep track of the scaling done so that the correct place for the decimal point is remembered.

If a floating-point representation is used in a computer, the scaling problem is somewhat alleviated. For example, we could represent 0.625 as 0.625×10^0 and 0.400 as 0.400×10^0, where the exponent of the 10 would also be kept as part of the number in a floating-point representation. On adding these numbers we would obtain 0.1025×10^1, and the exponent on the 10 would automatically record any necessary scaling. Also, if we have two numbers 0.5×10^2 and 0.25×10^{-3}, forming the product in floating-point is simply $(0.5 \times 0.25) \times 10^{2+(-3)} = 0.125 \times 10^{-1}$, that is, the decimal place of the product is determined by simply adding $2 + (-3)$.

Another method of representing numbers, known as the modular or residue number system, is of current interest [3, 4]. In these systems the radix is a different number for each position in a number rather than a constant r for all positions. Some interesting properties of modular number systems result from number theoretic considerations of these systems. We describe briefly some of these basic properties by an example without discussing the theoretical basis for these properties. When the radix of each position is relatively prime* to the radix of any other position, it has been shown that no carries are required from one position to the next for addition and subtraction. Rather, each position is added (subtracted) separately, modulo† the radix of that position, in addition (subtraction) to give the sum (difference). We illustrate a modular number system in Table 1.3.1, where the radix for the right column is 3 and the radix for the left column is 5.

In this system $5 \times 3 = 15$ different numbers can be represented so that 0 to 14 is the range of the number system. Adding any two numbers whose decimal sum is no greater than 14 can be accomplished in this

---

* Two positive integers m and n are called relatively prime if there exist no positive integers $k > 1, r > 1$, and $s > 1$ such that $kr = m$ and $ks = n$.
† Given two numbers a and b which are less than r,

$$a + b \text{ modulo } r = \begin{cases} a + b & \text{if } a + b < r \\ a + b - r & \text{if } a + b \geq r \end{cases}$$

modular system without carries. For example, if we wish to add $9 + 4 = 13$, we add

$$
\begin{array}{rl}
9 = & 40 \\
+4 = & +41 \\
\hline
13 = & 81 \qquad mod = 31,
\end{array}
$$

where the modulo representation of 8 is $8 - 5 = 3$ and the 1 is unchanged

Table 1.3.1 A Modular Number System

Decimal Number	Modular Number 5 3
0	0 0
1	1 1
2	2 2
3	3 0
4	4 1
5	0 2
6	1 0
7	2 1
8	3 2
9	4 0
10	0 1
11	1 2
12	2 0
13	3 1
14	4 2

by the modulo operation. Note that 31 is the modular representation for 13, as can be checked in Table 1.3.1. Similarly, adding $2 + 5$,

$$
\begin{array}{rl}
2 = & 22 \\
+5 = & 02 \\
\hline
7 = & 21
\end{array}
$$

since $4 = 1 \bmod 3$, and 21 is the modular representation for 7. For subtraction

$$
\begin{array}{rl}
9 = & 40 \\
-5 = & -02 \\
\hline
4 = & 41
\end{array}
$$

since $(0 - 2) \bmod 3 = 1$, and 41 is the modular representation for 4, as seen in the table.

When numbers are represented in circuits, it may be extremely advantageous not to require a carry from one position to the next (this being a chief advantage of the modular number system). However, this system has some disadvantages in operations of division and in comparing the magnitude of two numbers. Furthermore, if two numbers whose sum falls outside the range of the number system are added together, a wrong answer results with no immediate indication, such as a carry beyond the range of the system, to indicate the error; thus, for example, adding the decimal numbers

$$\begin{array}{r} 11 = 12 \\ +13 = 31 \\ \hline 24 \quad 40 \end{array} \quad \text{(mod)}.$$

It is a simple matter to see that 24 is outside the range of 0 to 14, but 40 is the modular representation for 9, which is wrong (and there was not even any modulo operation required on the most significant digit!).

1.4 EFFICIENCY OF THE BASE

Returning to the positional number notation where a mixed number is equal to $\sum_{i=-f}^{p} n_i r^i$, we wish to determine which base r is most efficient; that is, for a fixed number of numbers M, which base r requires a minimum amount of digital circuitry to express the M numbers? To attack this problem, an estimate is required for the amount of circuitry needed to represent different bases. We shall assume that the amount of circuitry is directly proportional to the base, which we denote by $K_1 r$, where K_1 is some proportionality constant. This assumption is quite realistic for existing types of digital circuitry. The total number of circuits denoted by N can thus be expressed as

$$N = K_1 rn,$$

where n is the number of digit positions in the number. With n digit positions the number of different numbers which we can represent is $M = r^n$. Now we wish to minimize N for fixed M by finding a suitable base r, and since n is a function of r, we determine n in terms of r as follows:

$$M = r^n.$$

Taking logarithms,

$$\ln M = \ln r^n = n \ln r = K_2,$$

where K_2 is a constant since M is a constant. This gives

$$n = \frac{K_2}{\ln r}.$$

Thus

$$N = K_1 \frac{K_2}{\ln r} r = K_3 \frac{r}{\ln r}.$$

To find the best base r we differentiate by r, giving

$$\frac{dN}{dr} = \frac{K_3 \left[(\ln r) - r \cdot \dfrac{1}{r} \right]}{(\ln r)^2}$$

$$= K_3 \frac{(\ln r) - 1}{(\text{in } r)^2}.$$

Setting the derivative equal to zero gives

$$\frac{K_3[(\ln r) - 1]}{(\ln r)^2} = 0$$

so that

$$(\ln r) - 1 = 0$$

or

$$\ln r = 1.$$

Thus the most efficient base r is $r = e = 2.71828 \cdots$. Since it is more convenient to use an integer base, we can easily calculate that the base $r = 3$ is the most efficient integer base, and $r = 2$ and $r = 4$ are equally efficient and only slightly less efficient than $r = 3$. From other electronic and tolerance considerations the base $r = 2$ is the most advantageous and the most often used base in electronic computers. The positional notation number system using base 2 is called the *binary number system*, which we now discuss further.

1.5 THE BINARY NUMBER SYSTEM

The binary number system, with base $r = 2$, uses only the digits 0 and 1, and is thus a very simple number system. Almost all electronic computers use either the binary number system directly or a binary encoding of some other number system. The reasons for using the binary number system are rather straightforward. First, some of the early computers used relay contacts and these operate in essentially a binary manner (the contact being either open or closed). We can associate readily the digit 0 of the binary system with the open contact and 1 with the closed contact. In electronic computers many tubes, transistors, diodes, resisters, or similar devices are used. Since each such component has a certain variability in its operation because of tolerances, aging, and other effects, it is desirable to use a small base r in the number representation so that we need sense only a small number of r different possible states of a circuit

Table 1.5.1 Binary Equivalents for Some Decimal Numbers

Decimal Number	Binary Number
0	0
1	1
2	10
3	11
4	100
5	101
6	110
7	111
8	1000
9	1001
10	1010
11	1011
12	1100

to determine the number being represented. The base r equals 2 allows the most possible variation in the circuit because only two possible values of the circuit need to be sensed, for example, a conducting versus a nonconducting state of a circuit. Thus many two-state circuits were designed for computers which were extremely reliable in their operation, even though the device characteristics might vary considerably as a result of aging or other effects, simply because the circuit needed to indicate only two possible states. Table 1.5.1 gives the binary forms of a few decimal numbers.

As is seen readily from the table, the number of binary positions required to represent a number grows rather rapidly. Approximately 40 binary positions are required to represent a 12-digit decimal number; that is, 2^{40} is approximately equal to 10^{12}. Since it would be very inconvenient to write such long strings of 0's and 1's, we often indicate the binary number in the octal system, for it is very simple to convert between octal and binary. For example, the binary number

$$(000\ 001\ 011\ 100\ 111)_2 = (0\ 1\ 3\ 4\ 7)_8,$$

where the subscripts indicate the radix. To convert from binary to octal we simply group the binary digits in groups of three and then replace each group of three digits with its octal equivalent. Reversing the process converts octal to binary. Unfortunately, it is not quite as simple to convert between binary and decimal representations since 10 is not a power of 2. Such conversion is necessary, however, since it would be extremely confusing if we would not be able to place data into the computer and receive results from the computer in decimal form.

To convert from a decimal integer to a binary integer we need to record only the successive remainders on successive division of the decimal number by 2. For example, given the decimal number 10, we convert this to binary as follows:

	Remainder
$2\lfloor 10$	0
$2\lfloor 5$	1
$2\lfloor 2$	0
$2\lfloor 1$	1

The first remainder is the least significant binary digit, etc., to the end of the calculation, giving the binary equivalent of 10 as 1010. This calculation can be justified by looking at the binary and decimal formulas for a number. Suppose that two equivalent representations are

$$\sum_{i=0}^{p} a_i 10^i = \sum_{j=0}^{m} b_j 2^j = b_m 2^m + \cdots + b_1 2^1 + b_0 2^0.$$

If the a_i digits are known, division by 2 yields

$$\tfrac{1}{2}\sum_{i=0}^{p} a_i 10^i = \tfrac{1}{2}\sum_{j=0}^{m} b_j 2^j = b_m 2^{m-1} + \cdots + b_1 + \frac{b_0}{2},$$

and thus b_0 is the remainder after the first division by 2. Successive divisions by 2 can easily be seen to produce the other binary digits.

Similarly, we can convert decimal fractions to binary fractions, but now since negative powers of the radix are used, we multiply rather than divide by 2, and find that the successive integral parts give the binary fraction. Thus

$$
\begin{array}{r}
0.3125 \\
2 \\
\hline
0.6250 \\
2 \\
\hline
1.2500 \\
2 \\
\hline
0.5000 \\
2 \\
\hline
1.0000
\end{array}
$$

so that $(0.3125)_{10} = (0.0101)_2$. For converting a decimal number to binary where the decimal number has both an integral and a fractional part, the conversion should be accomplished by converting each part separately and then adding them together.

Conversion from binary to decimal can be done in a similar way as that from decimal to binary, but here we would divide by 1010 (the binary equivalent of 10), using binary rather than decimal arithmetic. It should be noted that in converting from decimal to binary we used division and multiplication by 2, using decimal arithmetic, whereas in the conversion from binary to decimal, since the number is originally represented in binary form, the arithmetic (multiplication or division by 10) should be performed using binary arithmetic. Another way to convert is simply to express the number in its expanded form, thus

$$
\begin{aligned}
(101101)_2 &= 1 \cdot 2^5 + 0 \cdot 2^4 + 1 \cdot 2^3 + 1 \cdot 2^2 + 0 \cdot 2^1 + 1 \cdot 2^0 \\
&= 32 + 8 + 4 + 1 \\
&= (45)_{10}.
\end{aligned}
$$

For fractions the expanded form again can be used, thus

$$
\begin{aligned}
(0.101101)_2 &= 1 \cdot 2^{-1} + 0 \cdot 2^{-2} + 1 \cdot 2^{-3} + 1 \cdot 2^{-4} + 0 \cdot 2^{-5} + 1 \cdot 2^{-6} \\
&= \tfrac{1}{2} + \tfrac{1}{8} + \tfrac{1}{16} + \tfrac{1}{64} \\
&= 0.5 + 0.125 + 0.625 + 0.015625 \\
&= (0.703125)_{10}.
\end{aligned}
$$

We have mentioned binary arithmetic, and although it is very simple, using the same principles as decimal arithmetic, it should be described briefly. This is done best by giving the addition, subtraction, and multiplication tables.

Table 1.5.2 Binary Addition Tables for $a + b$

a \ b	0	1
0	0	1
1	1	0

Sum Digit

a \ b	0	1
0	0	0
1	0	1

Carry Digit

Table 1.5.3 Binary Subtraction Tables for $a - b$

a \ b	0	1
0	0	1
1	1	0

Difference Digit

a \ b	0	1
0	0	1
1	0	0

Borrow Digit

Table 1.5.4 Binary Multiplication Table for $a \cdot b$

a \ b	0	1
0	0	0
1	0	1

An example to illustrate binary addition is

$$
\begin{array}{ll}
0111001 = a & \\
1110101 = b & \\
\hline
1001100 & \text{Sum digits} \\
110001 & \text{Carry digits} \\
\hline
10101110 = a + b.
\end{array}
$$

Note that a final carry was produced in this example in the most significant position when adding the sum and carry digits.

Subtraction is illustrated in the following example.

$$
\begin{array}{llll}
& 1 \quad 1 \quad 1 & 0101 = a \\
\text{Borrow} \rightarrow & 1 \quad 1 \quad 1 & \\
\text{digits} & 0 \quad 1 \quad 1 & 1001 = b \\
\hline
& 1 \quad 1 & 1100 = a - b.
\end{array}
$$

The reader can check this result by either adding $(a - b) + b$ using binary addition or by conversion of the binary numbers to decimal.

Binary multiplication is illustrated in the following example.

$$
\begin{array}{r}
1\ 1\ 1\ 0\ 0\ 1 = a \\
1\ 0\ 1\ 0 = b \\
\hline
0 \\
1\ 1\ 1\ 0\ 0\ 1 \\
0 \\
1\ 1\ 1\ 0\ 0\ 1 \\
\hline
1\ 0\ 0\ 0\ 1\ 1\ 1\ 0\ 1\ 0 = a \cdot b.
\end{array}
$$

In Section 1.10 on the arithmetic unit further discussion is given on arithmetic operations, the use of complements, and absolute value representations for negative numbers.

The reader should consider how to perform binary division, using successive subtractions as is done in long division in the decimal system; for example,

$$
\begin{array}{r}
10111 \leftarrow \text{Quotient} \\
\text{Divisor} \rightarrow 1001\overline{)\ 11010001} \leftarrow \text{Dividend} \\
-1001 \\
\hline
1000 \\
-0000 \\
\hline
10000 \\
1001 \\
\hline
01110 \\
1001 \\
\hline
1011 \\
1001 \\
\hline
10 \leftarrow \text{Remainder}
\end{array}
$$

1.6   CODED NUMBER REPRESENTATIONS

In certain data processing calculations the computations performed by the computer on the input data are very simple, but the complexity of the problem is in the numerous data which are to be processed. When this occurs, it may be very inconvenient to transform the data to binary form, do the calculation, and then transform the results back to decimal form, since most of the time may be spent in the transformation processes rather than in the calculations. Thus some data processing machines use binary coded number representations for decimal digits rather than the binary number system since these binary coded representations are more readily transformed to decimal form. Table 1.6.1 shows several different coded decimal number representations.

There are also other coded number representations, and this table illustrates only some of the more common encodings. Note that at least 4 binary digits are required to encode the decimal digits, and thus 6 out of the 16 possible combinations of the 4 digits are not used in the binary coded decimal. This inefficient use of the digits means that more binary

Table 1.6.1 Binary Coded Decimal Representation

Decimal Number	8421	2421	5211	Excess 3	Two out of Five
0	0000	0000	0000	0011	00011
1	0001	0001	0001	0100	00101
2	0010	0010	0100	0101	00110
3	0011	0011	0110	0110	01001
4	0100	0100	0111	0111	01010
5	0101	1011	1000	1000	01100
6	0110	1100	1001	1001	10001
7	0111	1101	1011	1010	10010
8	1000	1110	1110	1011	10100
9	1001	1111	1111	1100	11000

digits are required to represent a large decimal number when using a binary encoded decimal representation than a binary representation. Consider, for example, the decimal number 8500. By using the 8421 encoding scheme,

$$8500 = 1000\ 0101\ 0000\ 0000,$$

which requires 16 binary digits. Using the binary representation, we obtain

$$8500 = 10000100110100,$$

which requires only 14 binary digits. In general, approximately 3.32 binary digits are required for each 4 binary digits of a coded decimal representation, which can be seen as follows. To represent a decimal digit in binary form we need 10 different possibilities. This requires x binary digits, where $2^x = 10$. Thus $x = \log_2 10$, which is approximately $x = 3.32$.

Another disadvantage in using a binary encoded decimal representation is that the arithmetic processes become more complex than in pure binary. Nevertheless, these schemes offer greater convenience in certain data processing operations simply because number representation conversions are not required. As we shall see later, certain of these encoding systems are very convenient for complement number representation, which is helpful in the subtraction process.

The two out of five representation, although using five digits rather than four, has the advantage of immediate single-error detection. When either a digit error from 0 to 1 or 1 to 0 occurs, this can immediately be noticed since either exactly three digits of the five will be a 1 or only one of the five digits will equal 1. More complex encodings, which we shall not discuss, known as error-correcting and detecting-codes, have been developed for either correcting or detecting larger numbers of errors [15].

1.7 NONNUMERIC DATA REPRESENTATION

In data processing machines we also desire to be able to record non-numeric information such as alphabetic characters, punctuation marks,

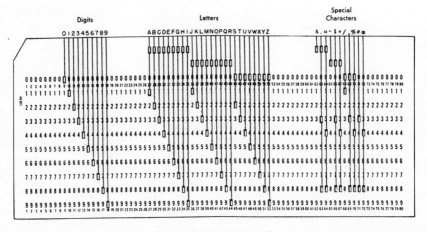

Figure 1.7.1   IBM card.

etc., so that easily readable documents may be printed by the machine. Various methods of binary encodings for these symbols, as well as digits, have been developed. One is the punched holes in the IBM card as shown in Figure 1.7.1. On this card there are 80 columns, where each column has 12 rows. Single punches in rows 0 through 9 are used to designate the decimal digits, certain combinations of two punches per column are used for letters, and other combinations of punches are used for special characters, as illustrated in Figure 1.7.1.

Table 1.7.1 International Teletype Code

Letter	Figures	Binary Coded Character	Punched Tape
E	3	00001	• o
Line Feed	Line Feed	00010	• o
A	=	00011	• o o
Space	Space	00100	• o
S	1	00101	• o o
I	8	00110	• o o
U	7	00111	• o o o
Carriage Return	Carriage Return	01000	o •
D	$	01001	o • o
R	4	01010	o • o
J	Bell	01011	o • o o
N	'	01100	o • o
F	!	01101	o • o o
C	:	01110	o • o o
K	(	01111	o • o o o
T	5	10000	o •
Z	"	10001	o • o
L	)	10010	o • o
W	2	10011	o • o o
H	£	10100	o o
Y	6	10101	o • o o
P	0	10110	o • o o
Q	1	10111	o • o o o
O	9	11000	o o •
B	?	11001	o o • o
G	&	11010	o o • o
Figures	Figures	11011	o o • o o
M	.	11100	o o • o
X	/	11101	o o • o o
V	;	11110	o o • o o
Letters	Letters	11111	o o • o o o

Another code for nonnumeric information is the international teletype code shown in Table 1.7.1. The binary characters are sent over teletype lines as timed electrical pulses and indicated by punched holes in paper tape.

In a computer it is common practice to interpret a binary word as nonnumeric information as well as a number. The interpretation of the computer instructions is probably the most familiar example of such nonnumeric interpretation. This will be discussed further in Section 1.11 on control units.

1.8 MEMORY UNIT

In the following sections we describe some of the methods used for implementing the various functional units of a digital computer discussed in Section 1.2. The memory unit stores most of the information in the computer, the data information for the calculation, and the set of instructions to be performed (called the *program*). The memory unit is usually organized in "words"; each word can store either a number (say by n positions of binary storage to store the n binary digits of a positional notation of a number) or an instruction for the computer which has been encoded in the form of a number. Usually, each word position in the memory is given an "address" designating its position. Along with the components which store the words, we have circuits which can

1. "Write" a word into a memory position whose address is designated.
2. "Read" a word from any designated address.

Some memories are arranged in a serial fashion such that the bits* of the word are obtained from the memory as a train of timed pulses. Other memories are parallel, that is, all the bits of a word are obtained simultaneously on a set of wires. Thus we can classify memories as either *serial* or *parallel*. Another common classification of memories is *random access* or *circulating-type* memories. Random access means that any word can be obtained from the memory as quickly as any other word, whereas in a circulating memory a given word is available at periodic intervals of time, where the period corresponds to the time for a signal to pass around the circulation path.

Several commonly used types of memory units are based on the principle of magnetics, where a bit is stored by magnetizing a piece of magnetic material in one direction or the other and some type of sensing mechanism is used to determine the direction of magnetization. Briefly, this principle of magnetization uses material which displays a relatively rectangular hysteresis loop as shown in Figure 1.8.1.

In this diagram if a set to 1 current is applied to the material, its magnetization will reach point A, and when the current is removed, the remaining magnetization is indicated by point 1. If a set to 0 current is

* Bits is a common contraction of the words binary digits.

applied, point *B* is attained; with the removal of the current, the residual magnetization of the material is indicated by point 0. Thus with no current applied, the magnetization can reside either at point 1 or point 0. These two different "directions of magnetization" are used to denote a binary digit.

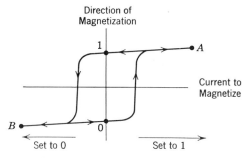

Figure 1.8.1   Square hysteresis loop.

One type of memory unit using magnetic storage is a magnetic drum. Here the magnetic material is placed on the surface of a cylinder (that is, the drum), and the cylinder is rotated by an electric motor or similar device. Reading and writing "heads" are placed around the drum. These heads are slotted metal loops with coils, so that a current in the coil for writing will cause magnetization of the drum's magnetic material

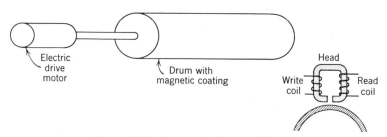

Figure 1.8.2   A magnetic drum and heads.

and a change in the direction of magnetization will be detectable in the reading coil of a head. In some drums, reading and writing functions are both done with a single head having multiple coil windings, whereas others use separate heads for each function. A diagram of a magnetic drum is shown in Figure 1.8.2.

Magnetic drums are used extensively to provide large amounts of relatively inexpensive storage capacity to modern digital computers. Other similar arrangements are also used, such as disks rather than drums, and magnetic tape units for both auxiliary storage and input and output uses. All these devices depend on the same principle of relative motion between the reading and writing windings and the magnetic material, and thus are circulating, rather than random access, type memories.

The magnetic core memory uses a small toroid (the core) of magnetic material having a nearly rectangular hysteresis loop to store a bit of information by having either the core magnetized in one direction or the other. Arrays of these cores are made to store many words. Wires are placed through these cores so that they can be magnetized as desired for

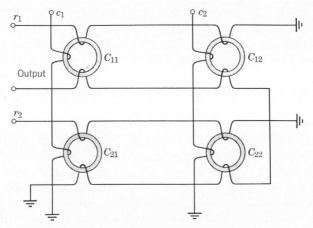

Figure 1.8.3   An array of four magnetic cores.

writing into the memory and the magnetization can be sensed for reading out of the memory. Consider the simple array of four cores depicted in Figure 1.8.3.

Now if a current of I_1 enters r_1 and a current of I_1 enters c_1, core C_{11} has a current of $2I_1$ affecting it and all others have a current of at most I_1. If the rectangular hysteresis loop is such that $2I_1$ causes a change in magnetization and I_1 does not, the core C_{11} would be set and the other cores would not. By similar control on the c_1, c_2, r_1, and r_2 wires, any one of the four cores can be set, and by reversing the currents in c_1, c_2, r_1, and r_2, the cores can be set in the other direction. This is called a *coincident current* arrangement for the core memory. Now if we want to "read" a core, say C_{11}, r_1 and c_1 can each be given a current of I_1. If this changes the magnetization in C_{11}, a large pulse appears on the output line. No large pulse appears if C_{11} is not changed in magnetization. Thus C_{11} is read, and it must then be reset if the reading changed its magnetization. This simple array of four cores shows how coincident currents can be used to write into the memory and to read out of the memory. Large arrays based on this principle are the most common type of high-speed random access memory for modern computers. The cycle time for reading or writing into a coincident core magnetic memory is approximately 2 to 10 μsec.

As seen in the description of Figure 1.8.3, the information is lost when reading a core. This is called *destructive readout*, and usually automatic circuits are built into the memory to reset the core to its original value. Some schemes, called *nondestructive readout* systems, have been devised for reading out of the cores without destroying the information; but since these have not proved to be as reliable, they are not widely used. If a speed of under 2 μsec is desired for the core memory, a reading scheme using higher currents is required and the coincident current techniques do not work. In these systems each word has its own read windings which are selected for reading out a word at high speed. These are known as *word arrangement* memories. The selection circuits are larger in this type of arrangement, but it does allow a faster reading of information. Writing is done in a coincident current fashion.

Several principles other than magnetics have been used in other types of memory devices known as *acoustical delay line* memories and *Williams tube* memories. The principle of the acoustic delay line is the transmission of sound waves through some medium and the recirculation of these sound waves. Tubes of mercury were commonly used as the medium. Quartz crystal transducers were placed at both ends to change electrical pulses into mechanical vibrations and to reconvert the sound waves into electrical pulses to be sent back to the first quartz transducer for re-circulation. The Williams tube storage is based on the presence or absence of an electric charge on a specified spot on the screen of a cathode-ray tube. This charge is placed on the screen by the electron beam and information is read by a capacitive pickup of voltage produced by re-directing the electron beam on the spot, where the voltage is dependent on the charge of the spot. Because both the acoustical delay line and the Williams tube memory systems have become nearly obsolete since the invention of magnetic core memories, we shall not consider them further.

The need to solve larger and larger problems on digital computers has necessitated both faster computers and larger capacity memory units. The arithmetic unit and control unit can be made to operate at speeds faster than those of conventional high capacity memory units. For these reasons, the quest for high-speed, large capacity memories at reasonable cost and for computer organizations that counteract the effects of a slow memory is of considerable current interest. The development of memory systems using cryogenic elements, tunnel diodes, and thin film magnetic elements may prove successful in the near future. These elements are extremely small and if mass-produced may give very large capacity memories, of random access type, which are both relatively inexpensive and fast. In addition, it may be possible to organize these memories to perform considerable logic in the memory unit itself or arrange them so that large amounts of information can be stored and yet be readily accessible even though the exact storage location of the information is not known. One such type is called an *associative memory*, where the information is obtained from the memory, not by knowing the address at which it is stored but by associating a distinguishing tag with the information and obtaining the information by comparison with the tag. This tag might be a part number, a man number, or a call number, depending on the particular application.

1.9   INPUT-OUTPUT UNITS

The input-output unit provides equipment to read the information and the computer instructions into the machine (the input) and to remove or display the results of the computation (the output). Many types of devices are available to perform these tasks and many machines have several different types of input and output equipment.

Usually the rate of processing information in the computer is much greater than that of either the input or output equipment. This is primarily because the input-output units usually require some mechanical operations, whereas the internal calculations proceed at electronic speeds. This speed differential is not critical if the information required for the problem and the results are small compared to the amount of calculation. This happens in a great many scientific calculations, so that on computers for scientific problems the input-output equipment may be rather slow without causing a great unbalance between input and output time versus computing time. In data processing and many business problems, a considerable amount of information must pass through both the input and output equipment with relatively little computing done on the data. In these computers the speed of the input-output equipment is quite critical. More sophisticated input-output equipment and logical organization of these units are required to maintain a reasonable balance between computing time and input-output time, without using the alternative of using slower circuits for computation. In the newer, faster computers being designed, the internal computational abilities have become so fast that rather sophisticated input-output equipment, and organization of this equipment, is required even for problems having relatively little input or output. The organizations allow input and output to proceed without stopping internal computation; for example, the computer might be recording the results of one problem while doing computing on a second problem and at the same time reading in information and instructions for a third problem. It is quite obvious that the organization of such a computer becomes rather complex, since one must insure that a mixup does not occur among all the various problems and that the correct information is available for the computer when it is called for, but if not, the computation will wait until it is available.

We shall discuss briefly some of the types of input-output equipment. For input the computer needs to be given numeric (and sometimes alphabetic and other symbolic) information in a fairly rapid and automatic fashion. Electric typewriters, keyboards, and teletype units are used to transform such information into electrical signals suitable for input to computers, these units are often used as one type of input to a computer. They are not very fast or automatic, however, since they are limited by the speed of an operator typing in the information and are not readily checked against operator error. Such a unit is very useful for checking and test purposes both as an input and output device. The Illiac (see Section 1.12), for example, has a teletype printer which can be used for output.

The use of punched paper tape, such as teletype tape, and punched cards gives a faster and more automatic means of input and output, and the equipment for preparing and reading punched cards and tape is readily available. This tape is obtainable with either 5 or 7 levels of holes across the tape, called a character, and with 10 characters per inch of tape. The tapes are prepared on modified teletype units and read into the computer with a photoelectric reader approximately 250 characters per second. For output, tape can be punched at about 100 characters per second on high-speed punching units. Similar systems are available for punched cards. The IBM cards, for example, are widely used for this purpose. They have 80 columns of holes on a card with each column having 12 positions, as shown in Figure 1.7.1. Card readers vary in speed from 100 to 600 cards per minute and card punches operate at from 100 to about 250 cards per minute. The punched card units have some advantages over punched tapes such as a somewhat higher information rate, but the punched card equipment is also quite a bit more expensive than punched paper tape equipment.

Although most computers have either punched tape or card input and output capabilities, magnetic tape units have become popular in recent years since they are much faster and are erasable. The recording and reading of information on magnetic tapes are done similarly as on magnetic drums, except that the information is recorded on a tape (or ribbon) about 1 in. wide and a transport mechanism moves the tape past the reading and writing heads at 100 in. per second or more. There are many different types of magnetic tape units with widely varying physical and electrical characteristics, which we shall not attempt to describe. Since they are one of the fastest commonly available type of input-output equipment, it is quite usual to have auxiliary equipment to transform the input information onto magnetic tape and then to use magnetic tape almost exclusively as the direct input medium to the computer; the computer then gives its output onto magnetic tape and the auxiliary equipment prints or plots the output information from the magnetic tape.

There are also some very high-speed output systems that use cathode-ray tubes to plot information for both a direct visual display and photographing. Others have a special cathode-ray tube called a Charactron and xerographic printers. The Stromberg-Carlson SC-5000 is an example. It can print 10,000 characters per second with as many as 150 characters per line.

1.10 ARITHMETIC UNITS

The arithmetic unit performs the calculations on the numbers or words in the computer. The main operations are addition, subtraction, multiplication, and division, and most computers have instructions for each operation; some machines, however, do not have division instructions, and others include a square root instruction. Many computers can also perform certain logical operations on words. We shall discuss how some of these arithmetic operations can be carried out, and see that the method of representing numbers in the computer has a great effect on how these operations are performed.

A classification of arithmetic units is commonly made as to whether the arithmetic unit acts on single digits at a time (serial mode) or upon all the digits of a word simultaneously (parallel mode). A serial mode of operation requires less equipment than a parallel mode since the next digits can be sequenced through the same circuits as those used for the first digits; but, of course, in the parallel mode greater speed can be achieved since all digits are treated simultaneously. Serial operation has become popular for medium and small size computers because they need less equipment in the arithmetic unit and the operations may be performed concurrently with the serial reading of information from a drum memory unit. Magnetic core memory units are usually operated to read a complete word of information and are thus very well suited to combine with a parallel arithmetic unit.

Many variations of number representations are found in computers.

The determining factors are the base used, the precision (or length of word), the range of numbers, a fixed- or floating-point, and the type of negative number representation. Usually, either a binary or a decimal base is used in computers. Decimal numbers are represented by some sort of binary encoding as was shown in Table 1.6.1.

In a fixed-point computer the numbers are represented in a positional notation in a word either as integers in the form

$$N_r = \sum_{i=0}^{p} n_i r^i,$$

where each word has $p + 1$ positions of radix r, or as fractions in the form

$$F_r = \sum_{i=-1}^{-f} n_i r^i,$$

where each word has f positions of radix r. Thus for a binary parallel computer using fractional fixed-point notation, the arithmetic unit would require the capability of adding two f position binary fractions simultaneously to give an f positional resultant plus an indication of whether the resultant exceeded the range of the computer.

For a floating-point computer a number N_r is represented by $n \times r^j$, where r is the radix of the number system. Here both n and j are stored in the machine to represent the number N_r. The n represents the digits of the number and j locates the radix point. A floating-point machine is more complex than a fixed-point machine because both the exponent and the digits enter into the calculations. The precision of the numbers is usually measured by the number of digits used to represent the n portion of the number; for fixed-point machines this is the same as the word length of the machine. In Illiac the word length is 40 binary digits. In the LGP-30 (see Section 1.13) the word length is 32 binary digits. Both the machines are fixed-point machines and the numbers n lie in the range $-1 \leq n \leq 1$. In floating-point machines, the range is greater because of the exponent representation. There are two common representations for negative numbers, either a complement representation or an absolute value and sign. Both the LGP-30 and the Illiac use binary complement number systems for negative numbers.

We describe the absolute value and sign representation and the complement representations using a binary fractional number n in positional notation where $n = n_0 n_1 \cdots n_f$. In both representations one of the binary digits is called the *sign digit*. As is customary we let the left-most digit n_0 designate the sign digit. In the absolute value and sign representation, n_0 equals 0 indicates a positive number, whereas n_0 equals 1 indicates a negative number. For absolute value and sign representation the numerical value of n can be expressed as

$$n = (1 - 2n_0) \cdot \sum_{i=1}^{f} n_i 2^{-i}.$$

Thus, if $n_i = 0$ for all $i = 1, \ldots, f$, n equals 0 both for $n_0 = 0$ and $n_0 = 1$. The range of numbers in this representation is thus

$$n_0 = 0, \qquad n_i = 1 \qquad \text{for the maximum,}$$

so that

$$n = (1 - 0) \sum_{i=1}^{f} 2^{-i} < 1$$

and

$$n = 1, \qquad n_i = 1 \qquad \text{for the minimum,}$$

so that

$$n = (-1) \sum_{i=1}^{f} 2^{-i} > -1,$$

giving a range $-1 < n < 1$.

In this representation, the number $+\frac{3}{8}$ would be written as 0.0110 and $-\frac{3}{8}$ as 1.0110. Furthermore, it should be noted that multiplication is particularly convenient here, for the value of the product is determined by the product of the two absolute values (that is, the $\sum_{i=1}^{f} n_i 2^{-i}$ part of the representations). In addition, the sign of the product is represented by a 0 if the sign representations of the two numbers agree and is represented by a 1 otherwise.

Two types of complement representations are used, the $(r - 1)$'s-complement and the r's-complement for a radix r system. Thus for a decimal system we have a 9's-complement system and a 10's-complement system; and in the binary system we have a 1's-complement and a 2's-complement system. To obtain the 9's-complement of a decimal number, each digit is subtracted from 9 and an extra digit is reserved for indicating the sign. Thus the 9's complement of 631 is $9999 - 0631 = 9368$, where the 9 in the most significant place indicates a negative number. By using a complement number system it is particularly simple to subtract two numbers. For example, if 631 is to be subtracted from 826, we simply have to add $826 + 9368$, with the extra rule that if a carry occurs on the most significant digit, it is added to the least significant digit. This rule is called an *end-around carry*. Thus

$$
\begin{array}{r}
826 \\
-631 \\
\hline
195
\end{array}
\qquad \text{is performed by} \qquad
\begin{array}{r}
826 \\
+9368 \\
\hline
10194 \\
+1 \\
\hline
0195
\end{array}
$$

Correspondingly, the 1's-complement of a binary number is obtained by replacing 0's by 1's and 1's by 0's which is equivalent to subtracting each position of the number from 1. Hence the 1's complement of 0.011010 is 1.100101, and if we wish to perform the subtraction 0.100000 − 0.011010, we again use the end-around carry and complementary representation as follows:

$$
\begin{array}{rcr}
0.100000 & & 0.100000 \\
-0.011010 & \text{is} & +1.100101 \\
\hline
0.000110 & & 10.000101 \, \cdot \\
& & +1 \\
\hline
& & 0.000110 \\
\end{array}
$$

Thus subtraction on a computer using an $(r-1)$'s-complement system can be performed by using the same circuitry as that required for addition, with the added requirement of the end-around carry.

The numerical value of n in 1's-complement representation is expressed as

$$ n = -n_0(1 - 2^{-f}) + \sum_{i=1}^{f} n_i 2^{-i}, $$

where we note that subtracting each digit from a 1 for negative numbers is expressed by the $-n_0(1 - 2^{-f})$ when $n_0 = 1$ for negative numbers. The reader may verify that the range of n is $-1 < n < 1$, as was the case in the absolute value and sign representation, and that we again have two representations for zero. Note, however, that $-\frac{3}{8}$ is represented as 1.1001, formed by subtracting 0.0110 from 1.1111. Does this check with the 1's-complement formula given for n?

The r's-complement of a number is found exactly as that for the $(r-1)$'s-complement except that a 1 is then added to the least significant digit. For example, the 10's-complement of decimal 631 is

$$
\begin{array}{r}
9999 \\
-631 \\
\hline
9368 \\
+1 \\
\hline
9369 \\
\end{array}
$$

and the 2's-complement of binary 0.011010 is

$$
\begin{array}{r}
1.111111 \\
-0.011010 \\
\hline
1.100101 \, . \\
+1 \\
\hline
1.100110 \\
\end{array}
$$

In this r's-complement system an end-around carry is not required for subtractions; therefore subtraction can be performed by simply adding the complement. For example, to subtract 631 from 826, we add the complement of 631 to 826, obtaining

$$
\begin{array}{r}
826 \\
-631 \\
\hline
195
\end{array}
\qquad
\begin{array}{r}
826 \\
+9369 \\
\hline
0195
\end{array}
$$

The carry to the left is outside of the range and thus lost in the computation.

The numerical value of n in 2's-complement form can be expressed as

$$
n = -n_0 + \sum_{i=1}^{f} n_i 2^{-i},
$$

and by the rule given for representing negative numbers, $-\frac{3}{8}$ would be expressed as 1.1010, which can be checked against the preceding formula. With this formula we see that $n = -1$ can be expressed by letting $n_0 = 1$ and $n_i = 0$ for $i = 1, \ldots, f$. Thus the range of numbers represented by the 2's-complement numbers is $-1 \leq n < 1$, and the unique representation for zero is $n_i = 0$ for $i = 0, \ldots, f$.

As has been seen, each of these methods of representing negative numbers gives a different representation. One advantage of the complement representations is that addition can be performed directly by adding the numbers in their binary representations (with provision for end-around carry for 1's-complement) and subtractions can be performed by complementing and then adding the numbers. An advantage of the absolute value and sign representation, however, arises in performing multiplication, whereas the complement representations introduce certain complications for multiplication.

In the arithmetic unit, an adder circuit is usually the central part of the unit. Ordinarily, storage for the numbers used in the computation and for the results is also provided. In a serial machine the numbers may be obtained directly from the memory; usually in parallel machines, however, several words of storage devices are included to store these numbers. These are called the arithmetic registers of the machine. Addition is performed directly by the adder circuit, subtraction is performed by using complementing and adding circuits, and multiplication and division by sequences of additions and subtractions. For a decimal machine, multiplication involves adding the multiplicand to itself as many times as indicated by the least significant digit of the multiplier, shifting the partial sum right, repeating for the next multiplier digit, etc. In a binary machine, the multiplicand is added or not depending on the multiplier digit being 1 or 0, respectively. Various methods for providing shortcuts to multiplication are used. Some machines use a table lookup for multiplication to decrease multiplication time, which requires considerable circuitry. In decimal machines, a shortcut can be used by replacing multiplier digits above 4 by their complements and by using subtractions and one additional addition in the next higher digit. This cuts the maximum multiplication time by approximately one-half. Similarly, for binary machines, each run of consecutive 1's in the multiplier can be multiplied by one subtraction followed by one addition in the digit just above the run of 1's, thus reducing the total number of additions and subtractions to form the product when the length of the strings of 1 is greater than 1.

As seen from Table 1.6.1, the 2421, 5211, and excess 3 encodings are extremely convenient to use when a complementary system is used for negative numbers. In each of these encodings the 9's-complement of any digit is obtained by simply complementing each of the 4 binary digits. For example, 0011 represents 3 in the 2421 system. The 9's-complement of 3 is 6, but 1100 represents 6 in the 2421 system. Therefore, if such an encoding is employed for the decimal machine, the adder circuit can also be used for subtraction if a simple binary complementing circuit is supplied for each binary digit and there is some provision for an end-around carry.

When performing numerical calculations on numbers represented in a computer, the range of numbers which the computer can handle is of great importance. If a fixed point representation is used, the range of the numbers is set both by the position in which the radix point is assumed and in the number of digits in a word.

When performing calculations, we must insure that the number stay within the range of numbers handled by the computer. The problem of so arranging a calculation is called *scaling* and was briefly mentioned in Section 1.3. This can be exemplified further if we assume a fixed-point fractional representation for numbers in 2's-complement form where a number n in the computer can be in a range $-1 \leq m < 1$. Results of various arithmetic operations may then form resultants which are outside this range. Let

$$z = x + y,$$

where
$$-1 \leq x < 1$$

and
$$-1 \leq y < 1,$$

where z is the sum of adding an augend x and an addend y of numbers in the computer. The sum z then has a range $-2 \leq z < 2$, depending on the values of x and y. To have correct addition in the computer we must insure that z is in the range $-1 \leq z < 1$. Thus a circuit should provide for detecting the condition that z is not in the required range, that is, when z *overflows* the range of the computer representation. It is common to have overflow detection circuits in a computer; similarly, if

$$z = x - y,$$

where z is the difference of the minuend x and the subtrahend y. Then with ranges

$$-1 \leq x < 1,$$
$$-1 \leq y < 1,$$

the difference z has range

$$-2 < z < 2,$$

and we must also check for overflow in subtraction.

When forming the product z,

$$z = x \cdot y,$$

where x is the multiplier and y is the multiplicand, it is obvious that the range of the product will be

$$-1 < z \leq 1$$

for x and y having correct ranges. Thus if both $x = -1$ and $y = -1$, z will equal 1, which is outside the range. This, however, is not the complete picture in multiplication since usually the product is formed by a successive addition process. Therefore we must also insure that the partial products will be in the correct range for the computer, except for the case $z = 1$. If we assume binary fractions are being used, a recursion formula for multiplication is

$$p_{j+1} = \tfrac{1}{2}(p_j + x_{m-j}y),$$

where m is the number of nonsign digits in the computer word, j is the recursion index $0 \leq j \leq m - 1$, and x_{m-j} is the $(m - j)$th bit of x where the bits are numbered as $0.x_1 x_2 \cdots x_m$; that is, for positive x

$$x = \sum_{i=1}^{m} 2^{-i} x_i.$$

We shall verify that this recursion formula does indeed form the product, but first we shall illustrate the recursion by letting

$$x = 0.0110,$$
$$y = 0.1101,$$

and assume $p_0 = 0$; note that here $m = 4$. Then

$$p_1 = \tfrac{1}{2}[0.0000 + 0 \times (0.1101)]$$
$$= \tfrac{1}{2}(0.0000) = 0.00000,$$
$$p_2 = \tfrac{1}{2}[0.00000 + 1 \times (0.1101)]$$
$$= \tfrac{1}{2}(0.11010) = 0.011010.$$

Note that the $\frac{1}{2}$ operation is done simply by "shifting" the number one place to the right.

$$p_3 = \tfrac{1}{2}[0.011010 + 1 \times (0.1101)]$$
$$= \tfrac{1}{2}(1.001110)$$
$$= 0.1001110.$$

Note here that 1.001110 is outside the normal range, but the multiplication by $\frac{1}{2}$ restores the result to correct range if a 0 is assumed to enter from the left in the shifting operation. Finally,

$$p_4 = \tfrac{1}{2}[0.1001110 + 0 \times (0.1101)]$$
$$= 0.01001110.$$

The product z is thus 0.01001110, which the reader can check as the correct answer. Note that the product in general has $2m$ bits, and thus two words would be required to store the true product. Alternatively, we might round off the product in some fashion and keep only m bits.

We now verify the recursion formula

$$p_{j+1} = \tfrac{1}{2}(p_j + x_{m-j}y).$$

From the recursion,

$$p_1 = \tfrac{1}{2}(p_0 + x_m y)$$
$$p_2 = \tfrac{1}{2}[\tfrac{1}{2}(p_0 + x_m y) + x_{m-1}y]$$
$$= 2^{-2}p_0 + y(2^{-2}x_m + 2^{-1}x_{m-1})$$
$$= 2^{-2}p_0 + y\sum_{i=1}^{2} 2^{-i}x_{i+(m-2)}.$$

Now assume the general form

$$p_k = 2^{-k}p_0 + y\sum_{i=1}^{k} 2^{-i}x_{i+(m-k)}$$

for $2 \leq k < m$. Then

$$p_{k+1} = 2^{-1}\left[\left(2^{-k}p_0 + y\sum_{i=1}^{k} 2^{-i}x_{i+(m-k)}\right) + x_{m-k}y\right],$$

which after some algebraic manipulation gives the form

$$p_{k+1} = 2^{-(k+1)}p_0 + y\left[\sum_{i=1}^{k+1} 2^{-i}x_{i+[m-(k+1)]}\right].$$

Since this is the same form assumed for p_k, we have proved by induction that this is the general form for p_k for any $k = 2, \ldots, m$. In particular the final result is

$$p_m = 2^{-m}p_0 + y\sum_{i=1}^{m} 2^{-i}x_{i+(m-m)}$$
$$= 2^{-m}p_0 + y\sum_{i=1}^{m} 2^{-i}x_i.$$

Hence with the 2's-complement representation, as assumed,

$$x = -x_0 + \sum_{i=1}^{m} 2^{-i} x_i$$

so that

$$\sum_{i=1}^{m} 2^{-i} x_i = x + x_0$$

and

$$p_m = 2^{-m} p_0 + y(x + x_0)$$
$$= 2^{-m} p_0 + yx + yx_0.$$

Now if x is a positive number, $x_0 = 0$ so that $p_m = 2^{-m} p_0 + yx$. Setting p_0 equal to 0 gives the desired product $p_m = yx$. If x is negative, then $x_0 = 1$, giving

$$p_m = 2^{-m} p_0 + xy + y.$$

Setting $p_0 = 0$ gives

$$p_m = xy + y.$$

Therefore to obtain the correct product the multiplicand y must be subtracted from p_m when x is negative. Note that, if a rounded product of m bits is desired, this is readily attained by setting $p_0 = \frac{1}{2}$, giving

$$p_m = 2^{-(m+1)} + xy + x_0 y.$$

The $2^{-(m+1)}$ will round up if the least significant m digits of the product are greater than or equal to $\frac{1}{2}$ and will round down otherwise, so that a nearly unbiased roundoff is attained. Furthermore, from the recursive formula it can be seen that the ranges are

$$-2 \le (p_j + x_{m-j} y) < 2$$

under suitable representation, where

$$0 \le x_{m-j} \le 1,$$
$$-1 \le y < 1,$$
$$-1 \le x_{m-j} \cdot y < 1,$$

and we assume $-1 \le p_j < 1$ so that in general

$$-1 \le p_{j+1} < 1,$$

so that all partial products fall correctly in the number range of the computer, if not both $x = y = -1$.

When both $x = y = -1$, the binary representation for both numbers is $1.00 \cdots 0$. Assuming $p_0 = 0$, then from the recursion formula it follows that all $p_j = 0$ for $0 \le j \le m - 1$ since $x_{m-j} = 0$ for this range of j. Thus $p_m = 0$. Now since $x_0 = 1$, the correction of adding y to p_m is required. This gives a result of a 1 in the sign bit and zeros elsewhere, which is the representation for -1. This error can be sensed by noting that the product sign bit is in error. The sign bit should equal zero since the product of two negative numbers x and y should give a positive number, and positive numbers have a 0 in the sign bit.

Finally, we should consider briefly the division process, for which several methods of successive subtractions can be used to obtain a quotient.

Let

$$q = \frac{x_0}{d},$$

where q = the quotient
x_0 = the dividend
d = the divisor

If $\qquad\qquad -1 \leq x_0 < 1$

and $\qquad\qquad -1 \leq d < 1,$

then q has the range $-\infty \leq q \leq \infty$. Obviously, this is not satisfactory, since, first, we cannot divide by 0 and second, we would desire a quotient q in the range $-1 \leq q < 1$. This can be tested by insuring either that the absolute value of x is less than the absolute value of d or by using an overflow indication on the recursive division process.

Assuming positive binary fractions, let us consider the recursion formula

$$x_{j+1} = 2x_j - q_{j+1}d,$$

where

d = the divisor, $\quad -1 \leq d < 1$

j = the recursion index, $\quad 0 \leq j \leq m$

m = the number of nonsign bits

q_{j+1} = the $(j+1)$st quotient digit

$q = 0.q_1q_2 \cdots q_m$

x_j = the jth partial remainder.

For discussion let us assume that x_0 and d are both positive and $x_0 < d$. Then $0 < q < 1$. Given x_0 and d we first attempt to subtract d from $2x_0$; here such a subtraction would either form a negative number, meaning that the first quotient digit q should equal 0, or would remain positive, meaning that $q_1 = 1$. If $q_1 = 0$, we can restore $2x_0$ by adding d. To find q_2 we again double the partial remainder (either $2x_0$ or $2x_0 - d$) by shifting the partial raminder one place to the left. Again we try to subtract d, and using the same rules obtain either $q_2 = 0$ or $q_2 = 1$. We shall not go through the general verification of this recursion formula, but rather illustrate it as follows. Let

$$x_0 = 0.01101$$
$$d = 0.11000.$$

Then

$$
\begin{array}{rl}
2x_0 = & 0.11010 \\
-d = & -0.11000 \\
\hline
2x_0 - d = & 0.00010 \quad \text{positive partial remainder.}
\end{array}
$$

Therefore, $q_1 = 1.$

Now

$$
\begin{array}{rl}
x_1 = & 0.00010 \\
2x_1 = & 0.00100 \\
-d = & -0.11000 \\
\hline
2x_1 - d = & -0.10100 \quad \text{negative.}
\end{array}
$$

Thus we restore to obtain

$$x_2 = (2x_1 - d) + d = 0.00100$$

and
$$q_2 = 0$$
$$
\begin{array}{rl}
2x_2 = & 0.01000 \\
-d = & -0.11000 \\
\hline
& -0.10000 \quad \text{negative.}
\end{array}
$$

Therefore $x_3 = (2x_2 - d) + d = 0.01000$

and
$$q_3 = 0$$
$$
\begin{array}{rl}
2x_3 = & 0.10000 \\
-d = & -0.11000 \\
\hline
& -0.01000 \quad \text{negative.}
\end{array}
$$

Therefore $x_4 = (2x_3 - d) + d = 0.1000$

and
$$q_4 = 0$$
$$
\begin{array}{rl}
2x_4 = & 1.00000 \\
-d = & -0.11000 \\
\hline
& 0.01000 \quad \text{positive.}
\end{array}
$$

Thus $x_5 = 0.01000$

and $q_5 = 1.$

Our result is

$$q = 0.10001$$

with a partial remainder

$$x_5 = 0.0100,$$

or a true remainder of 0.0000001, since five doubling operations were performed. The result is easily checked by multiplication.

Our discussion illustrates the division process known as *restoring* division. To save time a *nonrestoring* division is usually performed in which the divisor is added to the doubled negative partial remainder until a positive partial remainder is obtained. By alternating the mode between positive and negative partial remainders in nonrestoring division considerable time can be saved by not having to waste extra steps to restore the partial remainder always to a positive remainder. The details of nonrestoring division and other arithmetic processes will not be covered here.

1.11 CONTROL UNITS

In describing the arithmetic unit in Section 1.10, it was seen that various sequences of operations are required in the arithmetic unit. For example, in multiplication a sequence of additions and shifts is required. One of the functions of the control unit is to provide signals that sequence the operations in the arithmetic unit. The control also obtains the correct information from the memory unit, performs counting operations, controls the operations of the input-output unit, and determines which instruction is to occur next.

To perform these tasks the control uses a program of instructions, which is stored in the memory. The control calls for an instruction; in its decoding the correct sequencing is set up and the correct operands are obtained for the operations to be performed. After completing an instruction, the control calls for the next instruction from the memory and proceeds with it. Usually this instruction is stored in the address, one greater than the present one; thus an "instruction counter" is used in the control to record the address of the next instruction. If it is to be some instruction other than the next one stored in the memory, then the instruction counter is modified by the control. Special instructions called *transfer instructions* are used to perform this function. There are two basic types of transfer instruction.

1. The "unconditional" transfer which always causes a modification.
2. The "conditional" transfer which may cause different types of modifications depending on the result of some previous calculation.

Early computers did not possess a control unit as such. The control was done either by loops of punched tape that had punches describing the operations, which were sequenced by what punches occurred next, or by the wiring of a plug-board to indicate the operation sequences. When large memories were incorporated into computers, a new concept of operation arose in which the instructions as well as the numbers were stored in the memory. This is called the *stored program* computer. This enables the sequences of instructions to be easily modified in the arithmetic unit, thereby giving great flexibility in sequencing operations; that is, the computer is used to modify its own instructions and sequencing of the instructions.

An instruction consists of two parts. One we can call the *order part*, which is a group of digits that indicates the type of operation to be performed. This part is decoded by the control and used to set up the proper sequence of operations in the arithmetic unit if the instruction is to read in some information or to read out some result, or in the memory unit if the instruction is to read or write in the memory. The second part is the *address part*. Some machines, such as the Illiac and LGP-30, are single-address machines in which the address part contains only one memory address. Other machines may have two, three, or four addresses. They usually indicate the location in memory of some particular operand. In a three-address machine, for example, if an addition instruction is to be performed, the addresses would refer to the addend, augend, and the location in the memory that the sum is to be stored. A three-address machine has several advantages for programming, for there are enough addresses to indicate memory locations for all the operands of the instruction. Many instructions, however, may not require three addresses and thus many address digits are wasted. Since it takes considerable time to obtain an instruction from the memory, it is often very inefficient to waste digits. For this reason, a single-address arrangement is often preferred. For example, Illiac uses single addresses and has two instructions in a single 40-digit word, as shown in the following diagram.

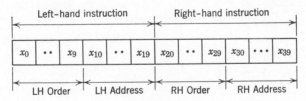

Thus, by bringing one word from the memory, two instructions are obtained. Normally the left-hand instruction is processed first, followed by the right-hand instruction. The 10 digits in the address parts allow $2^{10} = 1024$ memory locations to be addressed, which is the capacity of the Illiac Williams tube memory. For instructions to the Illiac drum memory, only one instruction can be given per word since the drum memory has too many locations to address with 10 digits.

We shall not give a detailed description of the instruction code and sequencing of a control unit because a great number of details on the manner of encoding the instructions would be necessary. We should, however, mention some additional features of control units which are commonly used. Probably the most important is that of *index registers* in the control. These are registers of the length of an address and are used to modify the memory location being consulted. They are usually arranged as counters so that they may be made to increase automatically (or decrease) by one each time the index register is consulted. By using these index registers, it is very easy to set up operations on a large block of numbers in the memory so that each use of the instruction will call for the number at the address $x + 1$ if x were the address consulted in the last use of this instruction. It is usually possible to sense the contents of the index register and to control the ending of the use of the operation. Without the use of index registers it is necessary to modify the instruction in the arithmetic unit.

Another feature of control which helps speed up computation is a "look ahead" feature or "advanced control" feature. Since it takes considerable time to obtain information from a memory unit, it is to one's advantage to have operands available in some sort of fast temporary storage as soon as they are needed for calculation. Thus an advanced control can be used to preprocess instructions which would normally be occurring next in sequence and bring to temporary storage the operands indicated by the addresses of the instruction in the advanced control. At the same time, the regular control unit can be performing the sequence of operations for the present instruction.

1.12 A PARALLEL COMPUTER, THE ILLIAC

In this and the following section we give a somewhat more detailed description of the general properties and structure of two rather basic types of computers. Here we describe the Illiac, a parallel asynchronous machine which was located at the University of Illinois Digital Computer Laboratory, and in the next section we describe the LGP-30, a serial synchronous machine.

The terms *synchronous* and *asynchronous* refer to two different methods of timing the circuits, or sequencing the operations, in a computer. A synchronous computer has a basic timing signal or "clock" built into the machine for timing the operations. The LGP-30 uses a special timing track on the drum to serve as the clock. An asynchronous computer has no basic clock, but it rather generates "end signals" for each operation it performs, and they are then used to start the next operation in the sequence.

Although the Illiac is called asynchronous, its electrostatic memory (Williams tubes) and drum memory both work synchronously. These devices need to be suitably interconnected with the asynchronous arithmetic unit and control.

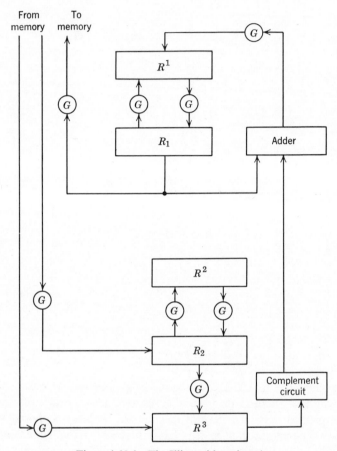

Figure 1.12.1   The Illiac arithmetic unit.

We describe briefly the Illiac in terms of its four basic functional units. A block diagram of the Illiac arithmetic unit is shown in Figure 1.12.1.

The G's represent gating circuits which control the transfer of information from one location to another. The five registers are R^1, R_1, R^2, R_2, and R^3. They each have 40 circuits called flip-flops, each being capable of storing one binary digit, that is, each flip-flop has two-stable states. One of these states is assigned the binary value 0 and the other the value 1. These states can be distinguished by different output voltages from the flip-flop, and thus these voltages are used to represent the binary digit. The left-most digit in these registers is a sign digit with the binary point following directly the sign digit as shown in the diagram. The 2's-

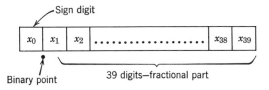

Sign digit

| x_0 | x_1 | x_2 | ···················· | x_{38} | x_{39} |

Binary point

39 digits—fractional part

complement number system is used. If the digits are numbered x_0 through x_{39}, using the formula of Section 1.10, the arithmetic number x is represented by

$$x = -x_0 + \sum_{i=1}^{39} 2^{-i}x_i.$$

Note that the sign digit equals 1 for negative fractions and 0 for positive fractions.

As an example of this number representation, $+\frac{3}{8}$ is represented as

$$+\tfrac{3}{8} = 0.0110$$

and

$$-\tfrac{3}{8} = 1.1010.$$

By using this formula, this can be checked as

$$\tfrac{3}{8} = x = -0 + 1 \cdot 2^{-2} + 1 \cdot 2^{-3}$$
$$= +\tfrac{3}{8}$$
$$-\tfrac{3}{8} = x = -1 + 1 \cdot 2^{-1} + 0 \cdot 2^{-2} + 1 \cdot 2^{-3}$$
$$= -1 + \tfrac{1}{2} + \tfrac{1}{8} = -\tfrac{3}{8},$$

where digits $x_4 \cdots x_{39}$ are all assumed to equal 0.

For addition, the addend is held in R_1 and the augend is held in R^3. The complement circuit is set not to complement. When the adder has had time to function, the result is gated first into R^1 and then into R_1. For subtraction, the same process occurs, except the complement circuit takes the digit-wise complement and a carry input of 1 is set into the least significant position of the adder. This creates the number in R_1 minus the number in R^3. Variations of addition and subtraction are possible in Illiac by controlling the initial value in R_1 to be 0, $\frac{1}{2}$, or the result of some previous operation.

For multiplication, we need the additional feature of adding successively in displaced positions. This is accomplished by shifting the numbers in R^1R_1 and R^2R_2. Both left and right shifts are provided as shown in Figure 1.12.2.

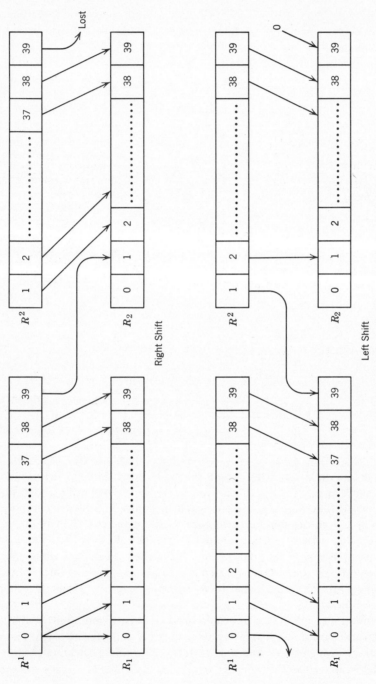

Figure 1.12.2   Right and left shifts in Illiac.

A right or left shift of a number in $R_1 R_2$ (which can be thought of as a 78-digit single register) is actually done by first gating $R_1 R_2$ up to $R^1 R^2$ and then doing the appropriate down shift.

In multiplication, the multiplier is placed in R_2 and the multiplicand is placed in R^3. If both are positive, multiplication proceeds as follows; x_{39} in R_2 is sensed. If this multiplier digit equals 1, R^3 is added to R_1 (R_1 is originally 0), giving a partial product P_1. $R_1 R_2$ is then shifted right one place. Now the new x_{39} in R_2 is sensed and the operation is repeated. If x_{39} in R_2 equals 0 at any time, the right shift occurs without any preceding addition. The process is continued through 39 steps, and the product then appears in $R_1 R_2$ as a double length number. Similar to the formulas in Section 1.10, this process can be formulated as partial products

$$P_{i+1} = \tfrac{1}{2}(P_i + Y_{39-i}X),$$

where X is the multiplicand, Y_{39-i} is the multiplier digit of the ith step, and P_i is the ith partial product. If P_0 represents the initial number in R_1, at the end of 39 steps we obtain:

$$P_{39} = 2^{-39}P_0 + \left(\sum_{i=1}^{39} 2^{-i}Y_i\right)X = 2^{-39}P_0 + XY.$$

The result is the desired double length product if $P_0 = 0$. If $P_0 = \tfrac{1}{2}$, a rounded product is obtained in R_1. If the multiplier or multiplicand is negative, care must be taken in forming the sign of the partial product and a correction is necessary if the multiplier is negative. This complicates the multiplication process since complements were used for negative numbers. Of course, if signed absolute representations were used, multiplication would consist of multiplying the nonsign parts as positive numbers and then calculating the final sign from the sign digits for the multiplier and multiplicand. For division, recursion relations similar to those in Section 1.10 can be developed. The general procedure is to place the dividend in R_1, subtract the divisor in R^3 as often as possible, and keep track of the number of subtractions in R_2, then to shift the remainder left and continue. At the end of the process, R_1 contains the remainder and R_2 contains the quotient.

In the Illiac control unit instructions are processed in pairs, two instructions per word. Figure 1.12.3 shows a block diagram for the Illiac control. Register R_3 holds the instruction pair currently being processed by the control. This instruction word has been brought to R_3 from the memory via the gate indicated, where this gate is operated after the right-hand instruction is completed. The position in memory of the instruction is determined by the control counter sending an address to the dispatch register, whereupon the address generator then sends signals to the

memory for reading the indicated word. With a new instruction word in
R_3, first the left-hand instruction (LHI) is gated to the decoder. The
decoder and arithmetic sequence control set up the correct sequence of
gates in the arithmetic unit to perform the instruction and the gating of

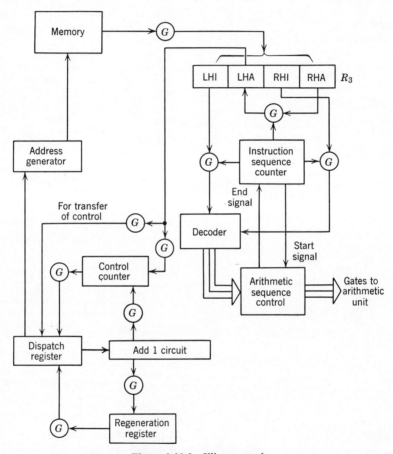

Figure 1.12.3   Illiac control.

the left-hand address (LHA) to the dispatch register either to read operands
from the memory or to store a result in the memory. After completing
the sequence of gates, an end signal is sent to the instruction sequence
counter, which then gates the right-hand instruction (RHI) to the decoder
so that this instruction can be performed. After completion of the RHI
the next pair of instructions is obtained from the memory by adding 1 to
the control counter address (as indicated by the add 1 circuit attached to
the dispatch register and control counter), and reading the pair of

instructions in the next memory location. For transfer of control instructions the sequence is slightly modified. Here the address of the instruction is gated into the control counter, indicating the address of the next instruction word.

Note that in both the block diagrams for the Illiac arithmetic and control units, Figures 1.12.1 and 1.12.3, we have described certain digital circuits by words such as adder, complement circuit, control counter, decoder, etc. The models of switching theory, developed in later chapters, give a more adequate and precise method of describing these circuits.

The Illiac memory is an electrostatic memory, and the words in this memory require periodic regeneration. During processing of instructions, therefore, the regeneration register gives addresses to the dispatch register. These addresses are consulted in the memory which also regenerates the word. By correct sequencing of the gates in this section of the control, the regeneration of successive addresses is interrupted when the memory needs to be consulted for other purposes.

The regeneration register, the dispatch register, and the address generator are the parts which control directly the memory and are actually located in the memory section of the computer. This memory is synchronous, and in addition to the control already mentioned, other synchronization circuits are included which enable us to transfer information from the synchronous memory to the asynchronous arithmetic and control units. The 1024 words of electrostatic storage are contained on forty cathode-ray tubes, one tube for each bit position of the word. On each tube a 32 × 32 raster of 1024 spots on the face of the tube is used to store the bits. When a word is to be read, the address generator simultaneously controls the placement of the electron beams on all forty tubes, and thus a complete word is either read out or stored in one cycle time of the memory. As discussed in Section 1.11, the address part of an Illiac instruction consists of 10 bits for each instruction. Since $2^{10} = 1024$, the address contains just enough bits to consult each of the 1024 words of the electrostatic memory.

The Illiac also has a drum memory which has 12,800 words of storage capacity. The instructions for the drum are special in that one drum instruction occupies the complete 40 bit word, for the address for a drum word requires more than the 10 bits allotted for addressing a word. Connections are made from the drum to the arithmetic register R_1. This register is synchronized with the drum during storage of information onto the drum and reading of information from the drum, where the synchronization is controlled by special "timing tracks."

Although functionally the drum unit is a memory device, in many ways it acts like a special input-output device on the Illiac since the input-output devices all are connected to R_1 and drum instructions are very closely related to the Illiac input-output instructions.

For input the Illiac uses five-level teletype-punched paper tape. The special code used on this tape, which is much more convenient for the computer, differs greatly from the international teletype code shown in Table 1.7.1. With this code base 16 numbers are represented in a normal 8421 weighted binary encoding using four of the holes; the fifth hole is punched only for letters and special characters. The paper tape is read into register R_1 of Illiac by a photoelectric tape reader. For numeric information only 4 bits are read from the tape at one time, and these are placed in the least significant four places of R_1. Register R_1 then shifts left four places, after which another 4 bits are read from the tape. Special reading of letters and characters is accomplished by reading the fifth hole bit into the sign bit of R_1.

The main output device of Illiac is a high-speed paper tape punch. This unit is connected to the four most significant digits of R_1. Under an output instruction, data are punched four digits at a time from R_1 in the same numeric code as used on input. Thus for decimal output we could read directly the tape as an 8421 code where a hole is interpreted as a 1 and no hole as a 0. If we desire a direct printout from the computer, a special output converted teletype printer can be switched in to print, rather than punch, the output.

Another special output device on Illiac is a cathode-ray tube output which can be used as a very fast output device to plot curves or display information in any desired two-dimensional form. It is possible to view directly this output and also photograph it for a permanent record. This output has a 256 × 256 raster of possible positions, where the horizontal position is controlled by the last 8 bits of R_1 and the vertical position by the next set of 8 bits of R_1.

It should be mentioned that all the input-output devices are synchronous in nature, and thus special input-output control circuits are required to synchronize these units with R_1. In addition, as is common with most computers, additional "peripheral" equipment is used to prepare the input and output for the computer. The Illiac has modified teletype equipment and special devices using photoelectric tape readers and high-speed punches.

1.13 A SERIAL COMPUTER—THE LGP-30

The LGP-30 is an excellent example of a serial synchronous computer which can be easily and briefly described. The LGP-30, like the Illiac, uses a binary fractional complement number system. Each word has 32 bits. For numerical data a word represents a sign bit, 30 numerical bits, and a spacer bit, as shown in Figure 1.13.1.

The word may also represent an instruction. Each instruction has an order or command part using 4 bits and an address part using 12 bits. The instruction has only one address and thus the computer is called a

Figure 1.13.1   LGP-30 data word.

single-address computer. Because only one instruction per word is used, some spare bits occur in the word and may be used for other purposes. This is shown in Figure 1.13.2.

A magnetic drum which rotates at about 4000 rpm is used for the main memory of the computer. This drum also contains the arithmetic registers and timing tracks to synchronize the computer. The main memory has a 4096 word capacity which is distributed on 64 tracks along the axis of

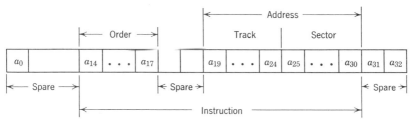

Figure 1.13.2   LGP-30 instruction word.

the drum and each track has 64 words. In the address part of the instruction bits a_{19} through a_{24} are used to select the track and a_{25} through a_{30} are used to select the track and a_{25} through a_{30} are used to select the particular word (or sector) on the track. As the drum rotates past the reading-writing heads, the words can be either serially read or written into. Four timing tracks are permanently recorded on the drum. One of these tracks, which is specially machined, provides 2049 pulses around the circumference of the drum to locate the 32×64 bits on each track. Three other timing tracks are used to position the 64 words around each track. The arithmetic registers consist of two one-word recirculating tracks and one special two-word recirculating track on the drum. These recirculating tracks are designed with two or more heads on the same track so that once a word is recorded on the track it will be read and rewritten continuously. Thus the words on these tracks are available as operands at the start of each word time. The arrangement of heads necessary for this operation is shown in Figure 1.13.3.

The recirculating tracks contain the following:

1. The control register, which holds the address for the next instruction.

2. The instruction register, which holds the instruction being executed and during multiplication or division holds the second operand.

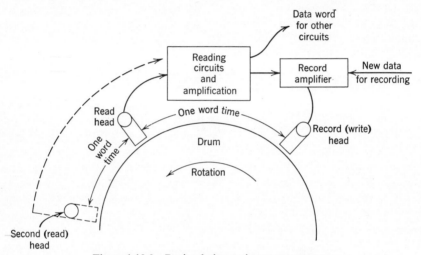

Figure 1.13.3   Recirculating register arrangement.

3. The accumulator register, which holds the resultant of the arithmetic operation. For multiplication or division the recirculation time of this register is increased to two word times. Thus, for example, the double length product can be recorded in this register. To expand the length to two word times, we simply switch to the second read head, advanced one word time from the first read head, as shown in Figure 1.13.3.

For external control of the computer, there are various switches and lights on a control panel. The input-output unit consists of a Flexowriter, that is, a typewriter with an integral paper tape punch and reader. Thus information can be read into the computer either by typing it on the typewriter or reading a punched paper tape. Similarly, the output can be obtained either as a printed record typed by the Flexowriter or as punched paper tape.

The detailed control and serial arithmetic are accomplished through very little circuitry consisting of fifteen temporary storage devices and associated logical circuitry. These storage devices are controlled from the digits in the recirculating registers and the timing tracks.

1.14 INCREASING COMPUTER SPEED

The need for faster computation ability, arising from extremely complex problems and a seemingly unending increase in the amount of computation being performed, has created extensive efforts toward increasing computer speed. These efforts range from new components and circuit configurations to new ideas in computer organization, arithmetic processes, and programming methods. In this section we describe briefly some of these approaches.

In parallel addition, m parallel stages of adder are used for adding m digit numbers. If two numbers are presented to the adder, a carry signal may have to be propagated from the least significant bit through each bit to the most significant bit. If the numbers are presented to the adder at time t_0 and if such a carry enters the most significant stage at t_1, we call the m stage carry time $C_m = t_1 - t_0$. Most parallel adders are arranged to allow the complete C_m time, plus some safety margin for every addition. Usually, however, a carry does not propagate the full length of the adder from the least significant stage to the most significant stage. It has been shown by Burks, Goldstine, and von Neumann that for a 40 binary-digit addition, the average maximum length of a sequence of 1's-carries is only 4.6 stages. Thus, if some way of detecting the completion of carries could be designed into the adder, a saving by a factor of about 8 could be obtained in carry propagation time during addition. To see how this can be done, consider the output carry table shown in Table 1.14.1, where A_k and B_k are the kth binary digits of the

Table 1.14.1 Table for Carry Digits

C_k	A_k	B_k	C_{k-1}	$\bar{C}_{k-1}$
0	0	1	0	1
0	1	0	0	1
1	0	1	1	0
1	1	0	1	0
0	0	0	0	1
1	0	0	0	1
0	1	1	1	0
1	1	1	1	0

addend and augend, C_k is the carry into the kth stage, and C_{k-1} is the carry out of the kth stage to the next higher order stage. We denote the least significant position of the number by subscript m, thus letting the subscript decrease with increasing significance, and the subscript 0 would correspond to the sign digit of the number. The entry $\bar{C}_{k-1}$ in the table denotes the binary complement of C_{k-1}. Table 1.14.1 illustrates that a carry ($C_{k-1} = 1$) to the next higher digit is required if two or more of the digits C_k, A_k, and B_k are equal to 1. By the arrangement shown for the first four rows, the value of C_{k-1} is equal to the value of C_k, and for the last four rows C_{k-1} is equal to 1 only when both A_k and B_k equal 1. Thus a carry $C_{k-1} = 1$ is generated in any stage where both A_k and B_k equal 1, irrespective of the value of C_k, and similarly a carry of 0, that is, $\bar{C}_{k-1} = 1$, is generated in any stage where $A_k = B_k = 0$ irrespective of the value of C_k.

An adder can be built which takes advantage of the fact that both $C_{k-1} = 1$ and $\bar{C}_{k-1} = 1$ can occur irrespective of the value of the incoming carry C_k. Furthermore, whenever $C_{k-1} = 1$ or $\bar{C}_{k-1} = 1$ has been generated in a stage it is apparent that the carry has been completed in that stage (this assumes that both C_{k-1} and $\bar{C}_{k-1}$ are set to 0 at the start of the addition). Thus a simple carry completion circuit can be built for each stage and also the complete parallel adder. With this circuit the end of addition can be signaled by the carry completion circuit; this completion signal depends on the particular numbers being added rather than having to wait for the maximum possible length of carry.

In a second method of speeding up addition, rather than generating a single number (the sum), two numbers are generated, one called a pseudo-sum and the other a pseudo-carry. Neither of these numbers requires a sequence of carries from stage to stage in their generation, and thus in such a method the carry propagation problem is eliminated. If a sequence of additions is performed, it is possible to leave the partial results in the pseudo-carry and pseudo-sum form and only combine these numbers into a single sum (called assimilation) just previous to storing the number in the memory. In assimilation carries must be propagated, but in a long number of additions only one carry propagate time is required, rather than one for each addition. This, of course, is very useful in speeding up multiplication.

We have presented two techniques to decrease addition time in a computer. The fast carry logic may, of course, be applied to carry assimilation to speed up this step when using the pseudo-sum, pseudo-carry representation. Other techniques are also available to speed up arithmetic operations; for example, multiplication can be speeded up by recoding the multiplier so that if a string of 1's occur in the multiplier as

$$2^{-(j+1)} + 2^{-(j+2)} + \cdots + 2^{-(j+k)},$$

rather than doing k successive additions, one addition and one subtraction are performed according to the relation

$$2^{-(j+1)} + 2^{-(j+2)} + \cdots + 2^{-(j+k)} = 2^{-j} - 2^{-(j+k)}.$$

One of the annoying factors in computers using the simple computer organization described in Section 1.3 is that certain units cannot be used to their fullest capacity at all times. For example, the arithmetic and control units may be tied up with the simple task of transferring data either from an input unit to the memory unit or from the memory unit to some output unit during input or output instructions. In addition, the rate of this transfer must be synchronized with the input and output equipment, and this is ordinarily much slower than the rate at which information can be transferred between the arithmetic unit and the memory. Another example is the imbalance between arithmetic speed and memory speed. The speed of fairly large capacity memory units is presently much slower than that at which some of the arithmetic processes can be performed in the arithmetic unit. Thus the arithmetic unit may often be waiting for operands from the memory.

Through other types of computer organization and the use of extra equipment, some of these problems of unmatched speeds among the various units can be eliminated. Separate input-output control equipment can be installed so that data can be read directly between the memory unit and the input-output units. In this way the arithmetic and control units may be performing arithmetic calculations at the same time that data are being transferred between the memory and the input-output units. Additional control equipment has also been proposed to determine what operands and instructions from the memory will be required after the instruction now being performed has been completed, and to transfer these operands and instructions to small capacity, highspeed memory devices so that these data will be available when required.

These two examples of variations on machine organization illustrate attempts to keep the computational units of the computer busy doing useful computation a higher percentage of the time. When two or more operations are being done simultaneously, methods must also be provided for insuring that the operations are not interfering with one another. This can be done with either additional circuits or specially prepared programs for the computer.

1.15 HISTORICAL REMARKS

Since we have introduced some of the basic notions of digital computers and since various methods of computation developed in the past may be useful for future digital systems, it may be interesting to give a brief discussion of their historical developments.

From very early times, various mechanisms have been devised to ease the drudgery of performing calculations by hand. The abacus is probably the earliest; it is still widely used, particularly in China and Japan. Basically, two methods of calculating have been mechanized. One method is illustrated by the mechanization of logarithms. Devices using this and other techniques of measurement are called "analog" or "measurement devices." A simple example of an analog device is the slide rule. We shall not discuss the historical development of analog devices here, but only some of the historical developments of the calculating device, called *digital machines*. The machines are called *digital* because arithmetic processes are carried out by mechanisms for representing and counting integers.

In the 1600's Pascal and Leibniz conceived primitive machines using the mechanical movement of wheels to indicate addition of integers. These machines, as well as other later developments in the 1800's, are the forerunners of the modern mechanical desk calculators. These machines could perform various arithmetic processes such as addition, multiplication, and division, but it was necessary for the operator to record intermediate results and set up the machine for the next calculation.

In the early 1800's, Charles Babbage devised two mechanical machines in an attempt to automate the entire process of calculation, which eliminated frequent operator intervention, giving a resulting increase in speed for completing a sequence of calculations. The Babbage machines failed mainly because of the inability to produce economically the mechanical parts of the machine.

The next big step in digital machines came when H. Hollerith of the United States Census Bureau proposed the use of punched holes in cards to store information and machines to sort and analyze these data. This idea was expanded by IBM, and similar ideas of Powers, an assistant of Hollerith, were developed by Remington Rand Company. An example is shown in Figure 1.7.1. Many types of card-handling machines then appeared which automatically performed the various operations required for business accounting calculations. These machines also began to be used in the 1930's and 1940's for scientific and statistical computations.

In 1939, through a joint effort of Harvard University and IBM, the development of a fully automated digital calculator was begun. This machine, the Automatic Sequence-Controlled Calculator (Mark I), was built by IBM, with Professor H. H. Aiken of Harvard University setting forth many of the machine requirements. This machine consisted principally of existing or modified electromechanical parts of standard IBM equipment, but these parts were used to produce a much more automatic machine than the previous business machines. It was put into operation at Harvard University in 1944. Professor H. H. Aiken subsequently developed several other computers: the Mark II, III, and IV. The Mark III and IV used electronic computing elements and magnetic drums for storage. Several other electromechanical machines were also constructed during the time of World War II. Two machines, the Bell Relay Computers Model 5, were built by Bell Telephone Laboratories, using mainly telephone relays and teletype equipment. These two computers were built to compute ballistic tables and were also used for other scientific calculations for the Army research laboratories. One of them was located at the Army Aberdeen Proving Grounds, and the other at the NACA Laboratories, Langley Field, Virginia.

All the previously mentioned machines used mechanical or electromechanical devices for representing digits and performing calculations, and were thus limited in speed. With the ever increasing need for more computations, a project was started at the University of Pennsylvania under the sponsorship of the United States Army to design and build the first electronic machine. This machine, the ENIAC, using about 18,000 vacuum tubes was built for the same purpose as the Bell Relay computers, but it was much faster. It was placed in operation early in 1946, and could perform approximately 300 multiplications per second on ten-digit decimal numbers.

The ENIAC was very fast compared with the previous electromechanical machines. The two main drawbacks of ENIAC were its large number of vacuum tubes, making it quite difficult to keep in repair, and its limited capacity to store numbers—either data or intermediate results. Originally, ENIAC could store only 20 ten-digit numbers, these being changeable during the calculation. This restriction made it very hard to organize certain computations on the ENIAC and thus various modifications were made later.

The next advances in digital computer development were made by using many fewer tubes than ENIAC and in storing more numbers. Methods for controlling a machine and for storing numbers using relatively few tubes were the two main problems at this stage of computer development.

The solution to the logical problem of control is due to John von Neumann, and the logical design of the next class of digital computers to A. W. Burks, H. H. Goldstine, and von Neumann [5].

Two methods of storing numbers were under concurrent development. One of these methods, called the "acoustic delay line," used the piezoelectric properties of quartz crystals to transform electric pulses into acoustic pulses and transmit these through a column of mercury, which at the other end of the column was reconverted into an electric pulse by a second crystal. With proper amplification and feedback to the first quartz crystal, a number could be stored as a recirculating sequence of acoustical pulses.

Before the ENIAC was completed, the University of Pennsylvania started another machine, the EDVAC, using acoustic delay lines for memory. Other machines using this memory principle were also built: namely, the SEAC by the National Bureau of Standards in Washington, D.C., the UNIVAC by Remington Rand Company (now Sperry-Rand Corporation), and the EDSAC at the University Mathematical Laboratory in Cambridge, England. The latter computer was the first of this type of machine to become operational in May 1949. Professors J. W. Mauchly and J. P. Eckert, two of the developers of the ENIAC and EDVAC at the University of Pennsylvania, formed their own company and built a computer called the BINAC; and, from this machine, the Remington Rand UNIVAC computers were developed.

Concurrent with the development of the acoustic delay line memory, another type of memory using electrostatic storage tubes, was being devised. Two examples are a special tube, called a "selectron," developed by J. Rajchmann at the RCA Research Laboratory, and an electrostatic storage system using standard cathode-ray tubes (later called "Williams tubes" in this type of memory) designed in 1949 by F. C. Williams at the University of Manchester, England. A group of machines was then built using the Williams tube type of memory. One such machine, based on the reports of Burks, Goldstine, and von Neumann, was completed under the direction of von Neumann at the Institute for Advanced Studies (IAS) at Princeton, New Jersey.

Following these general lines of design, M. V. Wilkes built the EDSAC at Cambridge University, the University of Illinois built the ORDVAC and the ILLIAC, and other similar computers were the MANIAC I and II at Los Alamos, New Mexico; the AVIDAC at the Argonne National Laboratories; and the ORACLE at Oak Ridge, Tennessee. IBM built the 701 and 702 computers, using both Williams tubes and magnetic drums for storage, ERA a Type 1103 machine, and Philco Corporation the TRANSAC 1000 and 2000. The Massachusetts Institute of Technology constructed the WHIRLWIND I, using a different type of cathode-ray tube storage.

Most machines using electrostatic storage or acoustic delay lines also had either magnetic drum or magnetic tape units (see Section 1.8), which enlarged their capacity to store numbers, since many of the problems required additional storage capacity. The magnetic drum and tape units were much slower, but also considerably cheaper than the electrostatic or acoustic storage; thus, in the 1950's, a number of medium-speed computers were built using only the magnetic drum for memory. Such computers are the ERA 1101 and 1102 built by the Engineering Research Associates of Minneapolis, Minnesota, the Librascope LGP-30, the DATATRON of Burroughs Corporation, and the IBM 650.

Soon a new magnetic device, the magnetic core came about. These magnetic cores proved not only to be relatively fast but also much more economical and reliable than the acoustic delay lines and electrostatic storage systems, and soon replaced them. Sperry-Rand Corporation built the UNIVAC II computers; IBM built the 704 and 705 and later the 709; and ERA built their 1103A and 1103AF, all with core storage systems. Other companies have also entered the computer field and many companies have developed transistorized machines. RCA built the BIZMAC and 500 series machines; Datamatic Corporation the DATA-MATIC 1000; National Cash Register Company with their NCR-304; Philco Corporation with the TRANSAC S-2000; and IBM built the 7090, to name a few.

Higher-speed computers have been developed in recent years which operate from ten to one hundred times as fast as their predecessors: Sperry-Rand's LARC; the IBM STRETCH, and the University of Illinois' Very-High-Speed computer are outstanding examples.

1.16 DIGITAL CIRCUITS IN COMMUNICATION

In the previous sections we have discussed one type of digital system, general-purpose digital computers. Digital systems are used in many, and an expanding number of, other applications. Since problems of digital systems, in general, are amenable to techniques of switching theory, we describe briefly some of them.

In this section we describe two applications in communication networks. The first is the interconnection of communication links, such as telephone lines, between various points. For example, in a telephone system, a digital system is employed to interconnect a "calling" telephone to the "called" telephone. Through a sequence of digits (input signals from the dialing of a telephone number) the calling telephone requests to be interconnected with some other telephone. The system to accomplish this interconnection is digital, since the input signals are digital and there are only a finite number of interconnections (outputs) which are possible.

A functional diagram of a telephone system is shown in Figure 1.16.1.

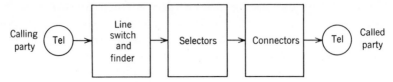

Figure 1.16.1   Functional diagram of a telephone system.

When the telephone receiver is lifted, the line switch and finder automatically connect the telephone line of the calling party to an idle line leading to a selector. The function of the selector is to hold all preceding switches operated and locked out from other calls, to apply a dial tone, to receive the numerical sequence of inputs from the dial of the telephone, and to find an idle line to the appropriate connector. The connector uses the last two digits of the dialed number to determine the exact connection to the called party, and it then tests the called party; if busy, there is a busy signal, and if idle, a ringing signal. When the called party answers, the connector removes the ringing signal and supplies a transmission current to both parties. On completion of the call, the connectors and selectors release the switches and lines involved in the connection. This brief description provides a simplified version of the operation of a telephone system. Its design and operation are complicated because there are a great many telephones in a system and a system may need to be modified and interconnected with other manual or automatic telephone systems.

The second application is in the transmission of digital information over transmission links in the presence of noise. Here we are interested in transmitting a digital signal from one location to another, but the signal on being received may be in error because of noise introduced in the transmission between the transmitter and receiver. Figure 1.16.2 shows a block diagram for such transmission.

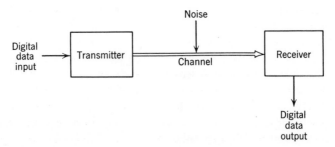

Figure 1.16.2   Noise in communication channel.

The exact errors which are introduced into a signal by the noise are usually not determinable by the receiver; but some scheme is desired for obtaining correct data at the output of the system. One such scheme is the use of error-correcting codes for the digital data. Many such coding schemes have been developed as discussed in [15]. These encode the digital data into a form which includes some extra (or redundant) digits so that certain errors in transmission may be detected and corrected by proper use of the digits. An extremely simple code is the two out of five code of Table 1.6.1 in which a single digit error is detectable by noting simply that not exactly two of the five digits are equal to one. In general, with

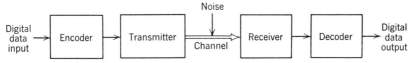

Figure 1.16.3   Error-correcting code system.

such a scheme one has to encode the digital data before transmission and "decode" the data at the receiver end, as shown in Figure 1.16.3.

Each error-correcting code gives specific rules for encoding and decoding the digital data, which are implemented respectively in the "encoder" and "decoder" blocks of Figure 1.16.3.

As we shall see later precise methods of prescribing the functions of blocks in these digital systems can be given.

1.17   SOME OTHER APPLICATIONS OF DIGITAL SYSTEMS

Digital circuits are often used in automatic process control equipment, digital control systems, pattern recognition systems such as character recognition machines, and information retrieval systems. For example, in automatic process control various continuous processes (such as in some parts of the manufacture of chemical substances, oil refining, and paper manufacture) certain measurable parameters of the system such as chemical composition and temperature can be used to determine the system performance and automatically vary control parameters to control the process. Often some of the measuring and control parameters are converted from continuous to digital signals, and special-purpose digital systems are used to perform the control function.

A common application of character recognition is in automatic processing of checks by the banking industry, in which specially designed characters are magnetically sensed in a digital manner, and digital systems use the signals obtained from these characters to determine the proper routing and processing of each check. Means for optical sensing of characters are also being perfected. In some of these, small black and white areas on a page are converted to binary electrical signals. Each of these signals is then correlated with signals from neighboring areas to determine the exact characters on the page. Various methods have been developed to enable recognition of either printed or handwritten characters.

Exercises

1. Convert the following decimal numbers into binary numbers; for fractions express the binary numbers to at least six places and indicate if the conversion is exact or not.

   (a) 57   (b) 0.40625

   (c) $\dfrac{15}{64}$ (d) 0.865

   (e) 432.5625   (f) 2048

2. Convert the decimal numbers of Exercise 1 into octal numbers.

3. Convert the following binary numbers into decimal numbers.

   (a) 0.101101   (b) 110.110

   (c) 100,000   (d) 111011.001101

4. On page 11 formulas and an argument are given which justify conversion from decimal integers to binary integers. Generalize these formulas and argument to convert from a base r system to a base s system.

5. Convert the following numbers to the radix indicated.

   (a) $(111)_3 = N_2$

   (b) $(175)_8 = N_2$

   (c) $(413.32)_5 = N_{10}$

6. Construct addition, subtraction, and multiplication tables for a radix 5 number system.

7. Construct addition tables for the 8421 binary-coded decimal system. Give an example which requires several adjacent carries.

8. Perform the following arithmetic operations in the bases indicated.

   (a) $(542)_6 + (322)_6$ (b) $(465)_7 - (66)_7$

   (c) $(320)_4 - (0.13)_4$ (d) $(110101.011101)_2 \div (101.1)_2$

9. A floating-point computer handles binary numbers of the form

$$x \cdot 2^y,$$

where the range of x is

$$-1 \leq x < 1$$

and the range of y is

$$-2^{10} \leq y < 2^{10}.$$

Calculate the ranges of the resultants for addition, subtraction, and multiplication and indicate how overflow might be detected.

10. Assume a 2's-complement system, binary fractional representation is used in computer arithmetic. For the conditions of adding two numbers together (where either number may be positive or negative) determine how the conditions of overflow (that is, when the sum s is not in the range $-1 \leq s < 1$) can be sensed.

REFERENCE NOTATIONS

Other and more detailed descriptions of digital computers are available in many sources; for example, in Chapter 2 of [2] Alt discusses the history, functional units, and number representations of digital computers. In [4] Brooks and Iverson discuss data processing on computers; Chapters 1, 3, and 5 especially should be of interest. Reference [5] is one of the first extensive reports on the design considerations for a computer. Gotlieb and Hume [9] also describe number representation and digital computers in Chapters 1 through 4. Also see Chapters 7–9 and 11 of Phister [16]. The material for Section 1.13 was obtained from [14], in which many more details of the LGP-30 are described. Richards [17] describes circuits and procedures for performing arithmetic, and in [20] Smith describes the various types of devices and circuits used in computers. Chapter 17 of [20] gives a particularly good discussion of attempts at increasing computer speeds. Particular methods of speeding up an adder are also discussed in [8] and [18]. A final example is the recent book by Ware [26]. Chapters 1, 2, 5, and 11–14 are of interest here.

The modular number system, only briefly mentioned in Section 1.4, can be further investigated through Garner's lucid article [7] or Szabo's more recent paper [23]. The original paper by Svoboda [22], however, may be somewhat more difficult to obtain. In [21] appears an interesting history of number systems, and in [6] and [19] there are interesting and somewhat more extensive histories of calculating machines; [19] also includes an extensive chronological bibliography on computers.

Descriptions of circuits used in telephone systems are given in [1]. Peterson [15] provides an excellent treatment for further study of error-correcting codes and associated circuitry; for a shorter discussion Kautz [13] may be useful. Finally, References [11, 12, and 25] illustrate some of the papers on the subjects of digital control and pattern recognition which were discussed in Section 1.17.

REFERENCES

1. Albert, A. L., *Fundamentals of Telephony*, McGraw-Hill Book Co. New York, 1943.
2. Alt, Franz L., *Electronic Digital Computers*, Academic Press, New York, 1958.
3. Bartee, Thomas C., *Digital Computer Fundamentals*, McGraw-Hill Book Co. New York, 1960.
4. Brooks, F. P., Jr., and K. E. Iverson, *Automatic Data Processing* John Wiley and Sons, 1963.
5. Burks, A. W., H. H. Goldstine, and J. von Neumann, *Preliminary Discussion of the Logical Design of an Electronic Computing Instrument*, Institute for Advanced Study, 1947.
6. Encyclopedia Britannica, "Calculating Machines," Vol. 4, pp. 548–554, 1960.
7. Garner, Harvey L., "The Residue Number System," *IRE Transactions on Electronic Computers*, Vol. EC-8, pp. 140–147, June 1959.
8. Gilchrist, B., J. H. Pomerene, and S. Y. Wong, "Fast Carry Logic of Digital Computers," *IRE Transactions on Electronic Computers*, Vol. EC-4, No. 4, pp. 133–136, December 1955.
9. Gotlieb, C. C., and J. N. P. Hume, *High-Speed Data Processing*, McGraw-Hill Book Co., New York, 1958.
10. Hohn, Franz E., *Applied Boolean Algebra, An Elementary Introduction*, The Macmillan Co., New York, 1960.

11. Jury, E. I., "Recent Advances in the Field of Sampled-Data and Digital Control Systems," *Automatic and Remote Control*, Vol. 1, *Proceedings of the First International Congress of the International Federation of Automatic Control*, Moscow, 1960, Butterworths, London, England, 1961, pp. 262–269.

12. Kamentsky, L. A., "The Simulation of Three Machines Which Read Rows of Handwritten Arabic Numbers," *IRE Transactions on Electronic Computers*, Vol. EC-10, pp. 489–501, September 1961.

13. Kautz, W. H., "Codes and Coding Circuitry for Automatic Error Correction within Digital Systems," in *Redundancy Techniques for Computing Systems*, edited by R. H. Wilcox and W. C. Mann, Spartan Books, pp. 152–195, 1962.

14. *Maintenance Manual for the Royal Precision Electronic Computer* (LGP-30).

15. Peterson, W. W., *Error Correcting Codes*, John Wiley and Sons, New York, 1960.

16. Phister, Montgomery, Jr., *Logical Design of Digital Computers*, John Wiley and Sons, New York, 1958.

17. Richards, R. K., *Arithmetic Operations in Digital Computers*, D. Van Nostrand Co., Princeton, New Jersey, 1955.

18. Robertson, James E., "Theory of Computer Arithmetic Employed in the Design of the New Computer at the University of Illinois," University of Michigan Engineering Summer Conference, "Theory of Computing Machine Design," June 13–17, 1960.

19. Serrell, R., M. M. Astrahan, G. W. Patterson, and I. B. Pyne, "The Evolution of Computing Machines and Systems," *Proceedings of the IRE*, Vol. 50, No. 5, pp. 1039–1058, May 1962.

20. Smith, Charles V. L., *Electronic Digital Computers*, McGraw-Hill Book Co., New York, 1959.

21. Smith, David Eugene and Jekuthiel Ginsbury, "From Numbers to Numerals and from Numerals to Computation," in *The World of Mathematics*, Vol. 1, pp. 442–464, Simon and Schuster, New York, 1956.

22. Svoboda, A., "Rational Numerical System of Residual Classes," *Stroje Na Zpracovani Informaci*, Sbornik V; 1957.

23. Szabo, N., "Recent Advances in Modular Arithmetic," in *Switching Theory in Space Technology*, edited by H. Aiken and W. F. Main, Stanford University Press, pp. 345–353, 1963.

24. Turing, A. M., "On Computable Numbers, with an Application to the Entscheidungsproblem," *Proc. London Math. Society*, Ser. 2, Vol. 42, pp. 230–265, 1936, and Vol. 43, pp. 544–546, 1937.

25. Unger, S. H., "Pattern Detection and Recognition," *Proceedings of the IRE*, pp. 1737–1752, October, 1959.

26. Ware, W. H., *Digital Computer Technology and Design*, John Wiley and Sons, New York, 1963.

2

Boolean Algebra with Applications to Elementary Switching Circuits

2.1 INTRODUCTION

As shown in Chapter 1, binary circuits and the use of the binary number system constitutes the most convenient method of representing information in electronic digital computers and also in many other types of digital systems for control or switching processes. One of the most elementary models for expressing the behavior of one type of digital system, called "combinational switching circuits," is based on Boolean algebra, which is somewhat similar to the standard algebra for real numbers but has several significant differences. As will be seen in this and subsequent chapters, Boolean algebra and related operations in this algebra provide a simple and precise foundation for the analysis of combinational switching circuits. To prepare the way for developing precise analysis and synthesis techniques of switching theory, we introduce in this chapter the basic concepts of Boolean algebra. In addition, to gain further understanding of these concepts, various theorems, applications, and methods of representing Boolean algebraic functions are discussed. Finally, certain special types of Boolean functions are described which have some importance in switching circuit theory.

2.2 THE BASIC POSTULATES OF BOOLEAN ALGEBRA

An elementary description of Boolean algebra is given by presenting a set of rules or *postulates* which define the various operations of the algebra on the elements in the algebra. In a later section we show that Boolean algebra can also be developed from the mathematical concepts of lattice theory and group theory; often these other mathematical concepts as well as Boolean algebra are useful in switching theory.

A Boolean algebra B is a set of undefined elements $a, b, c, \ldots$, with an equivalence relation (=) defined between the elements and with three operations called *union* denoted by the symbol ∨, *multiplication* denoted by the centered dot (·) or simply by juxtaposition, and *complementation* denoted by the symbol "—" (bar).* The equivalence relation satisfies the following properties for all elements of *B*.

(2.2.1) $a = a.$ (reflexive)

(2.2.2)   If $a = b$, then $b = a.$ (symmetric)

(2.2.3)   If $a = b$ and $b = c$, then $a = c.$ (transitive)

The principle of *substitution* is also satisfied; that is, if $a = b$, a may be replaced by b in any formula involving a, and an equivalent formula is produced.

The union operation and the multiplication operation are binary operations which satisfy the following postulates:

(2.2.4) $a \lor a = a,$ (idempotent laws)

               $a \cdot a = a.$

(2.2.5) $a \lor b = b \lor a,$ (commutative laws)

               $a \cdot b = b \cdot a.$

(2.2.6) $(a \lor b) \lor c = a \lor (b \lor c),$ (associative laws)

           $(a \cdot b) \cdot c = a \cdot (b \cdot c).$

(2.2.7) $a \cdot (b \lor c) = (a \cdot b) \lor (a \cdot c),$ (distributive laws)

           $a \lor (b \cdot c) = (a \lor b) \cdot (a \lor c).$

We assume that *B* contains two elements 0 and 1 which satisfy the following postulates:

(2.2.8) $1 \lor a = 1,$

                     $0 \cdot a = 0.$ (null elements)

(2.2.9) $0 \lor a = a,$

                     $1 \cdot a = a.$ (identity elements)

It should be noted that the 0 and 1 used here are elements of *B* and should not be confused with the quite different numbers 0 and 1 used in binary arithmetic of Chapter 1. That is, the 0 and 1 in binary arithmetic are elements in the algebra of numbers, whereas the 0 and 1 used here are elements of Boolean algebra.

---

* The union, multiplication, and complementation operations are also called the OR-operation, AND-operation, and NOT-operation, respectively.

The complementation operation is a unary operation which satisfies

(2.2.10) $a \vee \bar{a} = 1,$

                 $a \cdot \bar{a} = 0.$ (complementarity laws)

(2.2.11) $\overline{(a \cdot b)} = \bar{a} \vee \bar{b},$

                 $\overline{(a \vee b)} = \bar{a}\bar{b}.$ (dualization laws)

The dualization laws are also called deMorgan's laws.

(2.2.12) $\overline{(\bar{a})} = a.$ (involution law)

Some of these postulates of Boolean algebra are analogous to those of ordinary arithmetic when union ($\vee$) is taken as the sum ($+$) in arithmetic and multiplication ($\cdot$) is considered to be arithmetic multiplication. Thus, for example, the commutative laws (2.2.5) are those of arithmetic $a + b = b + a$ and $ab = ba$. The associative laws (2.2.6) also hold, but only the first of the two distributive laws carries over to arithmetic, that is, $a(b + c) = ab + ac$.

In comparison with arithmetic, however, some of the postulates of Boolean algebra seem quite unusual; for example, the idempotent laws (2.2.4), the null element postulate $1 \vee a = 1$, and the dualization laws (2.2.11). As we shall see, these postulates give Boolean algebra some of the particular properties of interest in switching theory.

We note that postulates (2.2.4) through (2.2.11) are given in pairs. By interchanging the OR- and AND- operations and also the 0- and 1-elements in one postulate of a pair, the other postulate is obtained. This procedure is known as the *principle of duality*. Since postulate (2.2.12) is unaffected by duality, it is said to be *self-dual*. By combining these postulates in various ways, using the principle of substitution, new laws or *identities* can be formed. For example, substituting $b \vee a$ for $a \vee b$ in the first associative law gives the identity $(b \vee a) \vee c = a \vee (b \vee c)$. In a similar fashion each identity we obtain from the postulates has a dual identity. Thus $(b \cdot a) \cdot c = a \cdot (b \cdot c)$ is also an identity. Since the dual identity follows directly from the principle of duality, a separate proof is unnecessary.

The postulates (2.2.1) through (2.2.12) do not contradict one another, that is, they are "consistent," but it is easily seen that they are not independent; that is, fewer postulates could be given for defining a Boolean algebra. To show this we prove (2.2.8) using postulates (2.2.5), (2.2.7) (2.2.9), and (2.2.10).

$$
\begin{aligned}
0 \cdot a &= 0 \vee (0 \cdot a) & &\text{by (2.2.9)} \\
&= (a \cdot \bar{a}) \vee (0 \cdot a) & &\text{by (2.2.10)} \\
&= (a \cdot \bar{a}) \vee (a \cdot 0) & &\text{by (2.2.5)} \\
&= a \cdot (\bar{a} \vee 0) & &\text{by (2.2.7)} \\
&= a \cdot (0 \vee \bar{a}) & &\text{by (2.2.5)} \\
&= a \cdot \bar{a} & &\text{by (2.2.9)} \\
&= 0 & &\text{by (2.2.10).}
\end{aligned}
$$

Thus the second null element postulate is proved using only four other postulates. By duality the other null element postulate is also true, and thus postulate (2.2.8) is unnecessary as a postulate for Boolean algebra if the four postulates used in the proof of (2.2.8) are given.

We may be able to delete other postulates as well and later prove them as theorems in the system. However, we make no attempt here to develop Boolean algebra from a minimum set of postulates.

2.3 SOME THEOREMS AND IDENTITIES

An arithmetic of the 0- and 1-elements, resulting quite directly from substitution into the postulates, is given in the following identities:

$$
\begin{aligned}
0 \vee 0 &= 0 \\
1 \vee 1 &= 1 \\
0 \vee 1 &= 1 \vee 0 = 1 \\
0 \cdot 0 &= 0 \\
0 \cdot 1 &= 1 \cdot 0 = 0 \\
1 \cdot 1 &= 1 \\
\bar{0} &= 1.
\end{aligned}
$$

(2.3.1)

For example, this last identity of (2.3.1) can be proved as follows:

$$
\begin{aligned}
0 \vee \bar{0} &= 1 & &\text{by (2.2.10)} \\
0 \vee \bar{0} &= \bar{0} & &\text{by (2.2.9)} \\
\therefore \bar{0} &= 1 & &\text{by substitution.}
\end{aligned}
$$

Theorem 2.3.1 The element 1 in (2.2.8) is unique.

PROOF. Suppose two different elements 1 and $1'$ existed in B such that for any element in B we had

$$1 \vee a = 1$$

and any element b in B we had
$$1' \vee b = 1'.$$

Now let $a = 1'$ and $b = 1$. Then
$$1 \vee 1' = 1$$
and
$$1' \vee 1 = 1'.$$

However, since $1 \vee 1' = 1' \vee 1$ by (2.2.5), we have by substitution that
$$1 = 1',$$

and thus the 1-element is unique.

By a similar argument, or by duality, we obtain the following theorem.

Theorem 2.3.2   The element 0 in (2.2.8) is unique.

Let us now prove an identity which is often called the *law of absorption*.

(2.3.2) $a \vee ab = a.$

PROOF. $a \vee ab = a \cdot 1 \vee ab$ by (2.2.9) and by substitution
$$\begin{aligned} &= a(1 \vee b) \quad \text{by (2.2.7)} \\ &= a \cdot 1 \quad\quad \text{by (2.2.8)} \\ &= a \quad\quad\quad \text{by (2.2.9.)} \end{aligned}$$

By duality we have

(2.3.3) $a(a \vee b) = a.$

Some other useful identities in transforming and simplifying Boolean expressions are

(2.3.4) $a \vee \bar{a}b = a \vee b,$
$$a(\bar{a} \vee b) = ab,$$
(2.3.5) $ac \vee \bar{a}b \vee bc = ac \vee \bar{a}b.$

The EXCLUSIVE OR-operation, denoted by the symbol $\oplus$, can be defined as follows:
$$a \oplus b = \bar{a}b \vee a\bar{b}.$$

This operation is very useful. For example, the least significant binary digit of the sum of two binary digits a and b has the value $a \oplus b$. This can be verified by referring back to the binary addition tables (Table 1.5.2). There it is noted that the binary sum equals 1 if $a = 0$, $b = 1$ and $a = 1$, $b = 0$, and the sum is 0 otherwise. The function $a \oplus b$ is identical to the sum digit since it equals 1 if either term $\bar{a}b$ or $a\bar{b}$ equals 1, and $\bar{a}b$ equals 1 when $a = 0$ and $b = 1$, and similarly $a\bar{b}$ equals 1 when

$a = 1$ and $b = 0$. This operation is commutative, associative, and distribution with the AND-operation (see Exercise 7). Some basic identities involving exclusive or are

(2.3.6)
$$\overline{a \oplus b} = ab \vee \bar{a}\bar{b},$$
$$a \oplus a = 0,$$
$$a \oplus 1 = \bar{a},$$
$$a \oplus b \oplus ab = a \vee b.$$

The proof of the identity $a \oplus a = 0$ is as follows:

$$a \oplus a = \bar{a}a \vee a\bar{a} \qquad \text{by definition}$$
$$= 0 \vee 0 \qquad \text{by (2.2.10)}$$
$$= 0 \qquad \text{by (2.2.9)}.$$

Note that $a \oplus a = 0$ serves as a cancellation law for the $\oplus$-operation; thus $a \oplus b = a \oplus c$ implies that $b = c$.

Cancellation is not valid in general for the OR- and AND-operations. That is, $a \vee b = a \vee c$ does not imply that $b = c$; also $a \cdot b = a \cdot c$ does not imply that $b = c$. For example, if $a = 1$, $b = 1$, and $c = 0$, then $a \vee b = a \vee c$ since $1 \vee b = 1 \vee c$ for any b and c, but $1 \neq 0$. A type of cancellation law does hold, however, as expressed in the next theorem.

Theorem 2.3.3   If $a \cdot b = a \cdot c$ and $a \vee b = a \vee c$, then $b = c$.

PROOF.
$$\overline{(a \cdot b)} = \overline{(a \cdot c)} \qquad \text{by hypothesis}$$
$$\bar{a} \vee \bar{b} = \bar{a} \vee \bar{c} \qquad \text{by dualization}$$
$$(a \vee b)(\bar{a} \vee \bar{b}) = (a \vee c)(\bar{a} \vee \bar{c}) \qquad \text{by substitution}$$
$$a\bar{b} \vee \bar{a}b = a\bar{c} \vee \bar{a}c$$
$$a \oplus b = a \oplus c$$
$$a \oplus a \oplus b = a \oplus a \oplus c$$
$$b = c.$$

Another binary relation between elements of B, called the *inclusion* relation and denoted by $\subseteq$, can now be defined.

$$a \subseteq b \quad \text{if and only if} \quad a \cdot b = a.$$

An equivalent definition is

$$a \subseteq b \quad \text{if and only if} \quad a \vee b = b.$$

Note that for the two elements 0 and 1 of B we have $0 \subseteq x$ and $x \subseteq 1$ for any x of B.

It is not difficult to prove that the inclusion relation forms a partial ordering on the elements of *B*. That is,

1. $a \subseteq a$ for all $a \in B$.
2. If $a \subseteq b$ and $b \subseteq a$, then $a = b$.
3. If $a \subseteq b$ and $b \subseteq c$, then $a \subseteq c$.

This partial ordering is proved in Section 2.8.

Another operation, called the *Sheffer stroke* operation, denoted by a /, is defined as follows:

$$a/b = \overline{(a \cdot b)}.$$

This is also called the AND-NOT- or NAND-operation. It is interesting that this operation alone is sufficient to define Boolean algebra. Such a single operation is called a *universal operation*. To prove that the Sheffer stroke is a universal operation we merely have to express $a \cdot b$, $a \vee b$, and $\bar{a}$ in terms of the Sheffer stroke alone. The following identities for this purpose are easily proved by the given definition and postulates of Section 2.2.

$$a \cdot b = (a/b)/(a/b),$$
$$a \vee b = (a/a)/(b/b),$$
$$\bar{a} = a/a.$$

It might also be mentioned that either the AND- and NOT-operations or the OR- and NOT-operations are sufficient sets of operations for a Boolean algebra. For example, using a dualization law, $a \vee b$ can be defined in terms of product and complementation as follows.

$$a \vee b = \overline{(\bar{a} \cdot \bar{b})}.$$

Another universal operation for Boolean algebra, the *Pierce arrow*-operation denoted by $\downarrow$, is defined as

$$a \downarrow b = \overline{(a \vee b)}.$$

This is also called the OR-NOT- or NOR-operation. The reader may verify the universality of this operation.

2.4 APPLICATION OF BOOLEAN ALGEBRA TO SET THEORY AND LOGIC

Table 2.4.1 lists some correspondences between the elements and operations of Boolean algebra and those of set theory, logic, and computer circuits. We briefly discuss the set theory and logic correspondences in this section, and in the next two sections we discuss correspondences with two types of switching circuits.

A set is an arbitrary collection of elements $S = \{a, b, c, \ldots\}$, where we denote that an element a belongs to the set S by $a \in S$. A set B is called a subset of A if $b \in B$ implies that $b \in A$. If B is a subset of A, we denote this relation by $B \subseteq A$. Using the notation 0 for the set containing no

Table 2.4.1

Boolean Algebra	Set Theory	Logic	Computer Circuits
Element	Set of elements	Statement	A signal with two possible values
AND-operation	Intersection	AND	AND-circuit
OR-operation	Union	OR	OR-circuit
NOT-operation	Complement	NOT	NOT-circuit or inverter
0-element	Empty set	False statement	One of the possible signal values
1-element	Set of all elements	True statement	The other possible signal value

elements (the empty set) and the notation 1 for the set of all elements, we can say that $0 \subseteq A$ and $A \subseteq 1$ for any set A. Certain operations on sets are also defined. Given two sets A and B we denote the set whose elements are in both A and in B by $A \cap B$, called the *intersection* of A and B. Similarly, the *union* of A and B, denoted by $A \cup B$, is the set whose elements are members of either A or of B or of both. Given a set A the set of all elements which is not in A is called the *complement* of A and is denoted by $\bar{A}$. Postulates governing the sets and operations may be given; these postulates, however, are identical to those given in Section 2.2 when the correspondences shown in Table 2.4.1 are used and thus are not listed here. As an example of the postulates for set theory the distributive law $a \cdot (b \vee c) = (a \cdot b) \vee (a \cdot c)$ would take the form $A \cap (B \cup C) = (A \cap B) \cup (A \cap C)$. That is, the set of elements consisting of elements in common with A and with the union of sets B and C is the same set as the union of the two sets $(A \cap B)$ and $(A \cap C)$.

A further understanding of these operations on sets may be gained by considering the *Venn diagram*, which is a graphical representation that illustrates set theory relations. The set of all points (1) is represented as

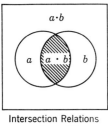

Intersection Relations
$a \cdot b = a \cap b$

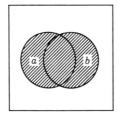

Shaded area
equals $a \vee b$
$a \vee b = a \cup b$

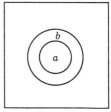

$a \subseteq b$ Relation

Figure 2.4.1   Venn diagrams.

the set of all points in a given rectangle, and subsets a, b, etc., are represented by areas within the rectangle. Some correspondences between Boolean algebra and set theory are shown in Figure 2.4.1.

The Venn diagram is very useful in visualizing some of the postulates and identities of Boolean algebra and set theory. However, these visualizations should not be used to constitute proof of an identity since the diagram may not display the most general situation.

The distributive law $a \vee (b \cdot c) = (a \vee b)(a \vee c)$ is demonstrated by the Venn diagrams in Figure 2.4.2. The identity is visualized as being true since the shaded areas are identical for both $a \vee (b \cdot c)$ and $(a \vee b)(a \vee c)$.

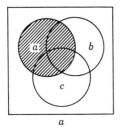

a

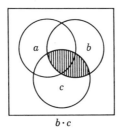

$b \cdot c$

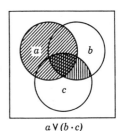

$a \vee (b \cdot c)$

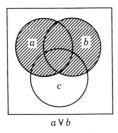

$a \vee b$

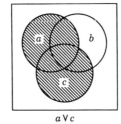

$a \vee c$

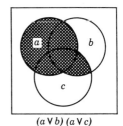

$(a \vee b)(a \vee c)$

Figure 2.4.2   Venn diagrams for the distributive law
$a \vee (b \cdot c) = (a \vee b)(a \vee c)$.

Similarly, the identity $a \vee \bar{a}b = a \vee b$ is shown in Venn diagrams in Figure 2.4.3.

In the application of Boolean algebra to logic, declarative statements are represented by the elements a, b, c, ... These statements can be combined with connectives such as "and," "or," and "not." Some statements we know are true such as, "Two multiplied by two is four."

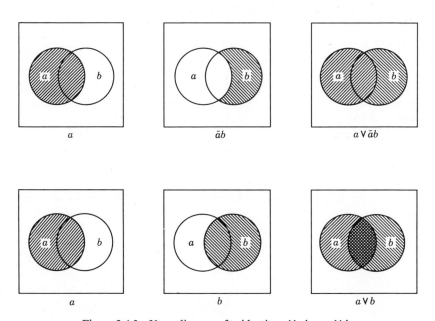

Figure 2.4.3   Venn diagrams for identity $a \vee \bar{a}b = a \vee b$.

Some statements are known to be false, such as, "All apples are green." Finally, some statements are undecidable, such as, "This statement is false." We shall restrict out treatment to decidable statements.

The use of the grammatical connectives "and," "or," and "not" are formalized in logic to obey certain postulates, and as in set theory there is a correspondence between Boolean algebra and logic as shown in Table 2.4.1. To illustrate this correspondence we consider two different combinations of two statements which seem to have the same meaning. Let

$a =$ two multiplied by two is four

and

$b =$ an apple is a fruit

be the two statements. Then the statement that "It is not true that two multiplied by two is four or that an apple is a fruit" is equivalent to, or has the same meaning as, the statement that "Two multiplied by two is not four and an apple is not a fruit." That these two statements are equal corresponds to the following postulate in Boolean algebra.

$$\overline{(a \vee b)} = \bar{a} \cdot \bar{b}$$

Another relation between statements is one of formal implication. Thus, if a and b are statements, we may say that a implies b or alternatively if a is true, then b is true. The $\subseteq$ relation, $a \subseteq b$ of Boolean algebra, can be interpreted as formal implication. Thus, if a is true, then from the definition $a \vee b = b$ with $a = 1$ we obtain $b = 1$ (or true). Note that if a is false ($=0$), then b can be either true or false since $0 \vee b = b$ holds for any b of B. From this discussion we see that a implies b can also be expressed as $\bar{a} \vee b$ being equal to 1. In addition, note that a implies b is true whenever a itself is false. Even though this may seem intuitively wrong, it emphasizes that one must heed the definition rather than intuition, for by the definition of $a \subseteq b$ we see that a being false is interpreted as $a = 0$ and by definition $a \vee b = b$ reduces to $b = b$ which is certainly true for element (or statement) b.

2.5 APPLICATION OF BOOLEAN ALGEBRA TO RELAY CONTACT NETWORKS

By assigning the Boolean element 0 to one of the two states of a switching device and the element 1 to the other state, the methods of Boolean algebra have been found to be extremely helpful in the design and analysis of circuits employing two-state devices. The relay contact is basically a two-state device, that is, it can be either open or closed.

For relay contacts, it is common to associate a 0 with the open contact and a 1 with a closed contact.* Thus, if we label a contact as x, $x = 0$ means that the contact is open and $x = 1$ that the contact is closed. We can realize the basic operations of union, multiplication, and complementation of Boolean algebra by rather simple contact networks, as illustrated in Table 2.5.1.

We must verify that these circuits may indeed be represented by the Boolean operations shown in the table. To do this we consider when there is a closed path between the two end terminals of the circuits shown in the left column. In the first circuit, of course, there is a closed path

* By duality of the algebra the 1 could equally well be associated with an open contact and the 0 with a closed contact. This was the original association made by Shannon in [22], but we choose the opposite association here since it is in more common usage.

when either a or b or both a and b are closed. Using the convention that a and b take on the values 0 and 1 when the contacts are open or closed respectively, we obtain the result that there is a closed path between the two terminals of the circuit under the three conditions $a = 0$, $b = 1$; $a = 1$, $b = 0$; and $a = 1$, $b = 1$; and no closed path only when $a = 0$ and $b = 0$. Now if we also associate a 1 to mean that a closed path exists

Table 2.5.1

Circuit	Boolean Operation
a ⎕ *b* (parallel contacts)	$a \vee b$
a —•— *b* (series contacts)	ab
$\bar{a}$ — A normally closed contact	$\bar{a}$

between the two terminals of the circuit and a 0 to mean that no such closed path exists, then the circuit action is described by the arithmetic identities of Section 2.3 on the 0 and 1 elements as $0 \vee 0 = 0$, $1 \vee 1 = 1$, $0 \vee 1 = 1 \vee 0 = 1$. This shows that the operation $a \vee b$ represents the parallel circuit in Table 2.5.1.

In the second circuit both contacts a and b must be closed for a closed path to exist between the two terminals of the circuit and by using a similar argument as for the previous circuit we see that we can denote this by ab. Finally, in the last circuit the complement represents a circuit whose path is closed when the relay is off; this relay contact is called a "normally closed contact." With this use of the Boolean operations we have extended the use of the 0 and 1 of B from representing open and closed contacts to that of representing open and closed paths in two terminal circuits. As already seen the arithmetic becomes that of the 0 and 1 elements given in Section 2.3 since only the two conditions, open circuit or closed circuit, are to be represented. We should also note that the algebra represents only a closed or an open path, and no direction is assigned to the path. Since relay contacts are *bilateral*, however, current may flow in either direction when the contact is closed, and thus the omission of a direction to the path is proper.

With the interpretation given in Table 2.5.1, relay contact networks can easily be seen to satisfy the postulates (2.2.1) through (2.2.12) of Boolean algebra. For example, for the complementarity law $a \vee \bar{a} = 1$ it is readily seen that the circuit representing $a \vee \bar{a}$ always has a closed path since if a is open, then $\bar{a}$ is closed, and conversely, and the value 1 represents a closed circuit.

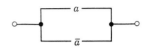

The use of the algebra is then readily extended to larger networks where, for example, the two-terminal parallel network

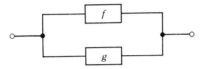

is described by $f \vee g$, where f and g can be two terminal networks previously described by the algebra. Thus if network f is

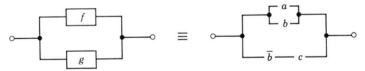

and network g is

the parallel connection of f and g becomes

This network then has a closed path when $(a \vee b) \vee \bar{b}c = 1$ and no closed path when $(a \vee b) \vee \bar{b}c = 0$, as can be checked by the reader. Similarly, series networks and series-parallel networks can be represented directly by expressions in Boolean algebra.

2.6 APPLICATION OF BOOLEAN ALGEBRA TO GATE-TYPE NETWORKS

In contrast to relay contacts, most electronic switching devices are *unilateral*, that is, current will flow only in one direction. Furthermore, the basic electronic circuits realize the operations of Boolean algebra (such as AND, OR, and NOT). This is in contrast to relay contact circuits where the contact positions represent the elements 0 and 1 of B and the operations of AND and OR are represented by series and parallel networks of elements. The electronic circuits are called *gate circuits* or *decision elements*. The correspondence with the Boolean operations is shown in Table 2.6.1.

Table 2.6.1

Decision Element	Boolean Operation
a ⟶ OR ⟶ b ⟶	$a \vee b$
a ⟶ AND ⟶ b ⟶	ab
a ⟶ NOT ⟶	$\bar{a}$

The unilateral properties of the circuits are indicated by arrows; those into an element indicate *inputs* to the element and those leaving an element indicate the *output* of the element. Since it is not our purpose to discuss the details of the electronic design of these circuits, with relation to the interconnection of active and passive electronic components comprising the circuits, it will suffice to model these circuits symbolically as in Table 2.6.1; we shall call any such unilateral element representing a Boolean expression, a *decision element*.

In relay contact circuits an open circuit was represented by the 0-element of Boolean algebra and the 1-element represented a closed circuit. In a similar way, signal values on the decision element inputs and outputs are represented by the Boolean 0 and 1. For example, if the signal values are voltage levels, each input or output may take on either a high or a low voltage with respect to some reference. As one possible convention, a high voltage may be represented by a 1 and a low voltage by a 0. In this case the OR-element would produce a high voltage level on its output if either or both inputs were a high voltage level; and the output would produce a low voltage level only when both inputs were at the low voltage level. By duality the opposite voltage convention could also be used, and then the AND-element for one convention becomes the OR-element for the other convention. Signal values which take on two different possible values may also be measured by other quantities such as current, position in mechanical movement, etc.; and suitable conventions of assigning the Boolean 0 and 1 to signal values is implied when it is said

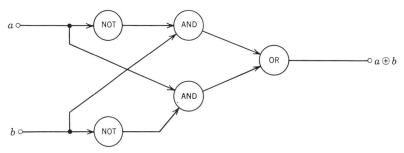

Figure 2.6.1   Logical diagram for $a \oplus b$.

that a decision element is represented by a Boolean expression. Note that the Boolean expression for a decision element uses the inputs of the element as variables in the expression*.

Similar to relay contact circuits we interconnect the basic elements into networks of elements, where Boolean algebra expressions may be used to represent certain aspects of these networks. Various types of these networks will be discussed later. We interconnect these decision elements by connecting outputs to inputs, never allowing two different outputs to be interconnected, and thereby we obtain a *logical circuit* or a *logical diagram*. A simple example of a logical diagram realizing the EXCLUSIVE OR-operation is shown in Figure 2.6.1.

This logical diagram corresponds to the definition $a \oplus b = \bar{a}b \vee a\bar{b}$ for exclusive or. We can show, however, that we can also express $a \oplus b$ by the identity

$$a \oplus b = \overline{(ab)}(a \vee b).$$

The corresponding logical diagram is shown in Figure 2.6.2.

Thus, by using the latter identity for "exclusive or," one NOT-circuit is saved over the logical diagram of Figure 2.6.1.

In our description of decision elements and their interconnection, we have made several idealizations of what actually occurs in a physical

* The output of an element may also be used as a variable in the Boolean expression if the element has a memory capability, but we shall not discuss this now.

circuit. We assume that the decision elements react instantaneously to the inputs, thus giving appropriate outputs at the same instant that inputs are applied. Actually, there will be some time delay that is associated with each decision element, but for now we neglect this. We also assume that there is no restriction on the number of inputs to which an output of a decision element can be attached, whereas circuit power considerations actually impose such restrictions. Finally, we assume that we have

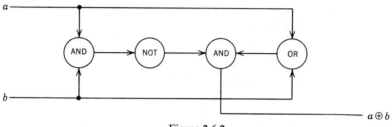

Figure 2.6.2

two-state devices, whereas actually a voltage or current will have to pass from one state to the other in a continuous fashion.

To specify the structure of logical diagrams in a more rigorous way, we define the set of decision elements as a given set of elements, each having a certain number m of inputs and one output, where each of these elements realizes some Boolean operation. Figure 2.6.3 shows such a decision element.

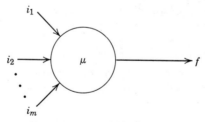

Figure 2.6.3   A decision element.

The symbol μ represents the logical Boolean operation describing the relationship between the output f and the inputs $i_1, \ldots, i_m$ of the decision element. To form a logical diagram, we interconnect the decision elements according to the following rules:

1. An output of a decision element can be attached to one or more inputs of decision elements.

2. The constant values 0 and 1 may be assigned to inputs of the decision elements.

3. No two outputs of decision elements can be interconnected.

After such a structure is formed, we have three types of branches in the logical diagram. The first are those decision element input branches to which no output of a decision element or constant value has been attached. These are called *input branches* to the logical diagram. The second type are those branches which are outputs of decision elements which are not attached to any inputs. These are called *output branches*. All remaining branches are called *internal branches*.

We shall discuss later some further restrictions on structure, classifying logical circuits into circuits without feedback, circuits with feedback, combinational circuits, and sequential circuits.

2.7 BOOLEAN FUNCTIONS AND CANONICAL FORMS

As seen in the previous two sections, Boolean expressions using the elements of B and the operations of Boolean algebra can be used to represent switching networks. In this section we formalize the notion of Boolean expressions into what are called *Boolean functions* and prove several theorems on special forms of Boolean functions.

Definition 2.7.1 A *Boolean function* of n-variables consists of a finite number of variables $x_1, x_2, \ldots, x_n$, each of whose domain* is B, where these variables are connected by a finite number of Boolean operations such as OR, AND, NOT, EXCLUSIVE OR, etc. For any set of values from B for $x_1, x_2, \ldots, x_n$, the value of the function is some element of B, and thus the range of the Boolean function is included in B.

For a Boolean function of n variables, we write $f(x_1, x_2, \ldots, x_n)$, and we shall often use simply the term function to mean Boolean function. For any given function, a number of different *expressions* for that function can be found. If we consider the two variable function

$$f(x_1, x_2) = x_1 \vee \bar{x}_1 \cdot x_2$$

then from Equation (2.3.4) we see that this function may also be expressed as

$$f(x_1, x_2) = x_1 \vee x_2.$$

That is, $x_1 \vee \bar{x}_1 x_2$ and $x_1 \vee x_2$ are two different expressions for the same Boolean function $f(x_1, x_2)$. By applying some of the postulates, we can

---

* The domain of a variable x_i means that x_i can take on, or be assigned, any and only the values in the domain, in this case any of the elements in B are considered as values for x_i.

also obtain

$$f(x_1, x_2) = x_1 \vee \bar{x}_1 x_2$$
$$= x_1 \cdot 1 \vee \bar{x}_1 x_2$$
$$= x_1(x_2 \vee \bar{x}_2) \vee \bar{x}_1 x_2$$
$$= x_1 x_2 \vee x_1 \bar{x}_2 \vee \bar{x}_1 x_2.$$

This last expression for $f(x_1, x_2)$ is called a *canonical form of the function.*

We now derive several theorems to show that any Boolean function can be expressed in several different "standard" or "canonical" forms.

Theorem 2.7.1   Any Boolean function $f(x)$ of a single variable x may be written in the form

$$f(x) = f(1) \cdot x \vee f(0) \cdot \bar{x}.$$

PROOF.   We first consider the form (*) $f(x) = f_1 x \vee f_0 \bar{x}$, where f_1 and f_0 are constant terms, and show that any $f(x)$ can be expressed in this way. The trivial functions 0, 1, x, $\bar{x}$ are functions of one variable and may be expressed in the form of (*) as follows:

$$0 = 0x \vee 0\bar{x} \qquad \text{where } f_1 = f_0 = 0.$$
$$1 = 1x \vee 1\bar{x} \qquad \text{where } f_1 = f_0 = 1.$$
$$x = 1x \vee 0\bar{x},$$
$$\bar{x} = 0x \vee 1\bar{x}.$$

Now assume that $g(x)$ and $h(x)$ are expressible in the form of (*). That is,

$$g(x) = g_1 x \vee g_0 \bar{x},$$
$$h(x) = h_1 x \vee h_0 \bar{x}.$$

We now prove that $\overline{g(x)}$, $g(x) \cdot h(x)$, and $g(x) \vee h(x)$ are expressible in the form of (*):

$$\overline{g(x)} = \overline{(g_1 x \vee g_0 \bar{x})}$$
$$= \overline{(g_1 x)} \cdot \overline{(g_0 \bar{x})}$$
$$= (\bar{g}_1 \vee \bar{x}) \cdot (\bar{g}_0 \vee x)$$
$$= \bar{g}_1 \bar{g}_0 \vee \bar{g}_1 x \vee \bar{g}_0 \bar{x} \vee \bar{x} x$$
$$= \bar{g}_1 \bar{g}_0 (x \vee \bar{x}) \vee \bar{g}_1 x \vee \bar{g}_0 \bar{x}$$
$$= (\bar{g}_1 \bar{g}_0 \vee \bar{g}_1) x \vee (\bar{g}_1 \bar{g}_0 \vee \bar{g}_0) \bar{x}$$
$$= \bar{g}_1 x \vee \bar{g}_0 \bar{x},$$
$$g(x) \cdot h(x) = (g_1 x \vee g_0 \bar{x})(h_1 x \vee h_0 \bar{x})$$
$$= (g_1 h_1) x \vee (g_0 h_0) \bar{x},$$
$$g(x) \vee h(x) = (g_1 x \vee g_0 \bar{x}) \vee (h_1 x \vee h_0 \bar{x})$$
$$= (g_1 \vee h_1) x \vee (g_0 \vee h_0) \bar{x},$$

and each of the final expressions for $\overline{g(x)}$, $g(x) \cdot h(x)$, and $g(x) \vee h(x)$ are in the form of (*).

Since the basic postulates of Boolean algebra were given only in terms of AND-, OR-, and NOT-operations, it follows that all Boolean functions can be formed from only these three operations; thus we can conclude that any Boolean function $f(x)$ can be expressed in the form of (*), that is,

$$f(x) = f_1 \cdot x \vee f_0 \cdot \bar{x}.$$

Now if x is set equal to 0, we obtain

$$f(0) = f_1 \cdot 0 \vee f_0 \cdot \bar{0} = f_0.$$

Thus $f_0 = f(0)$.

Setting $x = 1$ gives

$$f(1) = f_1 \cdot 1 \vee f_0 \cdot \bar{1} = f_1$$

Thus $f_1 = f(1)$, giving,

$$f(x) = f(1) \cdot x \vee f(0) \cdot \bar{x},$$

which proves the theorem.

Similarly, where $f(1, x_2, \ldots, x_n)$ and $f(0, x_2, \ldots, x_n)$ are functions of $x_2, \ldots, x_n$, the following theorem, known as *Shannon's expansion theorem,* can be proved.

Theorem 2.7.2 Any Boolean function $f(x_1, x_2, \ldots, x_n)$ can be written in the form

$$f(x_1, x_2, \ldots, x_n) = f(1, x_2, \ldots, x_n) \cdot x_1 \vee f(0, x_2, \ldots, x_n) \cdot \bar{x}_1.$$

By induction, applying this theorem on the unexpanded functions for all the n-variables, a function $f(x_1, x_2, \ldots, x_n)$ can be written in the form

$$\begin{aligned}
f(x_1, x_2, \ldots, x_n) = &f(1, 1, \ldots, 1) \cdot (x_1 \cdot x_2 \cdot \ldots \cdot x_n) \\
&\vee f(0, 1, \ldots, 1) \cdot (\bar{x}_1 \cdot x_2 \cdot \ldots \cdot x_n) \vee \\
&\ldots \vee f(0, 0, \ldots, 0) \cdot (\bar{x}_1 \cdot \bar{x}_2 \cdot \ldots \cdot \bar{x}_n).
\end{aligned}$$

This form is called the *disjunctive canonical form.* Using a convenient notation, we can restate it as follows.

Theorem 2.7.3 Every Boolean function $f(x_1, \ldots, x_n)$ can be expressed in the *disjunctive canonical form*

$$(2.7.1) \quad f(x_1, x_2, \ldots, x_n) = \bigvee_{e=(0,0,\ldots,0)}^{e=(1,1,\ldots,1)} f(e_1, e_2, \ldots, e_n) x_1^{e_1} \cdots x_n^{e_n}$$

where $e_i = 0$ or 1

$$x_j{}^0 = \bar{x}_j$$
$$x_j{}^1 = x_j$$

$e = (e_1, e_2, \ldots, e_n)$ is an n-tuple of 0's and 1's, and the union extends over all combinations of n 0's and 1's for the e_i's.

This theorem can be informally shown as follows. By applying the definition for EXCLUSIVE OR and other operations and postulates (2.2.11), (2.2.7), (2.2.12), (2.2.4), and (2.2.10), any function can be changed to an expanded form of product terms in which each is expressed as a product of variables or their complements where no product term has the same variable appearing twice and these product terms are connected by the OR-operation. Since the original function has only a finite number of uses of the operation, there will be only a finite number of product terms in the expanded OR form of the function. Now some product term A may not contain occurrences of some variable x_i (or its complement). Such terms may have $(x_i \vee \bar{x}_i)$ joined to them, giving $A(x_i \vee \bar{x}_i)$. Then applying (2.2.7), the function again can be expressed in a union of product terms. By repeated application each term can be made to contain each variable or its complement, and by postulate (2.2.4) duplicate product terms may be eliminated. This form is stated in the theorem.

The value of $f(e_1, e_2, \ldots, e_n)$ is equal to either 0 or 1, as seen by the arithmetic rules of Equations (2.3.1). If $f(e_1, e_2, \ldots, e_n) = 0$, the term $x_1{}^{e_1} \cdots x_n{}^{e_n}$ is absent (has a 0 multiplier) in the canonical form and if $f(e_1, e_2, \ldots, e_n) = 1$, the term appears (has a 1 multiplier) in the canonical form. This canonical form of a Boolean function is called disjunctive because it is the disjunction (OR-operation) of product terms, where each product term contains each variable exactly once, either complemented or not. If a function is expressed as a disjunction of product terms, but each term does not necessarily contain each variable, such an expression is called a *disjunctive normal form*.

By duality with the disjunctive canonical form, we obtain the conjuctive canonical form.

Theorem 2.7.4   Every Boolean function $f(x_1, x_2, \ldots, x_n)$ can be expressed in *conjunctive canonical form*

(2.7.2)

$$f(x_1, x_2, \ldots, x_n) = \prod_{e=(0,0,\ldots,0)}^{e=(1,1,\ldots,1)} [f(\bar{e}_1, \bar{e}_2, \ldots, \bar{e}_n) \vee x_1{}^{e_1} \vee x_2{}^{e_2} \vee \cdots \vee x_n{}^{e_n}]$$

where the product extends over all combinations of n 0's and 1's for the e_i's.

The disjunctive (or conjunctive) canonical form can be easily shown to be a unique representation for a function. Thus, if we wish to check whether two functions $f(x_1, x_2, \ldots, x_n)$ and $g(x_1, x_2, \ldots, x_n)$ are equivalent, we can expand f and g to their disjunctive (conjunctive) canonical forms and compare the expressions.

To illustrate the canonical expansions and their use in determining the equivalence of two function expressions, consider the following example. Let

$$f(x_1, x_2, x_3) = \bar{x}_1 \bar{x}_2 \lor x_2 x_3 \lor x_1 \bar{x}_3$$

and

$$g(x_1, x_2, x_3) = \bar{x}_1(\bar{x}_2 \lor x_3) \lor x_1(x_2 \lor \bar{x}_3).$$

The disjunctive canonical expansion for f and g can be obtained by evaluating the $f(e_1, e_2, e_3)$ and $g(e_1, e_2, e_3)$ for each of the eight possible three-tuples (e_1, e_2, e_3) or by expanding the f and g by using postulates. We do the former for f and the latter for g.

$$f(0, 0, 0) = f(0, 0, 1) = f(0, 1, 1) = f(1, 1, 1)$$
$$= f(1, 1, 0) = f(1, 0, 0) = 1$$

and

$$f(1, 0, 1) = f(0, 1, 0) = 0.$$

Thus $f(x_1, x_2, x_3) = \bar{x}_1 \bar{x}_2 \bar{x}_3 \lor \bar{x}_1 \bar{x}_2 x_3 \lor \bar{x}_1 x_2 x_3 \lor x_1 x_2 x_3 \lor x_1 x_2 \bar{x}_3 \lor x_1 \bar{x}_2 \bar{x}_3.$

Also $g(x_1, x_2, x_3) = \bar{x}_1(\bar{x}_2 \lor x_3) \lor x_1(x_2 \lor \bar{x}_3)$

$$= \bar{x}_1 \bar{x}_2(x_3 \lor \bar{x}_3) \lor \bar{x}_1(x_2 \lor \bar{x}_2)x_3$$
$$\lor x_1 x_2(x_3 \lor \bar{x}_3) \lor x_1(x_2 \lor \bar{x}_2)\bar{x}_3$$
$$= \bar{x}_1 \bar{x}_2 x_3 \lor \bar{x}_1 \bar{x}_2 \bar{x}_3 \lor \bar{x}_1 x_2 x_3$$
$$\lor x_1 x_2 x_3 \lor x_1 x_2 \bar{x}_3 \lor x_1 \bar{x}_2 \bar{x}_3.$$

Checking term by term we immediately verify that $f(x_1, x_2, x_3)$ is equivalent to $g(x_1, x_2, x_3)$.

From Theorem 2.7.3 we see that for an n-variable function there are exactly 2^n possible canonical product terms and each of these terms may either appear or not appear in the disjunctive canonical form for the function. Thus it follows that there are exactly 2^{2^n} Boolean functions of n variables.

If we consider each x_i to take on only two values either 0 br 1, we can write the function in a tabular form called the *truth table* for a function. Let us consider a specific example:

$$f(x_1, x_2, x_3) = \bar{x}_1 \bar{x}_2 \bar{x}_3 \lor \bar{x}_1 x_2 x_3 \lor x_1 \bar{x}_2 x_3 \lor x_1 x_2 \bar{x}_3.$$

The truth table for this function is shown in Table 2.7.1. This tabular form is a convenient representation for a function.

In general, for an n-variable function the truth table contains 2^n rows, one column for each variable and one column for the functional value.

Table 2.7.1   A Truth Table

	x_1	x_2	x_3	f
0	0	0	0	1
1	0	0	1	0
2	0	1	0	0
3	0	1	1	1
4	1	0	0	0
5	1	0	1	1
6	1	1	0	1
7	1	1	1	0

Each row has a different set of 0 and 1 values for the $x_1, x_2, \ldots, x_n$, and it is convenient to arrange the rows in binary numerical form for these values so that the first row has binary value 0 and the last row has binary value $2^n - 1$. This binary value is noted for our example in the left-most column of Table 2.7.1. If we are interested in several functions additional columns can be added. For example, the binary operations can be displayed in truth table forms as in Table 2.7.2.

Table 2.7.2   Truth Tables for Binary Operations

	a	b	$a \vee b$	$a \cdot b$	$a \oplus b$	$a \subseteq b$	a/b	$a \downarrow b$
0	0	0	0	0	0	1	1	1
1	0	1	1	0	1	1	1	0
2	1	0	1	0	1	0	1	0
3	1	1	1	1	0	1	0	0

From the dualization laws a simple procedure can be shown to convert the disjunctive canonical form of a function f into the conjunctive canonical form for f. This procedure can be stated as follows: Take the union of all the terms not in the disjunctive canonical form for f, replace each occurrence of the OR-operation with the AND-operation and each occurrence of the AND-operation with the OR-operation and reverse complements on all the letters. Similarly, we can convert from the conjunctive canonical form to the disjunctive canonical form.

A similar procedure, resulting from the dualization laws, enables us to obtain the complement of any function where the functional expression does not contain any complemented parentheses. Thus, given a function f, having no complemented parentheses, the function $\bar{f}$ is obtained by replacing each occurrence of the OR-operation in f with the AND-operation, and each occurrence of the AND-operation in f with the OR-operation, and reversing the complements on all letters in f.

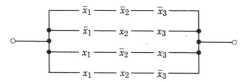

Figure 2.7.1   Relay contact circuit for $f(x_1, x_2, x_3)$ of Table 2.7.1.

The use of Boolean functions both in the relay contact network application and in the gate-type network application should be evident, for Boolean functions were implicitly used in Sections 2.5 and 2.6.

Consider, for example, the problem of designing a relay contact network to realize the function f shown in Table 2.7.1. From the disjunctive canonical expression

$$f(x_1, x_2, x_3) = \bar{x}_1\bar{x}_2\bar{x}_3 \vee \bar{x}_1 x_2 x_3 \vee x_1 \bar{x}_2 x_3 \vee x_1 x_2 \bar{x}_3,$$

we see that each term is represented by a series circuit of three contacts, and the OR-operations correspond to parallel interconnection. This gives the circuit shown in Figure 2.7.1.

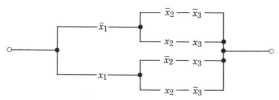

Figure 2.7.2   Another realization for $f(x_1, x_2, x_3)$ of Table 2.7.1.

Other expressions for $f(x_1, x_2, x_3)$ may give simpler relay contact circuits, however. By using some of the postulates, we see that

$$f(x_1, x_2, x_3) = \bar{x}_1(\bar{x}_2\bar{x}_3 \vee x_2 x_3) \vee x_1(x_2 \bar{x}_3 \vee \bar{x}_2 x_3),$$

which gives the relay contact circuit shown in Figure 2.7.2. This circuit would usually be considered simpler than that in Figure 2.7.1 because it requires only ten contacts rather than twelve contacts.

For a practical example, the sum and carry digits for a binary adder may be expressed as Boolean functions. Let the Boolean 0 represent the binary 0 and the Boolean 1 represent the binary 1 for the binary variables a_i, b_i, and c_i, where

$$a_i = \text{the } i\text{th augend digit,}$$
$$b_i = \text{the } i\text{th addend digit,}$$
$$c_i = \text{the carry into the } i\text{th digit.}$$

Then the sum for the ith position s_i and the carry from the ith position c_{i-1} are represented as Boolean functions in Table 2.7.3.

Table 2.7.3 Truth Table for Binary Sum and Carry Functions

a_i	b_i	c_i	s_i	c_{i-1}
0	0	0	0	0
0	0	1	1	0
0	1	0	1	0
0	1	1	0	1
1	0	0	1	0
1	0	1	0	1
1	1	0	0	1
1	1	1	1	1

As will be shown later using these functions leads to suitable functional expressions for representing either relay or logical networks, and different expressions for the same function represent different networks.

2.8 GROUP THEORY AND LATTICE THEORY CONNECTIONS WITH BOOLEAN ALGEBRA

The purpose of this section is, first, to show that Boolean algebra is equivalent to the mathematical concept of a ring with a unit in which the idempotence law also holds; and second, to show that Boolean algebra also corresponds to a particular type of distributive lattice. Toward this goal we introduce the basic concepts of abstract groups, rings, and lattices.

The treatment in this section is somewhat more precise and formal than that in some of the previous sections, and thus a reader having no previous introduction to abstract algebra may find this section rather difficult to read. Nevertheless, it is considered worthwhile to show these precise descriptions of Boolean algebra. Explanations of some of the mathematical concepts are included to help the reader.

Definition 2.8.1 An abstract *group* G consists of a set of elements $a, b, c, \ldots$, an equivalence relation, and a binary $+$-operation satisfying postulates (2.8.1) through (2.8.4).

(2.8.1) *Closure for $+$:* If a and b are elements of G, then $c = a + b$ is a unique element of G.

(2.8.2) *Associativity:* $(a + b) + c = a + (b + c)$ for a, b, and c elements of G.

(2.8.3) *Identity:* There is an element e of G such that for every a of G,

$$e + a = a + e = a.$$

(2.8.4) *Inverse:* For each a of G there exists an element a' of G such that

$$a + a' = a' + a = e.$$

Definition 2.8.2 A group G which also satisfies the commutativity postulate (2.8.5) is called a *commutative group* or *Abelian group*.

(2.8.5) *Commutativity:* $a + b = b + a$ for any two elements a and b of G.

Definition 2.8.3 A *ring* R is an Abelian group which has a second binary $\times$-operation satisfying postulates (2.8.6) and (2.8.7), and distributive postulates (2.8.8) and (2.8.9) for the $+$- and $\times$-operations.

(2.8.6) *Closure for $\times$:* If a and b are elements of R, then $c = a \times b$ is a unique element of R.

(2.8.7) *Associativity:* $(a \times b) \times c = a \times (b \times c)$ for elements a, b, and c of R.

(2.8.8) *Left distributivity:* $a \times (b + c) = (a \times b) + (a \times c)$ for elements a, b, and c of R.

(2.8.9) *Right distributivity:* $(b + c) \times a = (b \times a) + (c \times a)$ for elements a, b, and c of R.

Definition 2.8.4 A ring R which also satisfies postulate (2.8.10) is called a *ring with a unit*.

(2.8.10) *Unit:* There is an element i of R such that $a \times i = i \times a = a$.

If we consider the set of all integers as a set of elements, then it is an abstract group where the $+$-operation may be interpreted as the standard sum operation between two integers. In this case the element e is equal to the integer 0 and the element a' is the integer $-a$ for any integer a. For integers the standard multiplication operation satisfies for the $\times$-operation and thus we also have a ring. The unit element i for (2.8.10) is the integer 1.

Definition 2.8.5 A ring with a unit R, which also satisfies the idempotence postulate (2.8.11), is called a *Boolean ring*.

(2.8.11) *Idempotence:* $a \times a = a$ for all a of R.

Up to this point we have formally defined a Boolean ring, but it is not evident why we call such a ring Boolean. Certainly, the ring of integers discussed previously is not a Boolean ring since in general $a \times a \neq a$ for integers a. We now show, however, that by taking the group operation of $+$ to be the EXCLUSIVE OR-operation $\oplus$ of Boolean algebra defined previously, by letting the operation $\times$ be the AND-operation of Boolean algebra, and by letting the set of elements be the set of elements B, then these two operations satisfy the postulates of the Boolean ring. To show this we must verify postulates (2.8.1) through (2.8.11).

Since closure was assumed for the OR-operation and the NOT-operation postulate (2.8.1) is satisfied by the definition $a \oplus b = \bar{a}b \vee a\bar{b}$.

Postulate (2.8.2) is to be proved in Exercise 7 at the end of this chapter.

To prove postulate (2.8.3) let $e = 0$, then $0 \oplus a = a \oplus 0 = a$, since from the definition of $\oplus$

$$0 \oplus a = 1 \cdot a \vee 0 \cdot \bar{a} = a,$$

and
$$a \oplus 0 = \bar{a} \cdot 0 \vee a \cdot 1 = a.$$

Postulate (2.8.4) now requires that $e = 0$ so that $a \oplus a' = a' \oplus a = 0$. By letting $a = a'$, we obtain $a \oplus a = \bar{a}a \vee a\bar{a} = 0$ so that each element a is its own inverse under the $\oplus$-operation. Postulate (2.8.5) is also to be proved in Exercise 7. Now postulates (2.8.6) through (2.8.11) follow directly from those of Boolean algebra for the AND-operation. Note that both (2.8.8) and (2.8.9) are satisfied since $a \cdot b = b \cdot a$ for our Boolean algebra. The unit element of postulate (2.8.10) becomes the element 1 of B.

In a similar fashion starting out with a Boolean ring, with $\oplus$ and the AND-operation as the ring operations, we can obtain all the postulates of our Boolean algebra simply by defining the OR- and NOT-operations as follows.

Definition 2.8.6 For any two elements a and b of R define the OR-operation as

$$a \vee b = a \oplus b \oplus ab.$$

Definition 2.8.7 For any element a of R define the NOT-operation $^-$ as

$$\bar{a} = a \oplus 1.$$

Using these definitions, the formal proofs of the Boolean algebra postulates are quite straightforward and left as an exercise for the reader.

We thus see that a Boolean ring and a Boolean algebra are mathematically equivalent entities.

Definition 2.8.8   A ring with a unit F having at least two elements which also satisfies postulate (2.8.12) is called a *field*.

(2.8.12) *Inverses for* $\times$ *:*   For each element a of F except element e, there is an element a^{-1} of F such that $a \times a^{-1} = i$.

Note that the set of integers is not a field since a^{-1} of an integer is not in general an integer. If we consider the set of all real numbers, however, with addition as the $+$-operation and multiplication as the $\times$-operation, it can be shown that the set of real numbers is also a field.

Definition 2.8.9   A Boolean ring which also satisfies postulate (2.8.12) is called a *Boolean field*.

A Boolean field is a particularly simple type of Boolean algebra, as shown by the next theorem.

Theorem 2.8.1   A Boolean field has exactly two elements, 0 and 1.

PROOF.   If $a \neq 0$, then

$$a \cdot a^{-1} = 1 \qquad \text{by (2.8.12)}$$
and
$$a \cdot 1 = a \qquad \text{by (2.8.10).}$$

Thus

$$a \cdot 1 = a \cdot (a \cdot a^{-1}) = (a \cdot a) \cdot a^{-1}$$
$$= a \cdot a^{-1} = 1.$$

Therefore
$$a = 1.$$

Thus a either equals 0 or 1.

Boolean algebras with more than two elements can easily be seen to exist. For example, if B is assumed to be the set of all n-component vectors of 0's and 1's, then B satisfies the postulates of Boolean algebra where 0 is the vector of all 0's and 1 is the vector of all 1's. For cxample, consider the set of three-tuples

$$B = \{(0, 0, 0), (0, 0, 1), (0, 1, 0), (0, 1, 1), (1, 0, 0), (1, 0, 1), (1, 1, 0),$$
$$(1, 1, 1)\}.$$

Let (a_1, a_2, a_3), (b_1, b_2, b_3), and (c_1, c_2, c_3) be elements of B. That is, the a_i, b_i, and c_i are either 0 or 1. Then define the OR-, AND-, and NOT-operations as

$$(a_1, a_2, a_3) \vee (b_1, b_2, b_3) = (c_1, c_2, c_3),$$

where
$$c_i = a_i \lor b_i,$$
$$(a_1, a_2, a_3) \cdot (b_1, b_2, b_3) = (c_1, c_2, c_3),$$
where
$$c_i = a_i \cdot b_i,$$
and
$$\overline{(a_1, a_2, a_3)} = (\bar{a}_1, \bar{a}_2, \bar{a}_3).$$

As an example of these definitions we obtain:

$$(0, 0, 1) \lor (1, 0, 0) = (1, 0, 1)$$
$$(0, 1, 1) \cdot (1, 1, 0) = (0, 1, 0)$$
$$\overline{(0, 1, 0)} = (1, 0, 1).$$

With these definitions, and using the properties of the arithmetic for 0 and 1 elements, it is obvious that the idempotent, commutative, associative, and distributive postulates hold on B. Also, the complementarity, null element, identity element, and involution postulates hold if we define 0 in the Boolean algebra as $(0, 0, 0)$ and 1 as $(1, 1, 1)$.

The dualization postulate $\overline{(a \cdot b)} = \bar{a} \lor \bar{b}$ is proved as follows.

$$\overline{[(a_1, a_2, a_3) \cdot (b_1, b_2, b_3)]} = \overline{(a_1 \cdot b_1, a_2 \cdot b_2, a_3 \cdot b_3)}$$
$$= (\overline{a_1 \cdot b_1}, \overline{a_2 \cdot b_2}, \overline{a_3 \cdot b_3})$$
$$= (\bar{a}_1 \lor \bar{b}_1, \bar{a}_2 \lor \bar{b}_2, \bar{a}_3 \lor \bar{b}_3)$$
$$= (\bar{a}_1, \bar{a}_2, \bar{a}_3) \lor (\bar{b}_1, \bar{b}_2, \bar{b}_3)$$
$$= \overline{(a_1, a_2, a_3)} \lor \overline{(b_1, b_2, b_3)}.$$

The dual dualization postulate may be proved similarly. Thus all the postulates of Boolean algebra are satisfied for this eight element set B and the defined OR-, AND-, and NOT-operations, so this is a Boolean algebra.

Similar definitions obviously can be used on n-component vectors of 0's and 1's to give Boolean algebras with 2^n elements for any finite n. Although we shall not show this here, any Boolean algebra with a finite number of elements in B must have a power of two, 2^k, number of elements, and this Boolean algebra is isomorphic to the Boolean algebra of k-tuples of 0's and 1's. It is easy to show, for example, that no Boolean algebra with B having three elements exists. Let $B = \{0, 1, a\}$. From the postulates $\bar{a}$ must exist and $a \lor \bar{a} = 1$. Now if $\bar{a} = 0$, then since $\bar{1} = 0$, it follows that $a = 1$, contrary to assumption; thus $\bar{a} \neq 0$. Similarly, if $\bar{a} = 1$, then $a = 0$ contrary to assumption, and thus $\bar{a} \neq 1$. Thus the only possibility for $\bar{a}$ to exist is that $\bar{a} = a$, but then $a \lor \bar{a} = a \lor a = a \neq 1$, so that the complementarity postulate does not hold, proving that no three element Boolean algebra exists.

To describe the connection between Boolean algebra and lattice theory we must first define a partially ordered set.

Definition 2.8.10   A *partially ordered set* is a set S of elements $a, b, c, \ldots$ on which an equivalence relation and binary relation $\leq$ is satisfied, where $\leq$ satisfies postulates (2.8.13) through (2.8.15).

(2.8.13) *Reflexive:* $a \leq a$ for all a of S.
(2.8.14) *Antisymmetric:* $a \leq b$ and $b \leq a$ implies $a = b$ for a and b of S.
(2.8.15) *Transitive:* If $a \leq b$ and $b \leq c$, then $a \leq c$ for a, b, and c of S.

If for a set $a \leq b$ or $b \leq a$ for every pair of elements a, b of the set, then the set is said to be *totally* ordered. For example, the ordering by numeric value is a total ordering on the set of all integers. As an example of a partially ordered set consider the set of two-tuples of 0's and 1's $T = \{(0, 0)\,(0, 1)\,(1, 0)\,(1, 1)\}$ and define the ordering relation as follows.

$$(a_1, a_2) \leq (b_1, b_2) \quad \text{if and only if} \quad a_1 \leq b_1 \quad \text{and} \quad a_2 \leq b_2,$$

where a_i, b_i take on values 0 and 1 and $0 \leq 0, 1 \leq 1, 0 \leq 1$, but $1 \not\leq 0$. It is easily seen that this relation satisfies (2.8.13) through (2.8.15) and is thus a partially ordered set.

Then we have
$$(0, 0) \leq (0, 0),$$
$$(0, 0) \leq (0, 1),$$
$$(0, 0) \leq (1, 0),$$
$$(0, 0) \leq (1, 1),$$
$$(0, 1) \leq (0, 1),$$
$$(0, 1) \leq (1, 1),$$
$$(1, 0) \leq (1, 0),$$
$$(1, 0) \leq (1, 1),$$
$$(1, 1) \leq (1, 1).$$

However,
$$(0, 1) \not\leq (1, 0)$$

and
$$(1, 0) \not\leq (0, 1).$$

Thus it is obvious that this set is a partially ordered set but not a totally ordered set under this $\leq$ relation.

Theorem 2.8.2   The inclusion relation $a \subseteq b$ for elements of a Boolean algebra B is a partial ordering on B.
    PROOF. In Section 2.3 we defined $a \subseteq b$ as $a \subseteq b$ if and only if $a \cdot b = a$. Postulate (2.8.13), that is, $a \subseteq a$, follows since $a \cdot a = a$ is postulate (2.2.4).

We can show postulate (2.8.14), that is, if $a \subseteq b$ and $b \subseteq a$, then $a = b$, as follows.

$$\left.\begin{array}{l} a \cdot b = a \\ b \cdot a = b \end{array}\right\} \quad \text{by definition of } \subseteq$$

and thus $a = b$ by substitution. Finally, postulate (2.8.15) can be shown as follows. By assumption $a \subseteq b$ and $b \subseteq c$, thus

$$b \cdot c = b.$$

Now
$$a \cdot b = a \cdot b,$$

Therefore
$$a \cdot (b \cdot c) = a \cdot b,$$

$$(a \cdot b) \cdot c = a \cdot b,$$

and since $a \cdot b = a$ by $a \subseteq b$, we obtain

$$a \cdot c = a,$$

proving that $a \subseteq c$.

Thus the thoerem is proved.

In a partially ordered set S a *lower bound* (l.b.) for a subset of elements X of S is any element a of S which satisfies $a \leq x$ for every x of X. A lower bound b for X is called a *greatest lower bound* (g.l.b.) for X if each lower bound c for X satisfies $c \leq b$. Similarly, an *upper bound* (u.b.) for X is any element u of B satisfying $x \leq u$ for every x of X; and a *least upper bound* (l.u.b.) for X is an upper bound v for which any other upper bound w for X satisfies $v \leq w$. For the set of two-tuples T discussed earlier the element $(0, 0)$ is a g.l.b. for T and the element $(1, 1)$ is a l.u.b. for T. Since the inclusion relation is a partial ordering on set B of our Boolean algebra, we can look for bounds on elements of B.

Theorem 2.8.3   The elements 0 and 1 are universal bounds, lower bounds, and upper bounds, respectively for B, thus, for any a of B,

$$0 \subseteq a \subseteq 1.$$

PROOF.   By definition of $\subseteq$ we have $0 \subseteq a$ means $0 \cdot a = 0$, which is postulate (2.2.8) and similarly $a \subseteq 1$ means $a \cdot 1 = a$, which is postulate (2.2.9).

Theorem 2.8.4   In a Boolean algebra the AND-operation $a \cdot b$ and the OR-operation $a \vee b$ of any two elements a and b of B are the g.l.b. and l.u.b., respectively, of the set of elements $\{a, b\}$.

PROOF.   From the postulates we know that $(a \cdot b) \cdot a = a \cdot b$ so that $(a \cdot b) \subseteq a$, and that $(a \cdot b) \cdot b = a \cdot b$ so that $(a \cdot b) \subseteq b$. Thus $(a \cdot b)$ is a l.b. for set $\{a, b\}$. Assume element c is a l.b. for $\{a, b\}$; then $c \subseteq a$ and $c \subseteq b$ so that

$$c \cdot a = c$$

and $c \cdot b = c.$

Thus $c \cdot b \cdot a = c,$

showing that $c \subseteq a \cdot b.$

Hence $a \cdot b$ is the g.l.b. for $\{a, b\}$. A similar argument proves that $a \vee b$ is the l.u.b. for $\{a, b\}$.

In the proof we said *the* g.l.b. and *the* l.u.b.; the reader can justify the use of the word *the* here by showing the uniqueness of g.l.b. and l.u.b.

From the following definition of a lattice, it is seen that B, under the inclusion relation, is a lattice.

Definition 2.8.11   A *lattice L* is a partially ordered set in which every two elements have a l.u.b. and a g.l.b.

We can further specialize the concept of a lattice by assuming a "meet" operation between two elements as giving the g.l.b. and a "join" operation as giving the l.u.b. between any two elements. Rather than introducing more terminology, following Theorem 2.8.4 we shall use the centered dot $(\cdot)$ and $\vee$ symbols for meet and join, respectively.

Definition 2.8.12   A lattice L is called a *distributive lattice* if the distributive postulates (2.8.16) and (2.8.17) hold for elements of L.

(2.8.16) $a \cdot (b \vee c) = (a \cdot b) \vee (a \cdot c).$

(2.8.17) $a \vee (b \cdot c) = (a \vee b) \cdot (a \vee c).$

In Theorem 2.8.3 we saw that B has universal bounds 0 and 1; more generally, if a lattice has universal bounds, these are called the zero (0) and identity (1) of the lattice.

Definition 2.8.13   A lattice L with a 0 and a 1 is called a *complemented lattice* if for every element a of L there is an element $\bar{a}$ of L such that $a \cdot \bar{a} = 0$, and $a \vee \bar{a} = 1$.

Thus in the sense of lattice theory we see that Boolean algebra is analogous to a *distributive complemented lattice*. The set T could be considered to be the set of elements for a four-element Boolean algebra, where the OR-, AND-, and NOT-operations arc defined similar to the example on three-tuples. In addition, the lattice may be pictured as a diagram where if $a \leq b$, then a appears lower than b in the diagram, and if there is no c such that $a \leq c$ and $c \leq b$, then a line connects a and b. For our lattice T we obtain the diagram in Figure 2.8.1.

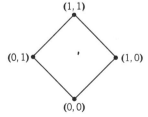

Figure 2.8.1   Diagram of four element lattice.

2.9   THE KARNAUGH MAP

In Section 2.8 we showed the connection between Boolean algebra and two abstract mathematical theories. In this and the next section we describe two graphical or geometric representations of Boolean algebra, showing how Boolean functions may be represented in these geometric forms. We also describe how the one geometric form, the Karnaugh map, may be used to obtain different expressions for a Boolean function and how the different expressions may be viewed as representing different relay and logical networks. Some elementary notions of simplification of networks are thereby introduced, but a more complete treatment is left to subsequent chapters.

The Karnaugh map is a graphical technique for representing Boolean functions for a few variables and obtaining simplified expressions, where identities of the type $a \vee ab = a$, $ab \vee a\bar{b} = a$, and $a \vee \bar{a}b = a \vee b$ are easily recognized graphically.

$x_1\,x_2$

00	01	11	10

Figure 2.9.1   A two variable map.

In truth tables for two variable functions there are four rows, as indicated in Table 2.7.2. A re-arrangement of the truth table can be made as shown in Figure 2.9.1, which is useful for simplification. This is called a *two variable Karnaugh map*.

Each of the four squares corresponds to one of the four combinations of the two variables. Similarly, a map for three variable functions has eight squares; as shown in Figure 2.9.2, and a map for four variable functions has sixteen squares, as shown in Figure 2.9.3. The maps are arranged so that adjacent squares differ in value for only one variable. For the two variable map consider the squares at opposite ends to be also adjacent. Then

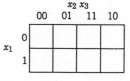

$x_2\,x_3$

	00	01	11	10
0				
1				

x_1

Figure   2.9.2   A   three variable map.

conversely, if two combinations of variable values differ in just one variable, the squares are adjacent. To maintain this property for the three and four variable maps, we consider opposite ends of each row or column to be adjacent as though the figure were inscribed on a torus.

To simplify labeling, designate rows or columns having a variable equal to 1 with a brace, so that the variable has value 0 elsewhere. This is shown in Figure 2.9.4.

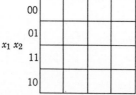

$x_3\,x_4$

	00	01	11	10
00				
01				
11				
10				

$x_1\,x_2$

Figure 2.9.3   A four variable map.

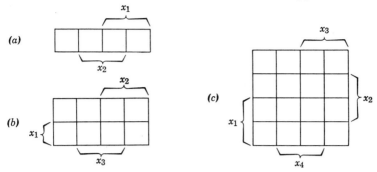

Figure 2.9.4   Simplified labels for maps.

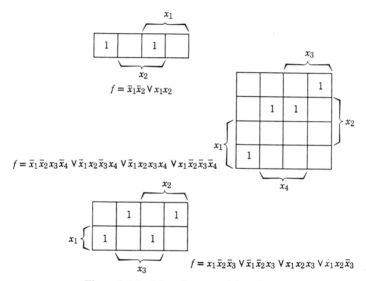

Figure 2.9.5   Maps for several functions.

To represent a function on a map, place 1's in the squares for which the function has value 1. The other squares are imagined to contain 0's (see Figure 2.9.5).

The squares in which 1's are written are called *p-squares* of the function, since the 1 represents a product of all the variables (some may be negated). Two adjacent 1's form a *one-dimensional p-subcube*, as shown in Figure 2.9.6.

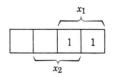

Figure 2.9.6   A one-dimensional *p*-sub-cube.

This one-dimensional *p*-subcube may be represented by the simple product term x_1, since the two 1 entries in the subcube correspond to $x_1 x_2$ and $x_1 \bar{x}_2$;

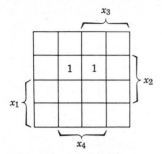

Figure 2.9.7 A one-dimensional *p*-subcube on a four variable map.

thus we graphically apply the identity $x_1 x_2 \vee x_1 \bar{x}_2 = x_1$. This principle can be extended to functions of more variables, as shown in Figure 2.9.7. The function for this map is

$$f = \bar{x}_1 x_2 \bar{x}_3 x_4 \vee \bar{x}_1 x_2 x_3 x_4$$

$$= \bar{x}_1 x_2 x_4.$$

Thus, the one-dimensional *p*-subcube corresponds to the product $\bar{x}_1 x_2 x_4$, with x_3 missing. In general, a one-dimensional *p*-subcube corresponds to a product term with exactly one of the variables (or its complement) missing. The variable missing is also readily determined from the map, it being the variable having different values for the two 1's of the subcube. Thus in Figure 2.9.7, x_3 has value 0 for the left-hand 1 and value 1 for the right-hand 1 of the subcube, whereas all other variables have equal values for both 1's.

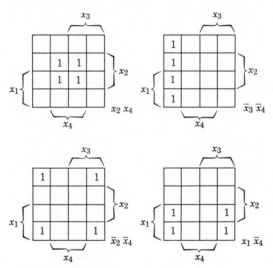

Figure 2.9.8   Some two-dimensional *p*-subcubes.

Four adjacent 1's, as shown in Figure 2.9.8, are called *two-dimensional p-subcubes* and each corresponds to a term having two variables missing as shown. The missing variables are those with a nonconstant value over the subcube. Note that in some of these subcubes the four 1's are "adjacent" only when the maps are considered to be inscribed on a torus, as previously explained. The functional identity for the upper left of these maps is

$$f = \bar{x}_1 x_2 \bar{x}_3 x_4 \vee \bar{x}_1 x_2 x_3 x_4 \vee x_1 x_2 \bar{x}_3 x_4 \vee x_1 x_2 x_3 x_4 = x_2 x_4.$$

In a similar way three-dimensional p-subcubes have eight 1's; some examples are shown in Figure 2.9.9.

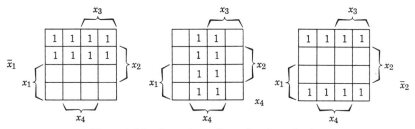

Figure 2.9.9   Some three-dimensional p-subcubes.

The terminology of "dimension" comes from a mapping of the p-subcubes onto an n-dimensional cube, where n is the number of variables of the function. Then a one-dimensional p-subcube corresponds to an edge having two adjacent vertices, a two-dimensional p-subcube corresponds to a two-dimensional subcube of the n-dimensional cube, etc. This cubical representation will be discussed in the next section.

By taking advantage of the higher dimensional p-subcubes, the functions can be "simplified." We shall say that one expression for a function is simpler than another expression if the total number of occurrences of variable letters is fewer in the first expression than in the second expression. Thus using the subcube expression $\bar{x}_1 x_2 x_4$ of Figure 2.9.7 is simpler than using the expression $\bar{x}_1 x_2 \bar{x}_3 x_4 \vee \bar{x}_1 x_2 x_3 x_4$. All that is required for a function

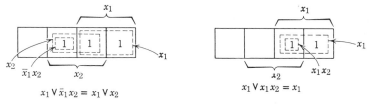

$$x_1 \vee \bar{x}_1 x_2 = x_1 \vee x_2 \qquad\qquad x_1 \vee x_1 x_2 = x_1$$

Figure 2.9.10   Map representation of some identities.

to be represented is that each 1 be in at *least* one of the p-subcubes used and that no squares without 1's are contained in any p-subcube used for the function. This is illustrated in Figure 2.9.10 for the identities $x_1 \vee x_1 x_2 = x_1$ and $x_1 \vee \bar{x}_1 x_2 = x_1 \vee x_2$, where the subcubes are shown in the dotted lines.

We say that the 1's of the map must be *covered* by p-subcubes to represent the function.   Figure 2.9.11 shows some functions represented by p-subcubes on three- and four-dimensional maps, where the p-subcubes used to represent the function are shown included in the dotted lines.   The

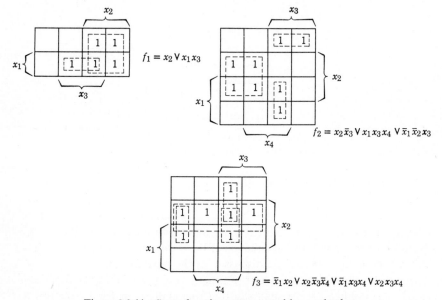

Figure 2.9.11   Some functions represented by p-subcubes.

representation obtained by picking p-subcubes of a function gives a disjunctive normal form expression for the function.   If the largest possible p-subcubes are chosen and as few p-subcubes are used as possible, a simplest disjunctive normal form is obtained.

Further simplification can be obtained by algebraic factoring of the function, and the structure of the Karnaugh map can aid in determining factorizations.   For example, consider f_3 of Figure 2.9.11.   This can be factored as

$$f_3 = x_2(\bar{x}_1 \vee \bar{x}_3\bar{x}_4 \vee x_3x_4) \vee \bar{x}_1x_3x_4,$$

or

$$f_3 = \bar{x}_1(x_2 \vee x_3x_4) \vee x_2(x_3x_4 \vee \bar{x}_3\bar{x}_4).$$

At this point it might be advisable to remark on the connection between the simplification of Boolean functions and the relay contact circuit and logical diagram representations of the expressions.   In Figures 2.7.1 and 2.7.2 we showed two relay contact networks represented by two different expressions for a Boolean function.   If an expression contains no sub-expressions which are complemented and larger than a letter, the

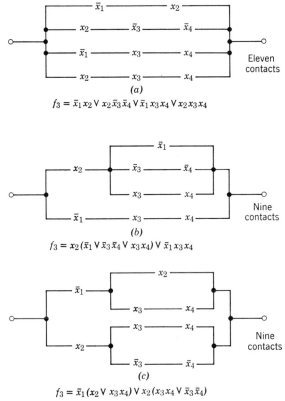

$$f_3 = \bar{x}_1 x_2 \vee x_2 \bar{x}_3 \bar{x}_4 \vee \bar{x}_1 x_3 x_4 \vee x_2 x_3 x_4$$

(a)

$$f_3 = x_2 (\bar{x}_1 \vee \bar{x}_3 \bar{x}_4 \vee x_3 x_4) \vee \bar{x}_1 x_3 x_4$$

(b)

$$f_3 = \bar{x}_1 (x_2 \vee x_3 x_4) \vee x_2 (x_3 x_4 \vee \bar{x}_3 \bar{x}_4)$$

(c)

Figure 2.9.12   Three relay contact network realizations for f_3.

expression can be thought of representing a series-parallel relay contact network. In this representation each appearance of a letter (or its complement) corresponds to a contact in the network. Thus expressions with fewer letter occurrences give circuits having fewer contacts, so that the function simplification can be viewed as an analogous simplification in the relay contact network. This is illustrated in Figure 2.9.12 for the three expressions obtained for f_3.

In a series-parallel relay contact network the number of contacts is certainly one of the important measures of the complexity of the networks, and although other measures also exist, there is a good correlation between simplification of the functional expression and that of the network.

There is no such simple measure of the complexity of logical diagrams which corresponds to the simplicity of the functional expressions. One simple measure is the total number of inputs (or arrowheads) to elements in the diagram, and this is somewhat governed by the simplicity of the

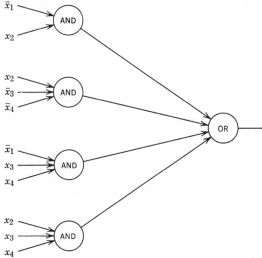

Figure 2.9.13   A logical diagram for $f_3 = \bar{x}_1 x_2 \vee x_2 \bar{x}_3 \bar{x}_4 \vee \bar{x}_1 x_3 x_4 \vee x_2 x_3 x_4$.

functional expression. In particular, if signal values are available for both the variable and its complement, then the number of letters in a disjunctive normal form expression is the same as the number of inputs to the AND-elements of a logical diagram which has one AND-element for each product term followed by one OR-element which gives the output. Such a "two-level" logical diagram for

$$f_3 = \bar{x}_1 x_2 \vee x_2 \bar{x}_3 \bar{x}_4 \vee \bar{x}_1 x_3 x_4 \vee x_2 x_3 x_4$$

is shown in Figure 2.9.13.

That the measure of complexity of the logical diagram is not identical to the simplicity of the functional expression—or not even equal when two expressions are of equal simplicity—is demonstrated by Figure 2.9.14, where logical diagrams are given using AND-, OR-, and NOT-elements.

If the complexity of the circuit is assessed by counting arrowheads, the first realization has complexity 16 and the second has complexity 17. Can you do better?

By considering the squares which do not have 1's and proceeding in an analogous fashion as before, dual forms (that is, conjunctive normal forms) can be obtained. For example, consider f_2 of Figure 2.9.11. The map for the inverse is shown in Figure 2.9.15. Thus we can express the inverse of f_2 as

$$\bar{f}_2 = \bar{x}_2 \bar{x}_3 \vee x_1 x_3 \bar{x}_4 \vee \bar{x}_1 x_2 x_3,$$

and by using the procedure, allied to duality, given in Section 2.3 to obtain the inverse function, f_2 is expressed as

$$f_2 = (x_2 \vee x_3)(\bar{x}_1 \vee \bar{x}_3 \vee x_4)(x_1 \vee \bar{x}_2 \vee \bar{x}_3).$$

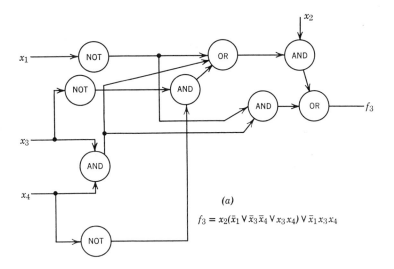

(a)

$$f_3 = x_2(\bar{x}_1 \vee \bar{x}_3\bar{x}_4 \vee x_3 x_4) \vee \bar{x}_1 x_3 x_4$$

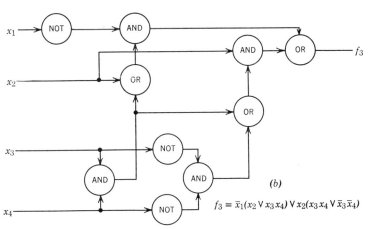

(b)

$$f_3 = \bar{x}_1(x_2 \vee x_3 x_4) \vee x_2(x_3 x_4 \vee \bar{x}_3 \bar{x}_4)$$

Figure 2.9.14   Two logical diagrams for $f_3 = \bar{x}_1 x_2 \vee x_2 \bar{x}_3 \bar{x}_4 \vee \bar{x}_1 x_3 x_4 \vee x_2 x_3 x_4$.

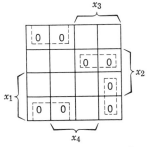

Figure 2.9.15   Inverse map for f_2.

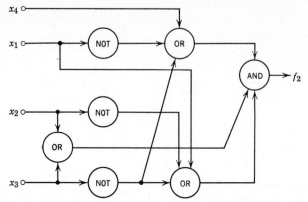

Figure 2.9.16   A logical diagram for $f_2 = (x_2 \lor x_3)(\bar{x}_1 \lor \bar{x}_3 \lor x_4)(x_1 \lor \bar{x}_2 \lor \bar{x}_3)$

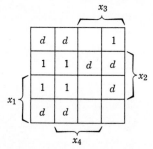

Figure 2.9.17   A map with don't cares.

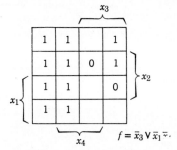

$f = \bar{x}_3 \lor \bar{x}_1 \bar{x}$.

Figure 2.9.18   A simplified function.

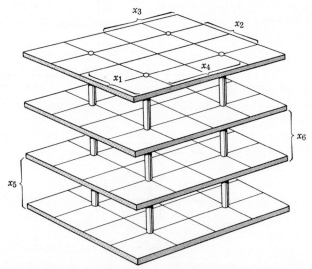

Figure 2.9.19.   A three dimensional Karnaugh map for six variables.

A logical diagram corresponding to this expression for f_2 is shown in Figure 2.9.16.

Up to this point we have considered logical diagrams obtained from Boolean functions. Sometimes in the operating specifications for a circuit, the output value of the circuit does not matter for certain input (variable) combinations. Such combinations are called *don't care combinations*. When don't care combinations occur in a design problem, the problem cannot be represented as a single Boolean function for we now have "on" conditions, which we represent by a Boolean function equaling 1, the "off" conditions, for which we desire a function to be 0, and the don't care conditions, for which the desired function can have either value 0 or 1. The don't care conditions may then be assigned values which cause simplification of the function (or circuit) to be designed.

On the Karnaugh map we can introduce a symbol d, and place a d in the squares for the don't care combinations. Then for simplification, 1's can be placed in any squares having d's in order to increase the size of any p-subcubes. To illustrate this use of don't cares consider the map of Figure 2.9.17.

By placing 1's and 0's for the d squares as shown in the map of Figure 2.9.18, a simplified function is obtained.

By the Karnaugh map method we have seen how to represent and simplify functions of two, three, and four variables. For more than four variables the maps become rather complex. We can extend the method to five and six variables by using two or four maps, respectively, of four variables. For this purpose a three-dimensional map of the form shown in Figure 2.9.19 is very convenient to use, where x_5 and x_6 are represented in the third dimension.

The p-subcube notation is easily seen to extend to three dimensions, so that functions up to six variables can be simplified on this map. Further extensions to more variables, although possible, become increasingly cumbersome. The algebraic techniques, to be discussed in Chapter 3, are more suitable for larger problems.

An example of a five variable problem using two four variable maps is given in Figure 2.9.20. This function is a Boolean function which re-presents the 2 digit being equal to 1 in the 5211 code for the five variables $x_1, \ldots, x_5$ of the two out of five code (see Table 1.6.1).

From the subcubes outlined by dotted lines it is seen that this function f_2 can be expressed as

$$f_2 = x_2\bar{x}_3 \vee x_3x_4 \vee x_1x_3,$$

or

$$f_2 = x_2\bar{x}_3 \vee x_3(x_1 \vee x_4).$$

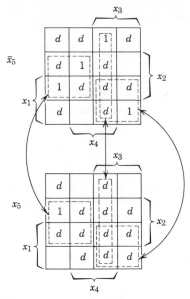

Figure 2.9.20   A five variable problem.

The reader may wish to give the relay contact networks and logical diagrams representing these functional expressions.

2.10 THE CUBICAL REPRESENTATION

Another geometric representation of a Boolean function is obtained by mapping a Boolean function of n-variables onto the n-dimensional unit cube (n-cube). Some of the concepts of this representation can be seen geometrically, but to circumvent the increase in geometric complexity encountered with an increase in the number of variables, as was seen in using the Karnaugh map, we shall rely on an analytic description of this mapping. With this analytic description, various operations will be defined in Chapter 3 which allow us to minimize Boolean functions.

For a Boolean function of n-variables $f(x_1, x_2, \ldots, x_n)$ to be mapped onto the n-cube, we set up a correspondence between the terms of the disjunctive canonical form and the vertices of the n-cube. We set up a coordinate system on the n-cube with coordinates $(e_1, e_2, \ldots, e_n)$ where $e_i = 0, 1$. We then make the correspondence between the term

$$x_1^{e_1} x_2^{e_2} \cdots x_n^{e_n}$$

and a vertex $(e_1, e_2, \ldots, e_n)$. Remember that $x_i^{e_i} = x_i$ if $e_i = 1$ and $x_i^{e_i} = \bar{x}_i$ if $e_i = 0$.

We designate by $f^{-1}(1)$ those variable combinations which cause f to equal 1 and conversely for $f^{-1}(0)$. Figure 2.10.1 shows this correspondence for $f = \bar{a}bc \vee a\bar{b}c \vee \bar{a}\bar{b}\bar{c} \vee abc$, where the $f^{-1}(1)$ vertices are enlarged.

Let Z_2 represent the space of Boolean elements 0 and 1. Then the space of n-tuples of 0's and 1's is the Cartesian product $Z_2 \times Z_2 \times \cdots \times Z_2$ of n Z_2's. This Cartesian product, representing the n-cube, we designate by

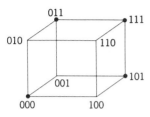

Figure 2.10.1   Cubical repre-
sentation for $f = \bar{a}bc \vee a\bar{b}c \vee$
$\bar{a}\bar{b}\bar{c} \vee abc$.

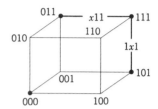

Figure 2.10.2   Cubical representation with 1-cubes.

Z_2^n. Then f is a mapping of the nth Cartesian product Z_2^n of the space Z_2 of integers modulo 2 into Z_2.

$$Z_2^n \xrightarrow{\;f\;} Z_2,$$

where $f^{-1}(1)$ is mapped onto 1 and $f^{-1}(0)$ is mapped onto 0. The elements of $f^{-1}(1)$ we shall call 0-*cubes* or *vertices*. For the example we have 000, 011, 101, and 111 as 0-cubes for the function in Figure 2.10.1.

Two 0-cubes are said to form a 1-cube if they differ in only one co-ordinate. Thus, as in the Karnaugh map, we can define k-dimensional p-subcubes, which from now on we shall call k-*cubes*.

For our example we have two 1-cubes formed for the pairs of 0-cubes 011, 111 and by 111, 101. We denote the 1-cubes by placing an x in the coordinate having different values. Thus we get $x11$ and $1x1$. This cubical representation is shown in Figure 2.10.2.

As seen in Figure 2.10.3 the geometrical representation for a 4-cube is rather complex; thus for functions having more than four variables, the analytic representation for the n-cube, rather than the geometric representation, seems best. We shall discuss this analytical representation at length in Chapter 3. In Figure 2.10.3 a four variable Boolean function is represented on a 4-cube. In this representation $f^{-1}(1)$ contains ten 0-cubes, twelve 1-cubes, and three 2-cubes. Each of the 2-cubes which appear contains two x's.

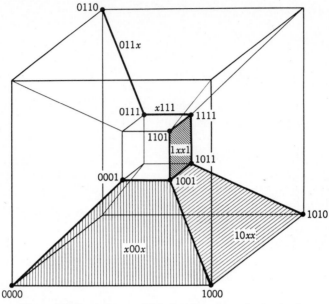

Figure 2.10.3   A four variable function mapped on a 4-cube.

2.11   SYMMETRIC FUNCTIONS

In this and the following section we define and discuss three special classes of Boolean functions that deserve particular consideration: symmetric functions, unate functions, and threshold functions. By restricting our attention to these classes, certain mathematical results can be obtained which do not hold for general Boolean functions. Furthermore, certain special design techniques for switching networks arise for such functions. These design techniques will be discussed later, but the classes of functions and some of their mathematical consequences can be discussed readily here.

Definition 2.11.1   A function $f(x_1, x_2, \ldots, x_n)$ is called *symmetric in the pair of variables* x_i, x_j if the function remains invariant under an interchange of the variables x_i, x_j, that is, if

$$f(x_1, x_2, \ldots, x_i, \ldots, x_j, \ldots, x_n) = f(x_1, x_2, \ldots, x_j, \ldots, x_i, \ldots, x_n).$$

For example, the function

$$f(x_1, x_2, x_3) = x_1 \bar{x}_2 x_3 \lor \bar{x}_1 x_2 x_3$$

is symmetric in x_1, x_2 since

$$f(x_2, x_1, x_3) = x_2\bar{x}_1x_3 \vee \bar{x}_2x_1x_3$$
$$= x_1\bar{x}_2x_3 \vee \bar{x}_1x_2x_3$$

so that $\qquad f(x_2, x_1, x_3) = f(x_1, x_2, x_3).$

This function, however, is *not* symmetric in x_1, x_3 since

$$f(x_3, x_2, x_1) = x_3\bar{x}_2x_1 \vee \bar{x}_3x_2x_1$$

is not equal to $f(x_1, x_2, x_3)$.

Definition 2.11.2 A function $f(x_1, x_2, \ldots, x_n)$ is called *totally symmetric* if it is symmetric in all pairs of variables x_i, x_j, $1 \le i, j \le n$.

Since any permutation of variables can be obtained by successive interchanges of pairs of variables, it immediately follows that a totally symmetric function is invariant under any permutation of variables.

We shall often simply refer to totally symmetric functions as *symmetric functions*, and refer to functions which are symmetric in some pairs but not in all pairs of variables as *partially symmetric functions*.

We readily see that the function

$$f(x_1, x_2, x_3) = x_1x_2 \vee x_1x_3 \vee x_2x_3$$

is totally symmetric. It is not immediately evident, however, that the function

$$f(x_1, x_2, x_3) = \bar{x}_1\bar{x}_2x_3 \vee x_1x_2x_3 \vee x_1\bar{x}_2\bar{x}_3$$

can also be considered to be a totally symmetric function. Indeed, it is not totally symmetric in the variables x_1, x_2, x_3. If we consider the variables to be $\bar{x}_1$, x_2, and $\bar{x}_3$, however, then

$$f(\bar{x}_1, x_2, \bar{x}_3) = \bar{x}_1\bar{x}_2x_3 \vee x_1x_2x_3 \vee x_1\bar{x}_2\bar{x}_3$$

is symmetric in these variables. The variables for which a function is totally symmetric are called the *variables of symmetry*. It may at times be difficult to determine what variables, if any, are the variables of symmetry for a given function. This problem we shall discuss later.

A particularly simple representation can be used to specify any totally symmetric function, as shown by the following theorem due to Shannon.

Theorem 2.11.1 A function $f(x_1, x_2, \ldots, x_n)$ is totally symmetric in the variables $(x_1, \ldots, x_n)$ if and only if it may be specified by a set of numbers $\{a_1, a_2, \ldots, a_k\}$ such that $f(x_1, x_2, \ldots, x_n) = 1$ if and only if exactly a_j $(j = 1, 2, \ldots, k)$ of the variables are equal to 1, and the remaining variables are equal to 0.

PROOF. Assume the function $f(x_1, x_2, \ldots, x_n)$ is totally symmetric and $f(x_1, x_2, \ldots, x_n) = 1$ when the first a_j variables are equal to 1 and the other variables equal 0. Then, $f = 1$ when any set of exactly a_j variables equal 1, since f is invariant under any permutation of variables. A similar argument proves the converse, thus proving the theorem.

For the function

$$f(x_1, x_2, x_3) = x_1 x_2 \lor x_1 x_3 \lor x_2 x_3$$

considered earlier, we readily see that $f = 1$ if and only if either two or three of the variables equal 1. Thus for this function the set of numbers $\{a_1, a_2, \ldots, a_k\}$ is the set $\{2, 3\}$. This function could then be represented by $S_{2,3}(x_1, x_2, x_3)$, where S stands for a totally symmetric function; 2, 3 stands for the set of numbers $\{a_1, a_2, \ldots, a_k\}$ (these are usually called *a-numbers*); and (x_1, x_2, x_3) are the variables of symmetry. The notation $S_{a_1, a_2, \ldots, a_k}(x_1, x_2, \ldots, x_n)$ is commonly used to represent a totally symmetric function. The function,

$$f(x_1, x_2, x_3) = \bar{x}_1 \bar{x}_2 x_3 \lor x_1 x_2 x_3 \lor x_1 \bar{x}_2 \bar{x}_3,$$

is thus represented by $S_1(\bar{x}_1, x_2, \bar{x}_3)$; that is, the function equals 1 if and only if exactly one of the variables of symmetry equals 1, or $f = 1$ only when $\bar{x}_1 = 1, x_2 = 0, \bar{x}_3 = 0$, or $\bar{x}_1 = 0, x_2 = 1, \bar{x}_3 = 0$, or $\bar{x}_1 = 0, x_2 = 0, \bar{x}_3 = 1$.

The *a*-numbers for an *n*-variable function can be selected from the numbers 0 through *n*. From this it follows that there are exactly 2^{n+1} symmetric functions of *n*-variables, where these variables are taken as the variables of symmetry. Of course, if the set of *a*-numbers includes all the integers from 0 through *n*, this Boolean function is the trivial Boolean function which is always equal to 1. Similarly, if the set of *a*-numbers is empty, the function is again trivial, that is, always equal to 0. Thus there are $2^{n+1} - 2$ nontrivial symmetric Boolean functions of *n*-variables. For $n = 2$, of the $2^{2^2} = 16$ functions of two variables, there are $2^3 - 2 = 6$ nontrivial symmetric functions. These are

$$S_0 = \bar{x}_1 \bar{x}_2 \qquad\qquad S_1 = x_1 \bar{x}_2 \lor \bar{x}_1 x_2 = x_1 \oplus x_2,$$
$$S_{0,1} = \bar{x}_1 \lor \bar{x}_2 \qquad\qquad S_{1,2} = x_1 \lor x_2,$$
$$S_{0,2} = x_1 x_2 \lor \bar{x}_1 \bar{x}_2 \qquad\qquad S_2 = x_1 x_2.$$

The following four theorems are almost immediate. The proofs are left to the reader.

Theorem 2.11.2 The union of two totally symmetric functions f and g, having the same variables of symmetry, is a totally symmetric function of the same variables of symmetry whose set of *a*-numbers is the union of the sets of *a*-numbers for *f* and *g*.

Using our notation, this is

$$S_{a_1,a_2,\ldots,a_j}(x_1, x_2, \ldots, x_n) \vee S_{a_1',a_2',\ldots,a_k'}(x_1, x_2, \ldots, x_n)$$
$$= S_{a_1'',a_2'',\ldots,a_p''}(x_1, x_2, \ldots, x_n),$$

where $\{a_1'', a_2'', \ldots, a_p''\} = \{a_1, a_2, \ldots, a_j\} \cup \{a_1', a_2', \ldots, a_k'\}$.

Theorem 2.11.3 The product of two totally symmetric functions *f* and *g*, having the same variables of symmetry, is a totally symmetric function of the same variables of symmetry whose set of *a*-numbers is the set of numbers appearing in both sets of *a*-numbers for *f* and *g*.

Using our notation this is

$$[S_{a_1,a_2,\ldots,a_j}(x_1, x_2, \ldots, x_n)] \cdot [S_{a_1',a_2',\ldots,a_k'}(x_1, x_2, \ldots, x_n)]$$
$$= S_{a_1'',a_2'',\ldots,a_p''}(x_1, x_2, \ldots, x_n),$$

where $\{a_1'', a_2'', \ldots, a_p''\} = \{a_1, a_2, \ldots, a_j\} \cap \{a_1', a_2', \ldots, a_k'\}$.

In these theorems we have used the notation $\cup$ and $\cap$ to represent set union and set intersection respectively.

Theorem 2.11.4 The inverse $\bar{f}$ of a totally symmetric function *f* of *n*-variables is also a totally symmetric function of the same variables of symmetry as *f*. The *a*-numbers for $\bar{f}$ are the numbers 0 through *n* which are not *a*-numbers for *f*.

To use symbols,

$$\overline{S_{a_1, a_2, \ldots, a_k}(x_1, x_2, \ldots, x_n)} = S_{a_1', a_2', \ldots, a_j'}(x_1, x_2, \ldots, x_n)$$

where $\{a_1', a_2', \ldots, a_j'\} = \{0, 1, \ldots, n\} - \{a_1, a_2, \ldots, a_k\}$.

Theorem 2.11.5 If *f* is a totally symmetric function

$$S_{a_1,a_2,\ldots,a_k}(x_1, x_2, \ldots, x_n),$$

f can also be represented as the totally symmetric function

$$S_{n-a_1,n-a_2,\ldots,n-a_k}(\bar{x}_1, \bar{x}_2, \ldots, \bar{x}_n).$$

As an example for these theorems consider the totally symmetric functions

$$f = S_{2,3}(x_1, x_2, \bar{x}_3, x_4)$$

and
$$g = S_{2,4}(x_1, x_2, \bar{x}_3, x_4).$$

Then

$$f \vee g = S_{2,3,4}(x_1, x_2, \bar{x}_3, x_4),$$
$$f \cdot g = S_2(x_1, x_2, \bar{x}_3, x_4),$$
$$\bar{f} = S_{0,1,4}(x_1, x_2, \bar{x}_3, x_4),$$

and

$$f = S_{1,2}(\bar{x}_1, \bar{x}_2, x_3, \bar{x}_4).$$

As was seen by the function $S_1(\bar{x}_1, x_2, \bar{x}_3)$ it may be rather difficult to determine whether a function is totally symmetric or not, and if so, for what variables the function is totally symmetric. From the definition for total symmetry it is evident that given the variables of symmetry, one can test for total symmetry by determining if the function is invariant under all possible interchanges of pairs of variables. There are $[n(n-1)]/2$ such interchanges. Now there are 2^n possible choices for the variables of symmetry, but from Theorem 2.11.5 we need consider only one-half (or 2^{n-1}) of these. Thus we could determine both whether the function is totally symmetric and the exact variables of symmetry by examining $\{[n(n-1)]/2\} \cdot 2^{n-1}$ possibilities. This number of possibilities becomes rather forbidding even for rather small n. Fortunately, all permutations can be generated by only two permutations rather than $[n(n-1)]/2$ interchanges. This then reduces the number of possibilities to 2 for testing whether a given function is totally symmetric in a given set of variables, or to $2 \cdot 2^{n-1} = 2^n$ possibilities to determine the exact variables of symmetry, if any. This is shown in the following theorem due to Povarov.

Theorem 2.11.6 A function $f(x_1, x_2, \ldots, x_n)$ is totally symmetric in the variables $x_1, x_2, \ldots, x_n$ if and only if

(2.11.1) $$f(x_1, x_2, \ldots, x_n) = f(x_2, x_1, x_3, \ldots, x_n)$$

and

(2.11.2) $$f(x_1, x_2, \ldots, x_n) = f(x_2, x_3, \ldots, x_n, x_1).$$

PROOF. A rather informal constructive verification of this theorem is given rather than a precise proof. If f is totally symmetric, it follows that

$$f(x_1, x_2, \ldots, x_n) = f(x_2, x_1, x_3, \ldots, x_n)$$

directly from the definition of total symmetry, and also

$$f(x_1, x_2, \ldots, x_n) = f(x_2, x_3, \ldots, x_n, x_1),$$

since f is invariant under all permutations of variables. To prove the converse we must show that all interchanges of pairs of variables may be obtained using only the two permutations (2.11.1) and (2.11.2). Suppose we wish to interchange x_i and x_j, $i < j$. Then repeat (2.11.2) until we obtain the function of the form

$$f(x_i, x_{i+1}, \ldots, x_j, x_{j+1}, \ldots, x_n, x_1, x_2, \ldots, x_{i-1}).$$

Applying (2.11.1) gives

$$f(x_{i+1}, x_i, x_{i+2}, \ldots, x_j, x_{j+1}, \ldots, x_n, x_1, x_2, \ldots, x_{i-1}).$$

By one application of (2.11.2) followed by one application of (2.11.1), we obtain

$$f(x_{i+2}, x_i, x_{i+3}, \ldots, x_j, x_{j+1}, \ldots, x_n, x_1, x_2, \ldots, x_{i-1}, x_{i+1}).$$

This can be repeated until x_i is moved to a position just preceding x_{j+1}. This gives

$$f(x_j, x_i, x_{j+1}, \ldots, x_n, x_1, x_2, \ldots, x_{i-1}, x_{i+1}, \ldots, x_{j-1}).$$

Now by repeating (2.11.2) we obtain the form

$$f(x_{j-1}, x_j, x_i, x_{j+1}, \ldots, x_n, x_1, x_2, \ldots, x_{i-1}, x_{i+1}, \ldots, x_{j-2}).$$

Then (2.11.1) moves x_j left one place. By repeated alternation of (2.11.2) and (2.11.1), and finally using (2.11.2), we have the desired form

$$f(x_1, x_2, \ldots, x_{i-1}, x_j, x_{i+1}, \ldots, x_{j-1}, x_i, x_{j+1}, \ldots, x_n)$$

and the theorem is verified.

By using this theorem let us verify that

$$f(x_1, x_2, x_3) = \bar{x}_1\bar{x}_2x_3 \lor x_1x_2x_3 \lor x_1\bar{x}_2\bar{x}_3$$

is indeed a symmetric function in the variables $\bar{x}_1, x_2, \bar{x}_3$. Applying Equation (2.11.1) of the theorem we replace $\bar{x}_1$ by x_2 and x_2 by $\bar{x}_1$, giving

$$f(x_2, \bar{x}_1\bar{x}_3) = x_2x_1x_3 \lor \bar{x}_2\bar{x}_1x_3 \lor \bar{x}_2x_1\bar{x}_3$$

so that indeed $f(\bar{x}_1, x_2, \bar{x}_3) = f(x_2, \bar{x}_1, \bar{x}_3)$. Applying Equation (2.11.2) we replace $\bar{x}_1$ by x_2, x_2 by $\bar{x}_3$, and $\bar{x}_3$ by $\bar{x}_1$, giving

$$f(x_2, \bar{x}_3, \bar{x}_1) = x_2x_3x_1 \lor \bar{x}_2\bar{x}_3x_1 \lor \bar{x}_2x_3\bar{x}_1,$$

and thus $f(\bar{x}_1, x_2, \bar{x}_3) = f(x_2, \bar{x}_3, \bar{x}_1)$, proving that this function is totally symmetric with variables of symmetry $\bar{x}_1, x_2, \bar{x}_3$. Is this function also symmetric in the variables $\bar{x}_1\bar{x}_2x_3$? We can check by applying the two tests of Theorem 2.11.6. For (2.11.1) we obtain:

$$f(\bar{x}_2, \bar{x}_1, x_3) = \bar{x}_2\bar{x}_1x_3 \lor x_2x_1x_3 \lor x_2\bar{x}_1\bar{x}_3,$$

but here $f(\bar{x}_2, \bar{x}_1, x_3) \neq f(\bar{x}_1, \bar{x}_2, x_3)$, so that the function is not totally symmetric in the variables $\bar{x}_1, \bar{x}_2, x_3$.

An expansion theorem for totally symmetric functions is given next.

Theorem 2.11.7   A totally symmetric function

$$S_{a_1,a_2,\ldots,a_k}(x_1, x_2, \ldots, x_n)$$

can be expressed in expanded form as

$$
\begin{aligned}
S_{a_1,a_2,\ldots,a_k}&(x_1, x_2, \ldots, x_n) \\
&= \bar{x}_1 \cdot S_{a_1,a_2,\ldots,a_k}(x_2, \ldots, x_n) \vee x_1 \cdot S_{a_1-1,a_2-1,\ldots,a_k-1}(x_2, \ldots, x_n),
\end{aligned}
$$

where $a_i - 1$ and a_j are eliminated in the expansion if $a_i = 0$ and $a_j = n$, respectively.

This theorem follows from the Shannon expansion theorem (Theorem 2.7.2) and Theorem 2.11.2.

In Chapter 5 we shall consider further methods for detecting symmetries in Boolean functions and some special techniques for switching circuit design representing symmetric functions.

2.12   UNATE AND THRESHOLD FUNCTIONS

As we have seen in previous sections, there may be many different expressions for any Boolean function, including the disjunctive canonical form and the conjunctive canonical form. If a Boolean function is expressed as a disjunction of one or more product terms, where each product term is the conjunction of several variables or complements of variables in which the same variable does not appear more than once, it is called a *disjunctive normal form*. Similarly, a dual of the disjunctive normal form is called a *conjunctive normal form*. The disjunctive and conjunctive canonical forms are particular examples of the disjunctive normal form and conjunctive normal form, respectively. Another example of a disjunctive normal form is

$$f = ab \vee \bar{b}c \vee a\bar{b}\bar{c} \vee d,$$

and an example of a conjunctive normal form is

$$g = (a \vee \bar{b})(\bar{a} \vee c \vee d)(\bar{a} \vee \bar{b} \vee \bar{c} \vee \bar{d}).$$

Either of these two forms is called a *normal form* for a Boolean function.

Normal form expressions are used in defining unate functions, as is seen by the following definitions.

Definition 2.12.1   A Boolean function $f(x_1, x_2, \ldots, x_n)$ is called *positive in* x_i if there exists a normal form expression for f in which x_i does not appear complemented.

Definition 2.12.2   A Boolean function $f(x_1, x_2, \ldots, x_n)$ is called *negative in* x_i if there exists a normal form expression for f in which x_i does not appear uncomplemented.

Definition 2.12.3   A Boolean function $f(x_1, x_2, \ldots, x_n)$ is called *unate in* x_i if it is either positive in x_i or negative in x_i.

Definition 2.12.4   A Boolean function $f(x_1, x_2, \ldots, x_n)$ is called *unate* if a normal form expression exists for f such that for each variable x_i of f, f is either positive in x_i or f is negative in x_i.

The function $f_1 = x_1 x_2 \lor x_1 \bar{x}_3$ is thus unate where this normal form expression is positive in x_1 and x_2 and is negative in x_3 whereas the function $f_2 = x_1 \bar{x}_2 \lor \bar{x}_1 x_2$ is not unate since no normal form expression exists for f_2 satisfying Definition 2.12.4. The function $f_3 = \bar{x}_1 x_3 \lor x_1 x_2 x_3$ is unate even though the normal form expression given for f_3 does not satisfy either the definition for f_3 being positive or negative in x_1. There does exist a normal form expression for f_3, however, namely, $f_3 = \bar{x}_1 x_3 \lor x_2 x_3$, which is obviously negative in x_1 and positive in x_2 and x_3, which is of the type satisfying Definition 2.12.4.

Theorem 2.12.1   A Boolean function $f(x_1, x_2, \ldots, x_n)$ is positive in x_i if and only if $f(x_1, x_2, \ldots, x_n)$ can be expressed as

$$f(x_1, x_2, \ldots, x_n) = x_i \cdot g(x_1, x_2, \ldots, x_{i-1}, x_{i+1}, \ldots, x_n)$$
$$\lor h(x_1, x_2, \ldots, x_{i-1}, x_{i+1}, \ldots, x_n).$$

PROOF.   Assume f is positive in x_i. Then f may be expressed as a disjunctive normal form positive in x_i. (If f is expressed in conjunctive normal form, successive application of the distributive law gives a disjunctive normal form, and if $\bar{x}_i$ did not appear in the conjunctive normal form, it also does not appear in the disjunctive normal form.) Now the disjunction of all terms in which x_i does not appear is

$$h(x_1, x_2, \ldots, x_{i-1}, x_{i+1}, \ldots, x_n),$$

and the disjunction of all terms in which x_i does appear is

$$x_i \cdot g(x_1, x_2, \ldots, x_{i-1}, x_{i+1}, \ldots, x_n).$$

Factoring x_i gives the desired form $x_i \cdot g$, thus defining g and proving half of the theorem. The converse is immediate.

Naturally, a similar theorem holds for $f(x_1, x_2, \ldots, x_n)$ being negative in x_i. Here we can express f as

$$f(x_1, x_2, \ldots, x_n) = \bar{x}_i \cdot g'(x_1, x_2, \ldots, x_{i-1}, x_{i+1}, \ldots, x_n)$$
$$\vee\, h'(x_1, x_2, \ldots, x_{i-1}, x_{i+1}, \ldots, x_n).$$

Consider the Boolean function $f(x_1, x_2, \ldots, x_n)$ mapped onto the n-dimensional unit cube as described in Section 2.10. We define a partial ordering of the vertices of the n-cube, which is useful in the study of unate functions as follows.

Definition 2.12.5 An n-*ordering* of the vertices of an n-cube is a partial ordering for which there exists a least vertex $(a_1, a_2, \ldots, a_n)$ and for every pair of vertices $(e_1, e_2, \ldots, e_n)$ and $(d_1, d_2, \ldots, d_n)$.

$$(e_1, e_2, \ldots, e_n) \le (d_1, d_2, \ldots, d_n)$$

if and only if either $e_i = a_i$ or $d_i = 1 - a_i$ or both, for every $i = 1, 2, \ldots, n$.

Using definitions given in Section 2.8 it is readily verified that the n-ordering is a partial ordering and that the n-ordering forms a lattice. One possible n-ordering of the n-cube is when

$$(a_1, a_2, \ldots, a_n) = (0, 0, \ldots, 0).$$

Then

$$(e_1, e_2, \ldots, e_n) \le (d_1, d_2, \ldots, d_n)$$

if and only if $e_i \le d_i$ for every i. As an example of n-orderings let us consider the 2-cube with vertices $(0, 0)$, $(0, 1)$, $(1, 0)$, and $(1, 1)$. If (a_1, a_2) is taken as $(0, 0)$, then the n-ordering is shown by the following lattice.

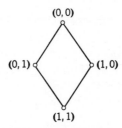

The vertex (a_1, a_2) is arbitrary for Definition 2.12.5, however, so let us consider the choice of $(a_1, a_2) = (0, 1)$. Then using the definition $(e_1, e_2) \le (d_1, d_2)$, we see that $(0, 1) \le (0, 0)$ since $e_i = a_i$ for both i (also here $d_2 = 1 - a_2 = 1 - 1 = 0$). Similarly, $(1, 1) \le (1, 0)$ since in this case the first component has value $1 - a_1 = 1 - 0 = 1$ for the right-hand vertex. The reader may check out the other relations in this n-ordering, where in this case the lattice resulting from this ordering is

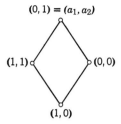

With this simple n-ordering, we can obtain the following theorem for unate functions.

Theorem 2.12.2 A Boolean function $f(x_1, x_2, \ldots, x_n)$ is unate if and only if $f \not\equiv 1$ and there exists an n-ordering such that for every $(e_1, e_2, \ldots, e_n)$ and $(d_1, d_2, \ldots, d_n)$ if $(e_1, e_2, \ldots, e_n)$ is associated with $f^{-1}(1)$ and

$$(e_1, e_2, \ldots, e_n) \leq (d_1, d_2, \ldots, d_n),$$

then $(d_1, d_2, \ldots, d_n)$ is also associated with $f^{-1}(1)$. Also if $(a_1, a_2, \ldots, a_n)$ is the least vertex of this n-ordering, then f is positive in x_i if $a_i = 0$ and f is negative in x_i if $a_i = 1$.

PROOF. If $f(x_1, x_2, \ldots, x_n)$ is unate, a disjunctive normal form D for f exists in which no variable appears both complemented and uncomplemented, thus $f \not\equiv 1$. Let $(a_1, a_2, \ldots, a_n)$ be a vertex on the n-cube for which $a_i = 0$ if x_i appears uncomplemented in D and for which $a_i = 1$ if x_i appears complemented in D. We can assume, without loss of generality, that no complemented terms appear in D and thus

$$(a_1, a_2, \ldots, a_n) = (0, 0, \ldots, 0).$$

Now if $(e_1, e_2, \ldots, e_n)$ is a vertex associated with $f^{-1}(1)$ and

$$(e_1, e_2, \ldots, e_n) \leq (d_1, d_2, \ldots, d_n),$$

some product term in D must be equal to 1, so that $f = 1$ for vertex $(e_1, e_2, \ldots, e_n)$. Now the same product term in D must also equal 1 for the vertex $(d_1, d_2, \ldots, d_n)$. This follows from the fact that

$$(e_1, e_2, \ldots, e_n) \leq (d_1, d_2, \ldots, d_n),$$

so that each variable that equals 1 in $(e_1, e_2, \ldots, e_n)$ also equals 1 in $(d_1, d_2, \ldots, d_n)$. Thus for f assumed unate the theorem is proved. Now assume $f \not\equiv 1$ and for every $(e_1, e_2, \ldots, e_n)$ and $(d_1, d_2, \ldots, d_n)$ if $(e_1, e_2, \ldots, e_n)$ is associated with $f^{-1}(1)$ and

$$(e_1, e_2, \ldots, e_n) \leq (d_1, d_2, \ldots, d_n),$$

then $(d_1, d_2, \ldots, d_n)$ is associated with $f^{-1}(1)$. Now we again assume, with no loss in generality, that

$$(a_1, a_2, \ldots, a_n) = (0, 0, \ldots, 0).$$

There is a set of vertices S associated with $f^{-1}(1)$ which is minimal in the n-ordering. Let

$$S = \{S_1, S_2, \ldots, S_k\}.$$

If D is the disjunction of product terms, where each S_i forms a product term with no complemented variables of exactly those variables whose coordinates equal 1 in S_i, then D is an expression for f and f is unate.

The function $f = x_1 x_2 \vee x_3 x_4$ is obviously unate directly from Definition 2.12.4 since it is positive in each of its variables. An n-ordering for this function satisfying Theorem 2.12.2 is obtained by letting $(a_1, a_2, a_3, a_4) = (0, 0, 0, 0)$. Then the set S mentioned in the proof is: $S = \{(1, 1, 0, 0), (0, 0, 1, 1)\}$. Note, for example, that $f = 1$ for vertex $(1, 1, 1, 0)$ and $(1, 1, 0, 0) \leq (1, 1, 1, 0)$ under the stated n-ordering.

Another class of Boolean functions, which is a subclass of unate functions (see Theorem 2.12.4), is called *threshold functions*. They are of considerable interest and have received wide attention for several reasons: (1) many types of circuit realizations for decision elements operate essentially on a threshold principle; (2) threshold functions seem to be closely related to neuronlike properties; and (3), threshold devices have been shown to be useful for increasing the reliability of redundant switching networks.

Definition 2.12.6 A Boolean function $f(x_1, x_2, \ldots, x_n)$ is called a *threshold function* if there exists a set of real numbers $w_1, w_2, \ldots, w_n$ and a real number T such that

$$f(x_1, x_2, \ldots, x_n) = 1 \quad \text{if} \quad \sum_{i=1}^{n} x_i w_i \geq T$$

and

$$f(x_1, x_2, \ldots, x_n) = 0 \quad \text{if} \quad \sum_{i=1}^{n} x_i w_i < T.$$

In this definition we assume the x_i to take on only the values 0 and 1, which were shown in the canonical forms to be sufficient to describe Boolean functions; furthermore, we assume that these 0 and 1 values are multiplied arithmetically with the w_i's and that the Σ are arithmetic sums.

In our cubical representation for Boolean functions we see that the equation

$$x_1 w_1 + x_2 w_2 + \cdots + x_n w_n = T$$

forms an $(n-1)$-dimension hyperplane through the n-cube. Now since $f = 1$ if

$$x_1 w_1 + x_2 w_2 + \cdots + x_n w_n \geq T$$

and $f = 0$ when

$$x_1 w_1 + x_2 w_2 + \cdots + x_n w_n < T,$$

we see that the hyperplane separates the vertices associated with $f^{-1}(1)$ and $f^{-1}(0)$ respectively. We thus obtain the well-known result.

Theorem 2.12.3   A hyperplane defined by the linear equation

$$x_1 w_1 + x_2 w_2 + \cdots + x_n w_n = T$$

separates the vertices of the n-cube associated with $f^{-1}(1)$ from those associated with $f^{-1}(0)$ if and only if $f(x_1, x_2, \ldots, x_n)$ is a threshold function as given in Definition 2.12.6.

Because of this theorem, threshold functions are often called *linearly separable functions.*

Theorem 2.12.4   The class of threshold functions is a subclass of the class of unate functions.

PROOF.   To prove this theorem we must show that any threshold function $f(x_1, x_2, \ldots, x_n)$ is also unate. Assume $f(x_1, x_2, \ldots, x_n)$ is not unate. Then there is some variable x_i for which f is not unate. Thus by Theorem 2.11.8 for f positive in x_i, there are no functions g and h such that

$$f(x_1, x_2, \ldots, x_n) = x_i \cdot g(x_1, x_2, \ldots, x_{i-1}, x_{i+1}, \ldots, x_n)$$
$$\vee\, h(x_1, x_2, \ldots, x_{i-1}, x_{i+1}, \ldots, x_n).$$

Thus there exists a set of values for

$$x_1, x_2, \ldots, x_{i-1}, x_{i+1}, \ldots, x_n$$

for which $f = 0$ when $x_i = 1$ and $f = 1$ when $x_i = 0$. Call these two sets of values

$$(a_1, a_2, \ldots, a_{i-1}, 1, a_{i+1}, \ldots, a_n)$$

and

$$(a_1, a_2, \ldots, a_{i-1}, 0, a_{i+1}, \ldots, a_n).$$

By the similar theorem for f negative for x_i we obtain a set of values

$$(b_1, b_2, \ldots, b_{i-1}, 0, b_{i+1}, \ldots, b_n)$$

for which $f = 0$, and the set

$$(b_1, b_2, \ldots, b_{i-1}, 1, b_{i+1}, \ldots, b_n)$$

for which $f = 1$. Note that these four points form a parallelogram in

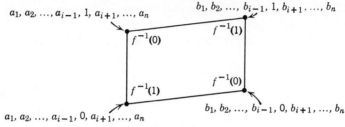

Figure 2.12.1

n-space as shown in Figure 2.12.1. Now for these four vertices of the n-cube, no hyperplane can be passed through this parallelogram such that the vertices for $f^{-1}(0)$ are separated (on one side) from those for $f^{-1}(1)$. Thus by Theorem 2.12.3 f is not a threshold function, and this contradiction proves the theorem.

As stated earlier, the function f

$$f(x_1, x_2, x_3, x_4) = x_1x_2 \lor x_3x_4$$

is obviously unate. It is not a threshold function, however, and we shall show this below. This example thus demonstrates that threshold functions are indeed a proper subclass of unate functions. To demonstrate that this function is not a threshold function we map the function onto a 4-cube, Figure 2.12.2, and then indicate four vertices which describe a parallelogram as in Figure 2.12.1.

The dotted lines describe a parallelogram where diagonal vertices 1100 and 0011 are mapped into $f^{-1}(1)$ and diagonal vertices 1010 and 0101 are

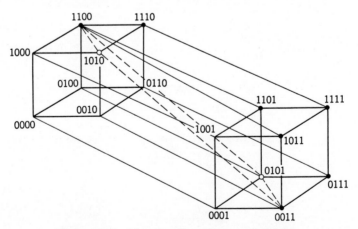

Figure 2.12.2   Mapping of $x_1x_2 \lor x_3x_4$ onto 4-cube.

mapped into $f^{-1}(0)$, thus showing that the function is not a threshold function.

Finally, let us consider a special type of threshold function for which all the w_i of Definition 2.12.6 are equal. In particular, those $f(x_1, x_2, \ldots, x_n)$ for which

$$f(x_1, x_2, \ldots, x_n) = 1 \quad \text{if} \quad \sum_{i=1}^{n} w_i x_i \geq T$$

and

$$f(x_1, x_2, \ldots, x_n) = 0 \quad \text{if} \quad \sum_{i=1}^{n} w_i x_i < T,$$

where $w_i = w_j = w > 0$ for $1 \leq i, j \leq n$ and $T \geq 0$.

In this case we obtain the simplified expressions

$$f(x_1, x_2, \ldots, x_n) = 1 \quad \text{if} \quad \sum_{i=1}^{n} x_i \geq \frac{T}{w}$$

and

$$f(x_1, x_2, \ldots, x_n) = 0 \quad \text{if} \quad \sum_{i=1}^{n} x_i < \frac{T}{w}.$$

Now for some integer p

$$p - 1 < \frac{T}{w} \leq p \quad \text{for} \quad p = 0, 1, 2, \ldots .$$

If $T/w = 0$, then $f(x_1, x_2, \ldots, x_n)$ is identically equal to 1. If $T/w > n$, then $f(x_1, x_2, \ldots, x_n)$ is identically equal to 0. When $0 < T/w \leq n$, then

$$f(x_1, x_2, \ldots, x_n) = 1 \quad \text{if} \quad p \text{ or more variables equal 1}$$

and $\quad f(x_1, x_2, \ldots, x_n) = 0 \quad$ if $\quad p - 1$ or fewer variables equal 1.

Since this description does not differentiate between different variables of the function, the function is a totally symmetric function. It can be represented as

$$f(x_1, x_2, \ldots, x_n) = S_{p, p+1, \ldots, n}(x_1, x_2, \ldots, x_n).$$

These special symmetric threshold functions are also called *simple voting functions* or *simple plurality functions*. If, in addition, n is odd and $p = (n + 1)/2$, then $f(x_1, x_2, \ldots, x_n)$ is called a *simple majority function*.

2.13 SWITCHING FUNCTIONS

As we have seen previously, particularly in Sections 2.5 and 2.6, when we consider Boolean function representations of switching networks, we are interested in representing the binary character of the elements or signal values with variables in a Boolean function. Since these values are binary and also the functional values are 0 or 1, they can be represented by the Boolean elements 0 and 1. Thus we can restrict the set B to the special set $B_2 = \{0, 1\}$ (that is, the Boolean field). Boolean functions of B_2 are also called *complete switching functions* because of this tie with switching networks.

As discussed in Section 2.9, certain combinations of values for the variables may not be specified for the design of a switching network and are thus called "don't care" conditions. Such a description is called a *partial switching function*. We denote complete and partial switching functions simply by the term *switching functions*. A partial switching function can be thought of as defining a class of Boolean functions of B_2, that is, the class of Boolean functions whose values equal that of the partial switching function for those combinations of values of the variables for which the partial switching function is defined. Thus if k combinations are undefined for a partial switching function f, there are 2^k Boolean functions in the class defined by f.

The reader should realize that complete switching functions are indeed a very restricted class of Boolean function; for example, see Exercise 21.

2.14 FUNCTIONAL DECOMPOSITION

It is often possible to express a function $f(x_1, x_2, \ldots, x_n)$ of n-variables as a composite function of functions, as in the following equation:

$$(2.14.1) \quad f(x_1, x_2, \ldots, x_n) = \phi_2(\phi_1(y_1, y_2, \ldots, y_s), z_1, z_2, \ldots, z_r),$$

where $Y = \{y_1, y_2, \ldots, y_s\}$ is a subset of the set of variables, $X = \{x_1, x_2, \ldots, x_n\}$, and $Z = \{z_1, z_2, \ldots, z_k\}$ is also a subset of the set of variables $\{x_1, x_2, \ldots, x_n\}$ such that $Y \cup Z = X$. In general, an n-variable function may be represented as a composite function in many ways. Such a composite representation is also called a *functional decomposition*.

Although we can consider functional decomposition for functions with finite or infinite range in which the variables have finite or infinite domains, we shall restrict our attention to switching functions.

If $f(x_1, x_2, \ldots, x_n)$ is a complete switching function, we are interested in finding functional decompositions for f in which ϕ_2 and ϕ_1 are both switching functions. If f is a partial switching function, f defines a class of complete switching functions and we are then simply interested in finding a decomposition $\phi_2(\phi_1(Y), Z)$, where ϕ_2 and ϕ_1 are switching functions and the class of complete switching functions defined by this decomposition is included in the class of complete switching functions defined by f. We shall abuse our terminology for this inclusion relation and simply write

$$f(X) = \phi_2(\phi_1(Y), Z)$$

since this should cause no confusion for partial switching functions.

Sometimes a composite expression can be found for a switching function f so that in the composite expression, ϕ_2 and ϕ_1 are essentially simpler switching functions. Thus, if we wish to design a logical circuit for a switching function, we may accomplish this by designing circuits for the

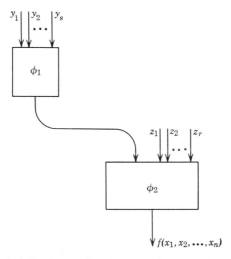

Figure 2.14.1   A logical circuit to realize the composite expression of Equation 2.14.1
for $f(x_1, x_2, \ldots x_n)$.

several simpler functions of the composite representation. For example, if $f(x_1, x_2, \ldots, x_n)$ is a switching function which can be expressed as in Equation (2.14.1), where ϕ_1 and ϕ_2 are also switching functions, then a logical circuit can be made to realize ϕ_1 and another logical circuit can be made to realize ϕ_2, such that by interconnecting these logical circuits as shown in Figure 2.14.1, we obtain a logical circuit which realizes the function f.

If we restrict the sets Y and Z of Equation (2.14.1) to be disjoint subsets of X (that is, having no x_i in both Y and Z), we obtain the particular composite expression given in Equation (2.14.2)

(2.14.2) $f(x_1, x_2, \ldots, x_n) = \phi_2(\phi_1(y_1, y_2, \ldots, y_s), z_1, z_2, \ldots, z_{n-s})$

since each of the n x_i's must appear either in set Y or set Z. We call the type of composite function expression for f given in Equation (2.14.2) a *simple disjoint-decomposition* (or s.d.-decomposition) for f.

We can restrict our attention to s.d.-decompositions for which $1 < s < n$ since the other three cases are trivial. The cases $s = 0$ and $s = n$ are obviously trivial. The case for $s = 1$ is also trivial since we know that any Boolean expression can be expressed as

$$f(x_1, x_2, \ldots, x_n) = x_i f(x_1, x_2, \ldots, x_{i-1}, 1, x_{i+1}, \ldots, x_n)$$
$$\lor \bar{x}_i f(x_1, x_2, \ldots, x_{i-1}, 0, x_{i+1}, \ldots, x_n),$$

from Theorem 2.7.2 and thus f can be expressed as

$$f(x_1, x_2, \ldots, x_n) = \phi_2(\phi_1(x_i), x_1, x_2, \ldots, x_{i-1}, x_{i+1}, \ldots, x_n)$$

by simply letting $\phi_1(x_i) = x_i$ and $\phi_2 = f$.

If a function f has at least one nontrivial s.d.-decomposition, we call f *s.d.-decomposable*.

As an example of a s.d.-decomposable function consider the function

$$f(x_1, x_2, x_3) = x_1 \bar{x}_3 \lor x_2 \bar{x}_3 \lor \bar{x}_1 \bar{x}_2 x_3.$$

If we let

$$\phi_1 = x_1 \lor x_2$$

and

$$\phi_2 = \bar{\phi}_1 x_3 \lor \phi_1 \bar{x}_3 = \phi_1 \oplus x_3,$$

f can be expressed as s.d.-decomposition

$$f(x_1, x_2, x_3) = \phi_2(\phi_1(x_1, x_2), x_3).$$

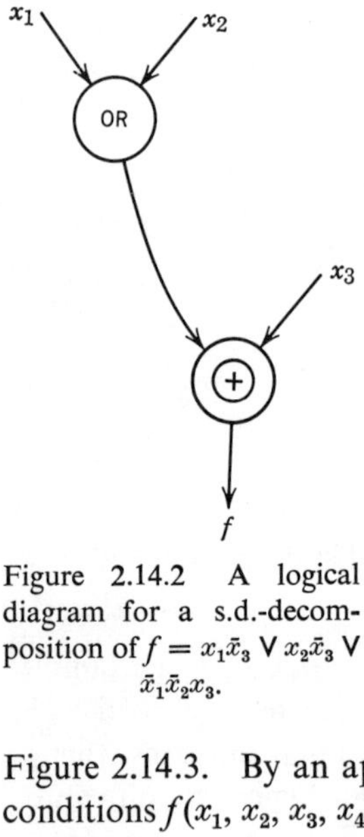

Figure 2.14.2   A logical diagram for a s.d.-decomposition of $f = x_1 \bar{x}_3 \lor x_2 \bar{x}_3 \lor \bar{x}_1 \bar{x}_2 x_3$.

A logical diagram for this functional expression is shown in Figure 2.14.2.

As another example of a s.d.-decomposition consider the four variable partial-switching function described by the Karnaugh map in Figure 2.14.3. By an appropriate assignment of values to the don't care conditions $f(x_1, x_2, x_3, x_4)$ can be expressed as

$$f = \phi_2(\phi_1, x_3, x_4),$$

where

$$\phi_1 = x_1 x_2$$

and

$$\phi_2 = \phi_1 \bar{x}_3 \bar{x}_4 \lor \bar{\phi} x_3 \bar{x}_4 \lor \bar{x}_3 x_4.$$

This can be verified by substituting $x_1 x_2$ into ϕ_2 for ϕ_1, giving

$$\phi_2 = x_1 x_2 \bar{x}_3 \bar{x}_4 \lor (\bar{x}_1 \lor \bar{x}_2) x_3 \bar{x}_4 \lor \bar{x}_3 x_4.$$

The resulting Karnaugh map is shown in Figure 2.14.4, where it is readily

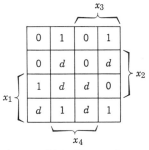

Figure 2.14.3 Karnaugh map
for a partial switching function
$f(x_1, x_2, x_3, x_4)$.

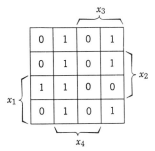

Figure 2.14.4 Karnaugh map
for $\phi_2(\phi_1, x_3, x_4)$.

seen that this satisfies the requirements of Figure 2.14.3. The resulting form of a logical diagram representing this decomposition is shown in Figure 2.14.5.

A slightly more general type of decomposition, called a *simple non-disjoint-decomposition* in which some x_i may appear both in Y and Z, is given in Equation (2.14.3).

(2.14.3) $f(x_1, x_2, \ldots, x_r, x_{r+1}, \ldots, x_s,$
$x_{s+1}, \ldots, x_n) = \phi_2[\phi_1(x_1, x_2, \ldots, x_s),$
$x_{r+1}, \ldots, x_n],$

where $x_{r+1}, \ldots, x_s$ are the variables common to ϕ_1 and ϕ_2 and there is no loss of generality in labeling the variables in this order.

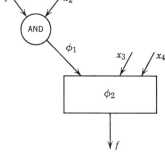

Figure 2.14.5 Logical diagram form
for $\phi_2(\phi_1, x_3, x_4)$.

We now show special forms for Karnaugh maps (also called decomposition charts in this context) which can be used to detect whether a given function is s.d.-decomposable. Let $\phi_i^0 = \phi_i^{-1}(0)$ and $\phi_i^1 = \phi_i^{-1}(1)$, then Equation (2.14.2) may be written as

(2.14.4) $f(x_1, x_2, \ldots, x_n)$
$$= \phi_1^0 \cdot \Gamma_0(z_1, z_2, \ldots, z_{n-s}) \vee \phi_1^1 \cdot \Gamma_1(z_1, z_2, \ldots, z_{n-s}),$$
where $\Gamma_0(z_1, z_2, \ldots, z_{n-s}) = \phi_2(0, z_1, z_2, \ldots, z_{n-s})$
$\Gamma_1(z_1, z_2, \ldots, z_{n-s}) = \phi_2(1, z_1, z_2, \ldots, z_{n-s})$

or as

(2.14.5) $f(x_1, x_2, \ldots, x_n)$
$$= \phi_1^0 \beta_0(z_1, z_2, \ldots, z_{n-s}) \vee \phi_1^1 \beta_1(z_1, z_2, \ldots, z_{n-s}) \vee \beta_x(z_1, z_2, \ldots, z_{n-s})$$
where $\beta_x = \Gamma_0 \cdot \Gamma_1,$ $\beta_0 = \Gamma_0 \cdot \overline{\Gamma}_1,$ $\beta_1 = \overline{\Gamma}_0 \cdot \Gamma_1.$

If either Equation (2.14.4) or (2.14.5) is satisfied, this is equivalent to the existence of the s.d.-decomposition of Equation (2.14.2) since these equations are simply modified expressions of (2.14.2).

We shall now give rules for the existence of a s.d.-decomposition by employing Karnaugh maps. Construct a Karnaugh map having 2^s rows and 2^{n-s} columns, where the rows correspond to the 2^s values for the variables $y_1, y_2, \ldots, y_s$ and the columns correspond to the 2^{n-s} values for the variables $z_1, z_2, \ldots, z_{n-s}$. Now place 1's in the positions corresponding to $f^{-1}(1)$ and 0's in the positions corresponding to $f^{-1}(0)$. For our previous example

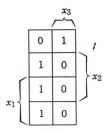

$$f = x_1\bar{x}_3 \vee x_2\bar{x}_3 \vee \bar{x}_1\bar{x}_2x_3 = \phi_2(\phi_1(x_1, x_2), x_3),$$

where

$$\phi_1 = x_1 \vee x_2$$

and

$$\phi_2 = \phi_1 \oplus x_3,$$

Figure 2.14.6 Karnaugh map for $f = x_1\bar{x}_3 \vee x_2\bar{x}_3 \vee \bar{x}_1\bar{x}_2x_3$.

we obtain the Karnaugh map shown in Figure 2.14.6, where $s = 2$, and $n - s = 1$.

Note that the right column is the component-by-component complement of the left column. Note that the two nonconstant columns of the Karnaugh map of Figure 2.14.4 for $\phi_2(\phi_1, x_3, x_4)$ are also complements. This general pattern carries over to the general case of s.d.-decomposition as shown by the following theorem due to Ashenhurst.

Theorem 2.14.1   A s.d.-decomposition of a switching function

$$f(x_1, x_2, \ldots, x_n) = \phi_2(\phi_1(y_1, y_2, \ldots, y_s), z_1, z_2, \ldots, z_{n-s}),$$

for a given set of variables $y_1, y_2, \ldots, y_s$, exists if and only if on the resulting Karnaugh map with 2^s rows and 2^{n-s} columns the don't care positions can be assigned 0 and 1 values such that every column is one of the following four types: (1) all zeros, (2) all ones, (3), equal to some column vector A, or (4) equal to the negation of A.

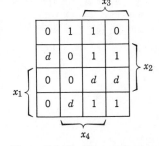

Figure 2.14.7 Karnaugh map for a switching function.

Obviously, the assignment of 0 and 1 values to Figure 2.14.3 as given in Figure 2.14.4 was done to satisfy this theorem.

Before we prove the theorem, let us consider another switching function as described by the Karnaugh map of Figure 2.14.7. Considering this example, we can assign 0 and 1 values to the d entries to satisfy Theorem 2.14.1. This assignment is shown in Figure 2.14.8. The second column may be considered to be A, then the fourth column is $\bar{A}$. The combinations of (x_1, x_2) for which rows in A equal 1 can be assigned to $\phi_1{}^0$ and the others to $\phi_1{}^1$. Thus

$$\phi_1 = 1 \qquad \text{for} \qquad \bar{x}_1 x_2 \vee x_1 x_2 \vee x_1 \bar{x}_2 = x_1 \vee x_2$$

and $\qquad \phi_1 = 0 \qquad \text{for} \qquad \bar{x}_1 \bar{x}_2.$

Now, using Equation (2.14.5), β_0 is equal to those combinations of (x_3, x_4) which contain column A. Similarly, β_1 is equal to those combinations of (x_3, x_4) which contain column $\bar{A}$, and finally β_x is equal to those combinations of (x_3, x_4) for which the column is all 1's. Thus

$$\beta_0 = \bar{x}_3 x_4$$
$$\beta_1 = x_3 \bar{x}_4$$
$$\beta_x = x_3 x_4$$

and by Equation (2.14.5) we can express the switching function as

(2.14.6) $\qquad \phi_2(\phi_1, x_3, x_4) = \bar{\phi}_1 \bar{x}_3 x_4 \vee \phi_1 x_3 \bar{x}_4 \vee x_3 x_4,$

where $\qquad \phi_1 = x_1 \vee x_2.$

To check Equation (2.14.6) we can substitute $x_1 \vee x_2$ for ϕ_1 and $\bar{x}_1 \bar{x}_2$ for $\bar{\phi}_1$, giving

$$f(x_1, x_2, x_3, x_4) = \bar{x}_1 \bar{x}_2 \bar{x}_3 x_4 \vee x_1 x_3 \bar{x}_4 \vee x_2 x_3 \bar{x}_4 \vee x_3 x_4.$$

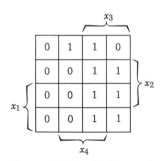

Figure 2.14.8 A Karnaugh map satisfying decomposition Theorem 2.14.1.

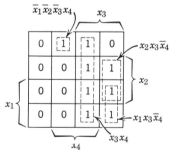

Figure 2.14.9 Verification of decomposition Equation (2.14.6).

This may be checked against the Karnaugh map of Figure 2.14.8 as done in Figure 2.14.9.

The logical diagram for Equation (2.14.6) is shown in Figure 2.14.10.

To prove Theorem 2.14.1, we can construct a decomposition if the conditions are satisfied just as done in the example. Let the values of

$y_1, y_2, \ldots, y_s$ corresponding to 1's in A be vertices in $\phi_1{}^0$, and the values of $y_1, y_2, \ldots, y_s$ corresponding to 0's in A be vertices in $\phi_1{}^1$. Let the column values of $z_1, z_2, \ldots, z_{n-s}$ for which A is a column correspond to vertices of β_0, and column values of $z_1, z_2, \ldots, z_{n-s}$ for which $\bar{A}$ is the column correspond to vertices of β_1, and column values $z_1, z_2, \ldots, z_{n-s}$ for which the column is all 1's correspond to vertices in β_x. Then Equation (2.14.5) describes the simple disjoint-decomposition. Now assume that no assignment of 0's and 1's to the d's can be made to satisfy the conditions of the theorem; but suppose a decomposition exists. There must be two column vectors A_k and A_l which are not all 0's or all 1's and not complementary. Thus in some pair of rows R_i and R_j we have the entries in these row and column entries

$$e_{ik} = e_{il},$$

but

$$e_{jk} \neq e_{jl}.$$

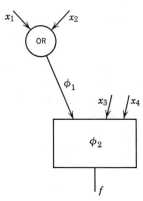

Figure 2.14.10   The logical diagram for the decomposition example.

Now if a decomposition exists, ϕ_1 has definite values assigned to rows i and j. Call these ϕ_{1i} and ϕ_{1j} respectively. Now either $\phi_{1i} = \phi_{1j}$ or not. If $\phi_{1j} = \phi_{1j}$, then no $\Gamma(z_1, \ldots, z_{n-s})$ can be assigned to columns k and l since $e_{jk} \neq e_{jl}$ and $e_{ik} = e_{il}$. If $\phi_{1i} \neq \phi_{1j}$, then $\Gamma(z_1, \ldots, z_{n-s})$ cannot be obtained since we do not have row independence between columns k and l. Thus a decomposition cannot exist, and the theorem is proved.

The test for s.d.-decomposition depends on a correct choice of 0's and 1's for the don't care positions in the Karnaugh map. The test may be carried out in a systematic manner, rather than by inspection, as follows:

1. Cross out all columns which do not have both 0 and 1 entries.

2. Choose a non-d-element, associate the row of this element with $\phi_1{}^0$, and the column with β_0 if the entry equals 1 or with β_1 if the entry equals 0. Then the following further row and column associations may be made:

  (a) If two elements in the same column are equal and $\phi_1{}^i, (i = 0, 1)$ is associated with one row containing one of these elements, then $\phi_1{}^i$ is also associated with the other row containing the other element.

  (b) If two elements in the same column are 0 and 1 respectively, and $\phi_1{}^i$ has been associated with the row containing one of these elements, then $\phi_1{}^{\bar{i}}$ is associated with the row containing the other element.

(c) If ϕ_1^i is assigned to a row containing some non-d-element, and the element is a 0, then the column for this element is associated with $\beta_{\bar{i}}$; if the element is a 1, then the column for this element is associated with β_i.

3. If a contradiction occurs in the process, such as associating both ϕ_1^i and $\phi_1^{\bar{i}}$ to some row, or β_i and $\beta_{\bar{i}}$ to some column, then no nontrivial simple disjoint-decomposition exists with this set of $y_1, y_2, \ldots, y_s$ variables.

If all rows have been assigned to ϕ_1^0 or ϕ_1^1, then the process terminates and the decomposition is exhibited by the ϕ_1^0, ϕ_1^1, β_0, β_1, and β_x, where

a	b	c	d 0 e 0	0 1	1 0	1 1
0	0	0	0	d	1	1
0	0	1	1	1	0	d
0	1	0	1	d	d	1
0	1	1	0	0	1	1
1	0	0	0	0	0	1
1	0	1	0	d	0	1
1	1	0	d	0	0	1
1	1	1	d	0	0	1

Figure 2.14.11   Map with $y_1, y_2, \ldots, y_s = a, b, c$.

β_x is formed from those column values for columns of all 1's (or 1's and d's) which were eliminated in Step 1. If Step 2 were continued as far as possible, but some rows were not associated with either ϕ_1^0 of ϕ_1^1, Step 2 should be repeated for a non-d-element in one of these rows. Step 2 is repeated until all rows have been associated with either ϕ_1^0 or ϕ_1^1, until a contradiction arises, or until all remaining rows are all d's. If no contradiction arises, a decomposition exists. The rows of all d's may be assigned to either ϕ_1^0 or ϕ_1^1, and also if repetition of Step 2 were required we could have made a ϕ_1^1 or ϕ_1^0 assignment arbitrarily. Thus, if Step 2 is used m times and there are n rows of d's, then 2^{m+n} choices of ϕ_1^0 and ϕ_1^1 are possible. In the special case of $m = 1$ and $n = 0$, we see that this corresponds to the one choice of a nonconstant column as either A or $\bar{A}$.

Consider another example, having five variables $abcde$, as shown in the map of Figure 2.14.11. In this example we note that the adjacent rows or columns need not be made to differ in only one value as in the Karnaugh maps discussed earlier. This is easily seen from the rules for decomposition just given. Here we also note that columns 1 and 3 *cannot* be made to be either identical column vectors or complementary column vectors; thus no s.d.-decomposition exists for $\{y_1, y_2, y_3\} = \{a, b, c\}$ for this example. Note also that if the set Y were $\{y_1, y_2\} = \{d, e\}$, Figure 2.14.11 also can be used to see that no s.d.-decomposition exists for $\{y_1, y_2\} = \{d, e\}$ since the *rows* (acting as columns) cannot be made to satisfy the decomposition theorem.

Now if a redundant appearance of variable a is introduced, and we revert to a nondisjoint-decomposition where $Y = \{a, b, c\}$ and $Z = \{a_1, d, e\}$, where $a_1 = a$, then we can modify the map of Figure 2.14.11 to that of 2.14.12.

$\begin{matrix} a_1 \\ d \\ e \end{matrix}$ $\diagdown$ abc	0000 0011 0101	1111 0011 0101
000	0*d*11	*dddd*
001	110*d*	*dddd*
010	1*dd*1	*dddd*
011	0011	*dddd*
100	*dddd*	0001
101	*dddd*	0*d*01
110	*dddd*	*d*001
111	*dddd*	*d*001

Figure 2.14.12   Map with redundant variable *a*.

By adding the redundant a, don't care conditions are introduced in the upper left and lower right blocks since $a = a_1$ and never will $a = 0$ and $a_1 = 1$ or $a = 1$ and $a_1 = 0$. We note that the decomposition theorem may now be satisfied, resulting in a nondisjoint-decomposition. Rather than introducing this redundancy directly, we can test for simple non-disjoint-decompositions using the following theorem.

Theorem 2.14.2   A switching function $f(x_1, x_2, \ldots, x_n)$ admits of a simple nondisjoint-decomposition of the form

$$\phi_2(\phi_1(w_1, w_2, \ldots, w_r, y_1, \ldots, y_s), w_1, \ldots, w_r, z_1, \ldots, z_{n-s-r})$$

if and only if, when the Karnaugh map having rows for combinations of $\{w_1, w_2, \ldots, w_r, y_1, \ldots, y_s\}$ is row partitioned according to the values of $w_1, \ldots, w_r$, each submap in the partition satisfied the conditions of Theorem 2.14.1.

Further application of decomposition for switching circuit design will be considered in Chapter 4.

2.15 SUMMARY

In this chapter we have introduced the concepts of Boolean algebra and shown how this algebra may act as a model both for relay contact switching circuits and networks of decision elements. Connections of this algebra to the mathematical disiplines of set theory, logic, group theory, and lattice theory were also discussed briefly. The concept of Boolean functions was considered at length, showing the geometric representation on Karnaugh maps, and the geometric and algebraic representation on n-cubes. Special types of Boolean functions and certain operations of decomposition were also introduced. All these notions will be useful in our study of switching theory techniques in the following chapters. Here we shall consider a special type of switching circuit called a "combinational" circuit for which Boolean functions serve as an adequate model. In Chapter 3, we shall use and extend the cubical representation discussed in Section 2.10, showing how normal form expressions for Boolean functions may be simplified using this notation. In Chapter 4, we consider more general Boolean functional expressions, and here the concepts of factoring and decomposition of Boolean functions will prove applicable. Finally, in Chapter 5, we shall study a generalized type of relay contact network called *bilateral switching networks* and shall find that special network structures and resulting simplifications are possible for symmetric functions.

Exercises

1. Prove that the two definitions for inclusion are equivalent. That is, that

$$a \subseteq b \quad \text{if and only if} \quad a \cdot b = a$$

is equivalent to

$$a \subseteq b \quad \text{if and only if} \quad a \vee b = b.$$

2. Prove the identities
  (a) $a \vee \bar{a}b = a \vee b.$
  (b) $ac \vee \bar{a}b \vee bc = ac \vee \bar{a}b.$
  (c) $\bar{a}\bar{c} \vee bc \vee a\bar{b} = \bar{a}b \vee ac \vee \bar{b}\bar{c}.$

3. Fill in each of the eight areas of the following Venn diagram with a product of the x-, y-, and z-variables.

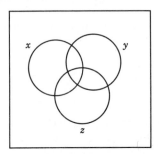

4. Illustrate by a shaded area on a Venn diagram the function

$$f = xy \lor \bar{x}\bar{y}$$

5. Determine whether $f = g$ for

$$f = \bar{a} \lor b \lor \bar{c}$$
$$g = \bar{a}(\bar{b} \lor \bar{c}) \lor bc \lor a\bar{c}$$

by comparing their disjunctive canonical expansions.

6. Express the function

$$f(x_1, x_2) = x_1 x_2$$

in conjunctive canonical form.

7. Prove that the EXCLUSIVE OR-operation is commutative, and associative, and also commutative with the AND-operation, that is, prove

$$a \oplus b = b \oplus a.$$
$$a \oplus (b \oplus c) = (a \oplus b) \oplus c.$$
$$a(b \oplus c) = ab \oplus ac.$$

8. Given the following Karnaugh map, find a simplified function and construct a logical diagram (using AND-, OR-, and NOT-elements for the simplified function.

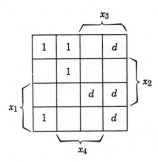

9. Do the same as Exercise 8 for the following.

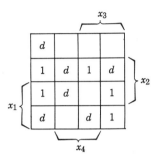

10. Construct Karnaugh maps for the following functions:

(a) $f = x_1 x_2 \lor x_1 x_3 \lor x_2 x_3$.

(b) $f = \bar{x}_2 \bar{x}_3 \bar{x}_4 \lor \bar{x}_1 \bar{x}_3 \bar{x}_4 \lor \bar{x}_1 \bar{x}_2 \bar{x}_4 \lor \bar{x}_1 \bar{x}_2 \bar{x}_3$.

(c) $f = \bar{x}_1 (x_2 x_3 \lor x_4)$.

(d) $f = x_1 \oplus x_2 \oplus x_3 \oplus x_4$.

11. Prove the uniqueness of the disjunctive canonical form for a function $f(x_1, x_2, \ldots, x_n)$.

12. For the two-terminal relay contact network shown, write the Boolean function for a closed path in the circuit. Using a Karnaugh map, obtain a simplified expression for the function and draw the resulting simplified relay contact circuit.

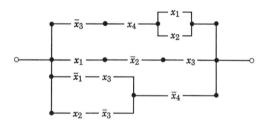

13. Prove that $x_1 \cdot f(x_1, x_2, \ldots, x_n) = x_1 \cdot f(1, x_2, \ldots, x_n)$ for any function $f(x_1, x_2, \ldots, x_n)$.

14. Prove that any Boolean function $f(x_1, x_2, \ldots, x_n)$ can be written in the "complement-free ring sum canonical form" as follows:

$$f(x_1, x_2, \ldots, x_n) = d_0 \oplus d_1 x_1 \oplus d_2 x_2 \oplus \cdots \oplus d_n x_n$$

$$\oplus d_{n+1} x_1 x_2 \oplus d_{n+2} x_1 x_3 \oplus \cdots \oplus d_{n(n+1)/2}\, x_{n-1} x_n$$

$$\oplus d_{(n(n+1)/2)+1} x_1 x_2 x_3 \oplus \cdots \oplus d_{2^n - 1} x_1 x_2 \cdots x_n,$$

where $d_i = 0$ or 1, $0 \le i \le 2^n - 1$.

15. Given the following logical diagram:

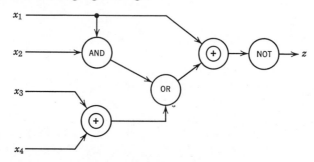

   (*a*) Derive a Boolean function for the output z as a function of the inputs x_1, x_2, x_3, and x_4.

   (*b*) Express this function in disjunctive normal form.

   (*c*) Assume that the inputs are so restricted that if $x_1 = 1$, then $x_3 = 1$, and also if $x_3 = 1$, then $x_1 = 1$; that is, $x_1\bar{x}_3 \vee \bar{x}_1 x_3$ never occurs, thus introducing certain don't care conditions. Write a simplified disjunctive normal form expression having a minimum number of appearances of variables (and complemented variables), using these don't care conditions.

16. The inclusion relation for Boolean algebra was shown to be a partial ordering (Theorem 2.8.2). For the Boolean algebra of two elements, $B = \{0, 1\}$ this relation is also a *total ordering*, that is, for every a, $b \in B$ either $a \subseteq b$ or $b \subseteq a$. Show that the inclusion relation is *not* a total ordering for some Boolean algebra with more than two elements.

17. Assume that a modular number system is used to represent the decimal digits, as shown in the following:

Decimal Digit	Modular Number 5	2
0	0	0
1	1	1
2	2	0
3	3	1
4	4	0
5	0	1
6	1	0
7	2	1
8	3	0
9	4	1

   (*a*) Using a positional number system for the modular-coded decimal digits, give the addition tables in the modular representation for the sum and carry digits for the case when the augend digit equals decimal 2.

(*b*) If the 5 radix is coded in binary as

$$x_1 x_2 x_3$$

$$0\ 0\ 0\ = 0$$
$$0\ 1\ 1\ = 1$$
$$1\ 0\ 1\ = 2$$
$$1\ 1\ 0\ = 3$$
$$1\ 1\ 1\ = 4$$

and $x_1 x_2 x_3$ are taken as Boolean variables, and the 2 radix is also treated as a Boolean variable x_4, then an adder circuit takes on the general form of the accompanying diagram.

Digits for Augend and Addend

Augend Addend   Augend Addend   Augend Addend

Carry | Adder Position | Carry | Adder Position | Carry | Adder Position | Carry

Sum Digits

Assuming the augend digit equals 2 (2, 0 modular), write the Boolean function f_c for the carry signal, where $f_c = 1$ when a carry of 1,1 (modular) is required. Note that f_c depends on the addend digits b_1, b_2, b_3, b_4, the augend digits a_1, a_2, a_3, a_4, and the carry in digit c, where we are assuming the augend digits fixed at

$$\boxed{a_1 \bar{a}_2 a_3}\ \boxed{\bar{a}_4}$$
$$2 \qquad 0 = 2$$
$$\text{Modular} \qquad \text{Decimal}$$

18. (*a*) Express the four variable Boolean function

$$f(x_1, x_2, x_3, x_4) = \bar{x}_1 \bar{x}_2(\bar{x}_3 \vee x_3 \bar{x}_4) \vee x_1 x_3 \bar{x}_4 \vee x_4(\bar{x}_2 x_3 \vee x_1 x_2 \vee \bar{x}_1 \bar{x}_3)$$

as a disjunctive normal form having a minimum number of appearances of variables (and complemented variables).

(*b*) Show a series-parallel relay contact circuit to realize the disjunctive normal form expression.

19. Prove, by mathematical induction on n, that the function

$$f(x_1, x_2, \ldots, x_{n+1}) = x_1 \oplus x_2 \oplus \cdots \oplus x_{n+1}$$

is equal to 1 if and only if an odd number of the variables x_1, x_2, $\ldots$, x_{n+1} are equal to 1.

20. Prove the extension of DeMorgan's laws that

$$\overline{(x_1 x_2 \cdots x_n)} = \bar{x}_1 \vee \bar{x}_2 \vee \cdots \vee \bar{x}_n$$

and

$$\overline{(x_1 \vee x_2 \vee \cdots \vee x_n)} = \bar{x}_1 \bar{x}_2 \cdots \bar{x}_n.$$

21. Suppose the set B of a Boolean algebra has four elements $B = \{0, a, b, 1\}$. Determine every Boolean function (if any) in this algebra which satisfies the following conditions:

(a) $f(x_1, x_2)$ where

$$f(a, 0) = a \qquad f(b, 0) = b,$$
$$f(a, 1) = 1 \qquad f(b, 1) = 1.$$

(b) $f(x_1, x_2, x_3)$ where

$$f(0, 0, 0,) = 1 \qquad f(1, 1, 1) = 0$$
$$f(a, a, 1) = b \qquad f(0, a, b) = 1$$
$$f(b, b, 0) = a.$$

(c) $g(x_1, x_2)$ where

$$g(0, 0) = 1 \qquad g(0, a) = a.$$

(d) $h(x_1, x_2)$ where

$$h(a, a) = 0 \qquad h(b, b) = 0$$
$$h(a, 0) = a \qquad h(1, b) = a.$$

22. Express the following Boolean functions as totally symmetric functions:

(a) $\bar{x}_1 \cdot S_{0,1,2}(x_2, x_3, x_4) \vee x_1 \cdot S_{2,3}(\bar{x}_2, \bar{x}_3, \bar{x}_4)$.

(b) $\overline{S_{2,3}(x_1, x_2, x_3, x_4)} \cdot S_{1,2,3,4}(x_1, x_2, x_3, x_4)$.

(c) $f(x_1, x_2, x_3) = x_1 x_2 x_3 \vee x_1 \bar{x}_2 \bar{x}_3 \vee \bar{x}_1 x_2 \bar{x}_3 \vee \bar{x}_1 \bar{x}_2 x_3$.

(d) $f(x_1, x_2, x_3, x_4) = \bar{x}_1 x_2 \vee \bar{x}_1 x_3 \vee \bar{x}_1 \bar{x}_4 \vee x_2 x_3 \vee x_2 \bar{x}_4 \vee x_3 \bar{x}_4$.

(e) $f(x_1, x_2, x_3) = \bar{x}_1 \bar{x}_2 \vee \bar{x}_2 \bar{x}_3 \vee x_1 x_2 \vee x_2 x_3$.

23. Let $f(x_1, x_2, \ldots, x_n)$ be a Boolean function, where the values of the variables are either 0 or 1, and where there exists a set of weights $w_1, w_2, \ldots, w_n$ ($w_i = +1$ or -1, $1 \leq i \leq n$) and a real number T such that

$$f(x_1, x_2, \ldots, x_n) = 1 \text{ if } \sum_{i=1}^{n} w_i x_i \geq T$$

and

$$f(x_1, x_2, \ldots, x_n) = 0 \text{ if } \sum_{i=1}^{n} w_i x_i < T.$$

This function is obviously a special type of threshold function. Is $f(x_1, x_2, \ldots, x_n)$ also a totally symmetric function? If so, prove, and indicate the variables of symmetry. If not, display some such $f(x_1, x_2, \ldots, x_n)$ which is not totally symmetric.

24. Does a s.d.-decomposition exist for the switching function given by the following Karnaugh map when

$$x_3$$

1	0	d	d
1	0	0	1
d	0	1	1
0	d	d	1

x_2

x_1

$$x_4$$

(a) $Y = (x_1, x_2)$?
(b) $Y = (x_3, x_4)$?
(c) $Y = (x_2, x_3)$?
(d) $Y = (x_1, x_4)$?
(e) Give a s.d.-decomposition for (a), (b), (c), and (d) whenever one exists and show the resulting logical circuit.

25. Find a nondisjoint-decomposition of the following partial switching function, if any exists, for $Y = \{x_1, x_2, x_3\}$ and $Z = \{x_1, x_4, x_5\}$.

x_4			
x_5	0 0 1 1		
$x_1 x_2 x_3$	0 1 0 1		
0 0 0	0 d 1 d		
0 0 1	1 1 0 d		
0 1 0	d 1 d 0		
0 1 1	1 d d 0		
1 0 0	0 0 d 1		
1 0 1	0 d 0 d		
1 1 0	d d 0 1		
1 1 1	1 0 1 d		

REFERENCE NOTATIONS

Basic developments of Boolean algebra can be found in many places, for example, [5, 8–11, 17, 18, 21]. Birkhoff and MacLane [5] in their widely known text on modern algebra give a particularly lucid and short exposition. The application to switching circuits dates back to Shannon [22], and various treatments of this application are found in many books [6–11, 18]. The geometric representations on Karnaugh maps is due to Karnaugh [12], and the n-cube representation may be found in [14] as well as in numerous articles by Roth discussed and referenced in the next chapter.

Symmetric functions, Section 2.11, were studied at length by Shannon [22, 23] and Caldwell [6]. Marcus [15] treats these to some extent, and Theorem 2.11.6 can be found in Povarov [19] where additional references to Russian works in switching theory may also be found. The group properties of symmetries of Boolean functions have been the subject of several recent works [1, 2,], where these properties lead to further techniques for detecting symmetries. Section 2.12 is based, to a large extent, on an article on unate functions by McNaughton [16].

Fuctional decomposition was first studied extensively by Ashenhurst [3]. Other work is illustrated in [7, 13, 20, 24]. Curtis's book [7] contains a multitude of design techniques and worked-out examples based on many different types of decompositions. Karp [13] extends and develops theorems for decomposition of functions on general finite domains; and Roth and Karp [20] describe a design technique based on successive decompositions. Some of these decompositions techniques will be further studied in Chapter 4.

REFERENCES

1. Arnold, R. F. and M. A. Harrison, "Algebraic Properties of Symmetric and Partially Symmetric Boolean Functions." *IEEE Transactions on Electronic Computers*, Vol. EC-12, pp. 244–251, June, 1963.
2. Arnold, R. F. and E. L. Lawler, "On the Analysis of Functional Symmetry." *Proceedings of the Fourth Annual IEEE Symposium on Switching Circuit Theory and Logical Design*, pp. 53–62, September, 1963.
3. Ashenhurst, R. L., "The Decomposition of Switching Functions," *Proceedings of an International Symposium on the Theory of Switching*, April 2–5, 1957, Vol. 29 of *Annals of Computation Laboratory of Harvard University*, pp. 74–116, 1959.
4. Birkhoff, G., *Lattice Theory*, American Mathematical Society Colloquium Publications, Vol. 25, New York, 1948.
5. Birkhoff, G. and S. MacLane, *A Survey of Modern Algebra*, Chapter XI, Revised Edition, The Macmillan Co., New York, 1953.
6. Caldwell, S. H., *Switching Circuits and Logical Design*, John Wiley and Sons, New York, 1958.
7. Curtis, H. A., *A New Approach to the Design of Switching Circuits*, D. Van Nostrand Co., Princeton, New Jersey, 1962.
8. Flegg, H. G., *Boolean Algebra and Its Applications*, John Wiley and Sons, New York, 1964.
9. Higonnet, R. A. and R. A. Grea, *Logical Design of Electrical Circuits*, McGraw-Hill Book Co., New York, 1958.
10. Hohn, F. E., *Applied Boolean Algebra, An Elementary Introduction*, The Macmillan Co., New York, 1960.
11. Humphrey, W. S., Jr., *Switching Circuits with Computer Applications*, McGraw-Hill Book Co., New York, 1958.
12. Karnaugh, M., "The Map Method of Synthesis of Combinational Logic Circuits," *Communications and Electronics*, No. 9, pp. 593–599, November 1953.
13. Karp, R. M., "Functional Decomposition and Switching Circuit Design," *IBM Research Report* RC-662, March 1962 and *SIAM Journal*, pp. 291–335, June 1963.
14. Lee, C. Y., "Switching Functions on the N-dimensional Cube," *Transactions of the AIEE*, pp. 289–291, Vol. 73, Part I, 1954.
15. Marcus, M. P., *Switching Circuits for Engineers*, Prentice-Hall, Englewood Cliffs, New Jersey, 1962.
16. McNaughton, R., "Unate Truth Functions," *IRE Transactions on Electronic Computers*, Vol. EC-10, pp. 1–6, March 1961.
17. Muller, D. E., Course Notes on Boolean Algebra, University of Illinois, Digital Computer Laboratory, 1954 (Unpublished).

18. Phister, M., Jr., *Logical Design of Digital Computers*, Chapters 3 and 4, John Wiley and Sons, New York, 1958.
19. Povarov, G. N., "A Mathematical Theory for the Synthesis of Contact Networks with One Input and k Outputs," *Proceedings of an International Symposium on the Theory of Switching*, April 2–5, 1957, Vol. 30 of the *Annals of Computation Laboratory of Harvard University*, pp. 74–94, 1959.
20. Roth, J. P., and R. M. Karp, "Minimization over Boolean Graphs," *IBM Journal of Research and Development*, Vol. 6, No. 2, pp. 227–238, April 1962.
21. Serrell, R., "Elements of Boolean Algebra for the Study of Information-Handling Systems," *Proceedings of the IRE*, Vol. 41, No. 10, pp. 1366–1380, October 1953.
22. Shannon, C. E., "A Symbolic Analysis of Relay and Switching Circuits," *Transactions of the AIEE*, Vol. 57, pp. 713–723, 1938.
23. Shannon, C. E., "The Synthesis of Two-Terminal Switching Circuits," *BSTJ*, Vol. 28, pp. 59–98, 1949.
24. Singer, T., "Some Uses of Truth Tables," *Proceedings of an International Symposium on the Theory of Switching*, April 2–5, 1957, Vol. 29 of *Annals of Computation Laboratory of Harvard University*, pp. 125–133, 1959.

3

Combinational Switching Circuits: Normal Form Circuit Design

3.1 INTRODUCTION

In this chapter we define a type of switching circuit called a *combinational circuit* and describe various combinational circuit structures. A procedure for the design of those switching circuits which correspond to disjunctive normal form or conjunctive normal form expressions of switching functions is then discussed in some detail. We call such circuits *normal form circuits*. As discussed briefly in Chapter 2 simplified circuits may be obtained by finding a simplified expression for the Boolean function which we want to realize in the form of a switching circuit. Thus for normal form circuits we shall be interested in finding simplified disjunctive or conjunctive normal form expressions. The algebraic approach we shall describe is based on the cubical representation given in Section 2.10, and can be considered to be an extension of the methods discussed for Karnaugh maps, Section 2.9. Other similar procedures for designing normal form circuits, using tabular methods and transformations on Boolean functions, have also been developed. In Section 3.8 we discuss one of these chart methods which is very convenient to use, especially for manual simplification of expressions. Further references on these methods are also included at the end of the chapter.

We prefer to discuss the algebraic method using the cubical representation rather than one of the other formulations for several reasons. First, we feel that the cubical representation is a convenient tool which gives both geometric and algebraic insight into switching theory problems, and this representation has not previously been readily available. Furthermore, this algebraic form readily lends itself to formal statements and proofs of the theorems underlying the simplification techniques, and treats functions of n variables throughout, rather than introducing additional complications as the number of variables increases. Of course, we must point out that there are usually many more steps required when

134

treating functions of many variables than that for functions of only a few variables, but this is to be expected. Finally, this approach can be readily adopted to mechanization on a digital computer since the cubical representation using 0's and 1's is well suited to the binary representation of numbers in computers. Several such computer programs using cubical representations have been developed.

Even though the cubical representation is stressed here, it should be clear to the reader that any results found in cubical terminology have analogous results in Boolean algebra and Boolean function terminology; and when the number of variables is sufficiently small, these results can be characterized by properties on chart and map representations. That these similarities exist follows simply from the fact that the cubical, map, and chart representations are different models for the same mathematical entity.

Before describing the design procedure, we give the definition of a "combinational switching circuit," and consider some of the possible relay contact and logical diagram structures for realizing combinational switching circuits. We then see that normal form circuits are a very simple type of combinational switching circuit.

Further theory and design procedures for other combinational switching circuit structures are discussed in Chapters 4 and 5.

3.2 THE STRUCTURE OF COMBINATIONAL CIRCUITS

In Sections 2.5 and 2.6 we described how relay contacts or decision elements could be interconnected to form a switching circuit. One such

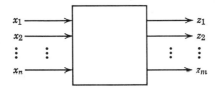

Figure 3.2.1   An n-input m-output switching circuit.

type of circuit is called a combinational switching circuit. Consider a switching circuit having n-inputs, $x_1, x_2, \ldots, x_n$, and m-outputs, $z_1, z_2, \ldots, z_m$, as shown in Figure 3.2.1.

Definition 3.2.1 A switching circuit is called a *combinational switching* *circuit** if the outputs can be expressed as m Boolean functions of the input variables $x_1, x_2, \ldots, x_n$.

That is, by the set of equations,

(3.2.1)

$$\begin{cases} z_1 = z_1(x_1, x_2, \ldots, x_n) \\ z_2 = z_2(x_1, x_2, \ldots, x_n) \\ \quad \cdot \\ \quad \cdot \\ \quad \cdot \\ z_m = z_m(x_1, x_2, \ldots, x_n). \end{cases}$$

This means that for each input combination $(e_1, e_2, \ldots, e_n)$ we obtain a unique output combination of the z_i's. (The e_i's are in the terminology of the disjunctive canonical expansion.) We could express Equation (3.2.1) in an equivalent truth table form, using 2^n rows for input combinations and $n + m$ columns: one column for each input and one column for each output.

Note that Definition 3.2.1 is a behavioral definition, that is, it describes only a relation between the inputs and outputs and does not describe any particular internal structure of the combinational circuit.   Also, as yet, no method is given to determine how, or if, the outputs of a given network may be expressed as Boolean functions of the inputs.   We shall now consider possible internal structures of combinational circuits, both for relay contact networks and logical diagrams.

Using relay technology, the n-input m-output combinational circuit can be realized by using n-relays and their contacts, as shown in Figure 3.2.2.

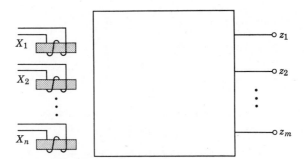

Figure 3.2.2   A relay combinational circuit.

---

* We shall usually drop "switching" here, and simply call such a circuit a *combinational circuit*.

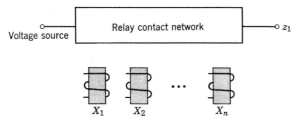

Figure 3.2.3   A two-terminal relay contact network.

The relays $X_1, X_2, \ldots, X_n$ are controlled by the $x_1, x_2, \ldots, x_n$ inputs respectively such that if $x_i = 1$, then relay X_i is energized, and if $x_i = 0$, then relay X_i is not energized. The box contains contacts only of the n-relays. The output z_i having value 1 is interpreted as meaning a closed path between ground or some voltage source (not shown) and the z_i terminal.

The *two-terminal relay contact network* is a special case of the m-output network just described, where $m = 1$. Figure 3.2.3 shows a two-terminal relay contact network.

Consider the two-terminal combinational circuit of Figure 3.2.4. Note that this two-terminal circuit is not a series-parallel contact circuit like that discussed in Section 2.5. Rather, this circuit is called a "bridge" circuit. In bridge circuits the analogy between the circuit structure and Boolean function is not direct as it is for series-parallel circuits. However, a Boolean function can be obtained to represent the closed paths between the two terminals by obtaining a product term for each possible path between the terminals and forming a disjunction of these product terms

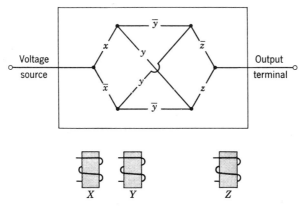

Figure 3.2.4   A two-terminal combinational relay circuit for $f = x \oplus y \oplus z$.

to obtain a function. Thus in Figure 3.2.4, the Boolean function representing the circuit is

$$f = x\bar{y}\bar{z} \lor xyz \lor \bar{x}y\bar{z} \lor \bar{x}\bar{y}z$$

$$= x \oplus y \oplus z.$$

This bridge circuit realization takes fewer contacts than would be required in a series-parallel circuit.* In Chapter 5 we shall study some methods for designing bridge-type contact circuits.

In Figure 3.2.5 we illustrate the simplest possible type of bridge circuit. It contains five contacts.

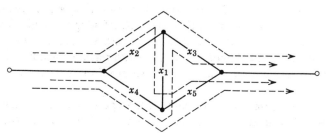

Figure 3.2.5   A simple bridge circuit.

The Boolean function for this circuit is found from the four possible paths between terminals, as marked on the figure. Note that two paths pass through each contact, and contact x_1 has one path in each direction, thereby utilizing the bilateral characteristic of the contact. The function represented by this circuit is thus

$$f = x_2 x_3 \lor x_1 x_2 x_5 \lor x_1 x_3 x_4 \lor x_4 x_5.$$

For Figure 3.2.4 we could also realize the function $f = x \oplus y \oplus z$ by first realizing an intermediate function g.

$$g = x \oplus y = x\bar{y} \lor \bar{x}y,$$

energizing a relay W with this function g, and then realizing f by

$$f = w\bar{z} \lor \bar{w}z.$$

Such a circuit is shown in Figure 3.2.6.

Both realizations (Figures 3.2.4 and 3.2.6) give the same static terminal behavior. Static terminal behavior means that if the inputs are held constant for a long time, then all the internal contacts and relays will attain some static condition, and it is this input to output condition

---

* We say that a function or expression *represents* a circuit and that a circuit *realizes* a function. Similarly, we use the terms circuit *realization* of a function and functional *representation* of a circuit.

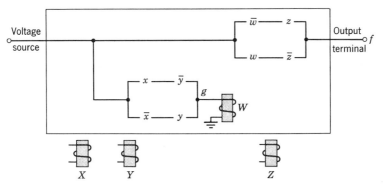

Figure 3.2.6 An alternative realization for $f = x \oplus y \oplus z$.

which is expressed by the Boolean function for the output. Usually, for relay networks, a relay requires some noticeable time to react to an energizing current. Thus the circuit shown in Figure 3.2.6 would require a longer time to attain a static condition (due to the reaction time of internal relay W) than the circuit shown in Figure 3.2.4 which has no internal relays. Since the output is a function of the input variables x, y, and z, both circuits are combinational circuits. By this example, we demonstrate that a combinational circuit may include internal relays such as W in Figure 3.2.6, rather than only relay contacts of the input variables. From Definition 3.2.1 the only requirement on a circuit to be combinational is that the outputs of the circuit may be expressed as Boolean functions of the input variables, and both circuits of Figure 3.2.4 and 3.2.6 satisfy this requirement. The circuit of Figure 3.2.6 may, in fact, be a preferred circuit for certain types of relays, since it requires only one "transfer contact"* per relay. (Note that Figure 3.2.4 required two transfer contacts on relay Y.)

Now we return to Figure 3.2.1 and consider combinational circuits using decision elements. For this realization, we consider the inputs $x_1, x_2, \ldots, x_n$ to be inputs to some decision elements. We would allow input x_i to be an input to as many elements as desired. (Sometimes we also assume that the complemented variables $\bar{x}_1, \bar{x}_2, \ldots, \bar{x}_n$ are available as inputs.)

A straightforward realization of an m-output circuit is to form a logical

---

* A transfer contact consists of a pair of contacts of one relay, one contact being the complement of the other, which are interconnected at one end to form a three-terminal configuration of the following type.

diagram for each z_i from some convenient functional expression for the z_i. Usually, however, we attempt to use less circuitry than this by finding functional expressions for the z_i which enable the same circuits to be used in realizing more than one output.

If a partial ordering can be imposed on the decision elements of a logical diagram in the manner to be described, then the logical diagram is said to contain no *feedback*. As we shall see, if a logical diagram does

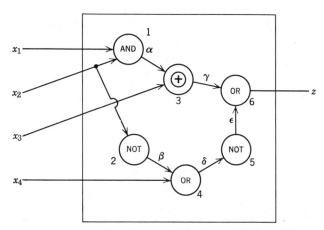

Figure 3.2.7   A single output logical circuit without feedback.

not contain feedback, the circuit can be shown to be combinational. We describe the partial ordering by the following numbering process. Pick an element having inputs only from the set of inputs $x_1, x_2, \ldots, x_n$ and label this element 1. Now pick an element having inputs only from the set $x_1, x_2, \ldots, x_n$ and some elements which have already been labeled, and label this with the next largest integer. Continue this process until all elements have been labeled. If we arrive at no termination of this numbering process before all elements are numbered, the circuit is combinational and has no feedback. The reader may be interested in showing that this numbering process actually corresponds to a partial ordering of the decision elements. A possible stalemate in this numbering could arise, however, when a next element to label could not be found, since each unlabeled element has inputs from other unlabeled elements. This situation will arise if and only if a circuit has feedback. Figure 3.2.7 illustrates the numbering process on a single-output circuit. The function z can be written as

$$z = (x_1 x_2 \oplus x_3) \vee (\overline{\overline{x}_2 \vee x_4}).$$

If a logical circuit has no feedback (note that we do not include storage elements in our logical circuits here), it is a combinational circuit. This can be shown by writing first the functional expressions for the decision elements in the order of the labeling. For our example of Figure 3.2.7 we have labeled outputs as α, β, γ, δ, ϵ and z, and can thus write

$$\alpha = x_1 x_2,$$
$$\beta = \bar{x}_2,$$
$$\gamma = \alpha \oplus x_3,$$
$$\delta = \beta \vee x_4,$$
$$\epsilon = \bar{\delta},$$
$$z = \epsilon \vee \gamma.$$

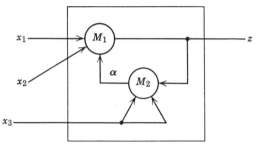

Figure 3.2.8   A single output logical circuit with feedback containing two majority elements.

We then substitute back into the output equation to produce an expression involving only the inputs.

$$z = \bar{\delta} \vee (\alpha \oplus x_3)$$
$$= \overline{(\beta \vee x_4)} \vee (x_1 x_2 \oplus x_3)$$
$$= \overline{(\bar{x}_2 \vee x_4)} \vee (x_1 x_2 \oplus x_3).$$

Although we can say that the logical circuit without feedback is combinational, we cannot, in general, say that a combinational logical circuit has no feedback. Similarly, in the relay case a combinational relay circuit can include internal relays, but a relay circuit containing internal relays is not necessarily combinational. We shall see this later. Now, consider the logical circuit shown in Figure 3.2.8. This satisfies all the conditions for interconnection of decision elements to form a logical diagram (see Section 2.6). The elements cannot be numbered according to the method just described, however, since each element has an input which is the output of the other element. We have a feedback loop from the output of M_1 to an input of M_2 to α. Here we have designated the output of M_2 as α. The decision elements M_1 and M_2 are considered to be majority elements, that is, the output of M_i equals 1 if and only if two or more of its inputs equal 1.

If we consider the input combinations of x_1, x_2, and x_3 as fixed values and assume a starting value on the α line, we can analyze the behavior

Table 3.2.1   Analysis for Figure 3.2.8

x_1	x_2	x_3	α	α'	z
0	0	0	0	0	0
0	0	0	1	0	0
0	0	1	0	1	0
0	0	1	1	1	0
0	1	0	0	0	0
0	1	0	1	0	0
0	1	1	0	1	1
0	1	1	1	1	1
1	0	0	0	0	0
1	0	0	1	0	0
1	0	1	0	1	1
1	0	1	1	1	1
1	1	0	0	0	1
1	1	0	1	0	1
1	1	1	0	1	1
1	1	1	1	1	1

of the circuit by determining the value of z and to what value α is tending (called α') with respect to the given values on x_1, x_2, x_3, and α. This is shown in Table 3.2.1. From this table we see that the starting value of α may be stable (that is, $\alpha' = \alpha$) for some combinations of inputs; for example, when $x_1 = x_2 = x_3 = \alpha = 0$; but for other input values α may tend to change; for example, when $x_1 = x_2 = x_3 = 1$ and $\alpha = 0$, then $\alpha' = 1$. In any possible starting condition, however, the changing of the value of α does not effect the output, and thus the output is determined by the values on x_1, x_2, and x_3 alone and can be expressed as

$$z = x_1 x_2 \bar{x}_3 \vee x_1 \bar{x}_2 x_3 \vee \bar{x}_1 x_2 x_3 \vee x_1 x_2 x_3.$$

Thus, the circuit is a combinational circuit with feedback.* Note, however,

---

* In some articles, a logical diagram without feedback is used as the definition for a combinational logical circuit, whereas in Definition 3.2.1 we impose no such structural condition.

that z could have been realized with a single majority circuit with inputs x_1, x_2, and x_3, thus eliminating the feedback.

We can summarize the structure of combinational circuits using relays or decision elements as follows:

1. Multiterminal relay contact networks (Figure 3.2.2). With a special case the two-terminal relay contact network (Figure 3.2.3).
2. Combinational relay networks having internal relays (example in Figure 3.2.6).
3. Combinational multioutput logical networks without feedback. (Example of single output case shown in Figure 3.2.7.)
4. Combinational logical circuit with feedback (example in Figure 3.2.8).

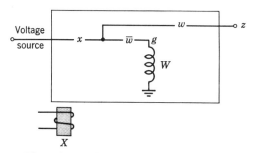

Figure 3.2.9   A relay circuit with an internal relay.

It should be noted that a relay contact network is a combinational circuit if it only has contacts of the input relays X_1, X_2, ..., X_n. If the relay circuit has internal relays, and contacts from the internal relays are used in the circuit, then the circuit may or may not satisfy the definition of a combinational circuit. Consider the circuit shown in Figure 3.2.9, having internal relay W. This circuit is not combinational since the output cannot be expressed as a Boolean function of the single input X. We can express z as $z = xw$, and letting g be the function to energize W, $g = x\bar{w}$, but since $\bar{w}$ is included in g we cannot eliminate the variable w from the equation for z. Indeed, under certain adjustments of the w and $\bar{w}$ contacts of the relay W, when $x = 1$ this circuit would oscillate, so that z would be changing continually from 0 to 1 and 1 to 0.

Logical circuits with feedback cannot have a partial ordering assigned to their elements as done for Figure 3.2.7; and some logical circuits with feedback may, indeed, not be combinational. This is exemplified by the circuit shown in Figure 3.2.10.

Neither EXCLUSIVE OR-element can be assigned number 1 for the partial ordering and thus the method of partial ordering does not apply to this circuit. Note also that the circuit is *not* combinational, since, for example, if $x_1 = x_2 = 0$ then z can take on the value 0 or 1. It will be $z = 0$ if initially $z = 0$ and $\alpha = 0$, and z will be $z = 1$ if initially $z = 1$ and $\alpha = 1$.

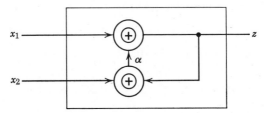

Figure 3.2.10   A noncombinational logical circuit with feedback.

Both these conditions are stable. For other input combinations the circuit may oscillate.

For the simple circuits of Figures 3.2.9 and 3.2.10 the simple analyses described suffice to determine that the circuits are not combinational. In larger examples having feedback, such an analysis may be considerably more complex. The combinational circuits of types 2 and 4, that is, those with feedback, are treated as degenerate cases of sequential circuit design. We shall discuss this further in Volume II. Most methods of combinational circuit design produce circuits without feedback of type 1 or 3 listed earlier, or special cases of such structures.

An important special structure for relay contact networks and logical circuits results from Boolean expressions in disjunctive normal form. In the relay contact case, each product in the Boolean function corresponds to a series connection of relay contacts, where x_i is a contact if x_i is in the product, and $\bar{x}_i$ is a contact if $\bar{x}_i$ appears in the product. By connecting all such series connections together in parallel the disjunctive normal form is realized. For the logical circuit realization assume that the variables and inverted variables are available as inputs, and that we have AND and OR-elements with as many inputs as desired. We realize each product of k-variables by a k-input AND-element, where x_i is an input if x_i is in the product and $\bar{x}_i$ is an input if $\bar{x}_i$ is in the product. The outputs of all the AND-elements are attached as inputs to one OR-element, and the output of the OR-element realizes the disjunctive normal form of the Boolean function. Such a circuit is called a *two-level* AND- OR *circuit*. An example of these structures is shown in Figure 3.2.11. Analogous circuits result from conjunctive normal forms, and we denote both these types of circuits as normal form circuits.

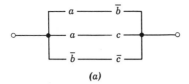

(a)

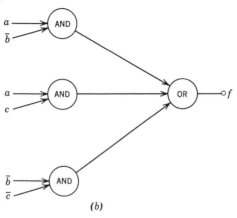

(b)

Figure 3.2.11 Relay contact and logical circuit realizations for $f = a\bar{b} \vee ac \vee \bar{b}\bar{c}$.

3.3 CUBICAL COMPLEXES

In Section 2.10 we introduced the cubical representation for Boolean functions. We shall be interested here in performing algebraic operations in this representation and showing how simplified disjunctive normal form expressions can be obtained by them. To formalize the concept of simplification and prove some theorems we introduce further terminology. For review, we set up a coordinate system on the n-cube with coordinates $(e_1, e_2, \ldots, e_n)$, where $e_j = 0, 1$. Then the term

$$x_1{}^{e_1} x_2{}^{e_2} \cdots x_n{}^{e_n}$$

was made to correspond to vertex $(e_1, e_2, \ldots, e_n)$. The Boolean function can then be viewed as a mapping of the n-cube $Z_2{}^n$ into the set of element 0, 1 called Z_2

$$Z_2{}^n \xrightarrow{f} Z_2,$$

where $f^{-1}(1)$ is mapped into 1 and $f^{-1}(0)$ is mapped into 0. The subcubes of $f^{-1}(1)$ are called 0-cubes, 1-cubes, 2-cubes, etc.

We wish to define a cubical complex $K(f)$, and we shall do this inductively. We start with the 0-cubes. Two 0-cubes are said to form a 1-cube
if they differ in only one coordinate. Thus, given 0-cubes 101 and 111,
differing only in the second coordinate the pair 101 and 111 form a 1-cube.
We represent this 1-cube as $1x1$, where x means the entry in the second
coordinate (also called a component) can be either a 1 or a 0. The 0-cubes
which form a 1-cube are called *faces* of the 1-cube. The x indicates a
free component, and the others are called *bound*. The space of all 0-cubes
is called K^0, and the space of all 1-cubes is called K^1. In the example
given in Figure 2.10.1,

$$ K^0 = \begin{Bmatrix} 000 \\ 011 \\ 101 \\ 111 \end{Bmatrix} \quad \text{and} \quad K^1 = \begin{Bmatrix} 1x1 \\ x11 \end{Bmatrix}. $$

Two 1-cubes of K^1 form a 2-cube if the free component is in the same
coordinate for both 1-cubes and if exactly one bound component disagrees.
The 1-cubes which form a 2-cube are called *opposite faces of the 2-cube*.
In our example we have no 2-cubes, but if $0x01$ and $0x11$ were 1-cubes,
then $0xx1$ would be a 2-cube. The space of all 2-cubes is called K^2. This
process continues inductively to give K^r, the space of all r-cubes, $0 \le r \le$
n. The operations of obtaining the faces of an r-cube and obtaining an
$r + 1$-cube from K^r can be formalized as follows.

Let $(a_1, a_2, \ldots, a_n) = c^r$ be an r-cube, $a_i = 0$, 1 or x, and there are
r x's. Then we can find the faces of c^r with the *ith face operator*

$$ \partial_i{}^p(a_1, \ldots, a_n) = \begin{cases} (a_1, \ldots, a_{i-1}, p, a_{i+1}, \ldots, a_n) & \text{if } a_i = x, \\ \phi & \text{if } a_i \ne x, \end{cases} $$

where $p = 0$ or 1. We can find a cube c^{r+1} with the *ith coface operator*

$$ \delta_i(a_1, \ldots, a_n) = $$

$$ \begin{cases} (a_1, \ldots, a_{i-1}, x, a_{i+1}, \ldots, a_n) = c^{r+1} & \text{if } a_i \ne x \text{ and } c^{r+1} \subseteq K(f), \\ \phi & \text{if } a_i = x \text{ or if } c^{r+1} \nsubseteq K(f). \end{cases} $$

The *cubical complex* $K(f)$ is defined by the collection $K^0, K^1, \ldots, K^r, \ldots,$
K^n and the face and coface operators.

It is the existence of the face and coface operators which, given a cube,
allows us to determine algebraically cubes of higher and lower dimension
in a cubical complex. Note that these algebraic operations, together with
the collections of cubes, make up the algebraic system called a *cubical*

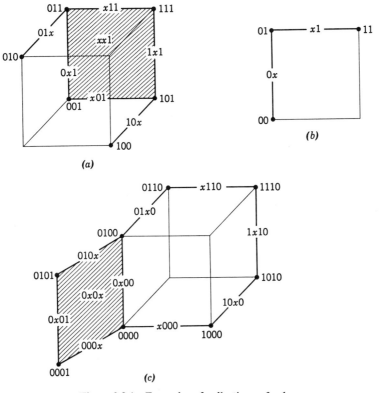

Figure 3.3.1   Examples of collections of cubes.

complex. The collection of *r*-cubes for a cubical complex can be depicted on the *n*-cube. Several examples are shown in Figure 3.3.1.

For Figure 3.3.1*a*,

$$
K^0 = \begin{pmatrix} 010 \\ 011 \\ 111 \\ 001 \\ 101 \\ 100 \end{pmatrix}, \qquad
K^1 = \begin{pmatrix} 01x \\ 0x1 \\ x11 \\ 1x1 \\ x01 \\ 10x \end{pmatrix}, \qquad
\begin{aligned} K^2 &= \{xx1\}, \\ K^3 &= \phi. \end{aligned}
$$

For Figure 3.3.1*b*,

$$
K^0 = \begin{Bmatrix} 00 \\ 01 \\ 11 \end{Bmatrix}, \qquad
K^1 = \begin{Bmatrix} 0x \\ x1 \end{Bmatrix}, \qquad
K^2 = \phi,
$$

For Figure 3.3.1c,

$$K^0 = \begin{Bmatrix} 0000 \\ 0001 \\ 0101 \\ 0100 \\ 0110 \\ 1110 \\ 1010 \\ 1000 \end{Bmatrix}, \qquad K^1 = \begin{Bmatrix} 000x \\ 0x01 \\ 010x \\ 0x00 \\ 01x0 \\ x110 \\ 1x10 \\ 10x0 \\ x000 \end{Bmatrix}, \qquad \begin{aligned} K^2 &= \{0x0x\}, \\ K^3 &= \phi, \\ K^4 &= \phi. \end{aligned}$$

Considering Figure 3.3.1c we can illustrate the face and coface operators.

$$\partial_2{}^0(0x0x) = 000x$$

$$\partial_2{}^1(0x01) = 0101$$

$$\partial_3{}^1(0x0x) = \phi$$

$$\delta_4(0x00) = 0x0x$$

$$\delta_4(0x01) = 0x0x$$

$$\delta_4(000x) = \phi$$

$$\delta_2(10x0) = \phi$$

With the preceding definition for a cubical complex and the mapping of a Boolean function onto an n-cube, we see that two Boolean functions are equivalent if and only if their complexes are identical. Furthermore, we see that for two Boolean functions f and g, the operation $f \cdot g$ corresponds to $K(f \cdot g) = K(f) \cap K(g)$ and similarly $K(f \vee g) = K(f) \cup K(g)$. Also, $K(\bar{f}) = \overline{K(f)}$, where $\overline{K(f)}$ is the complex described by all the vertices not contained in $K(f)$, and $\cap$ and $\cup$ are set intersection and union, respectively. Thus the algebra of Boolean functions is represented by this algebra of cubical complexes on the n-cube.

We illustrate the correspondence between $f \cdot g$ and $K(f \cdot g) = K(f) \cap K(g)$ by the example shown in Figure 3.3.2, where $f = \bar{x}_1 \bar{x}_2 \vee x_2 x_3$ and $g = x_2 \bar{x}_3 \vee \bar{x}_1 x_3$. With this example

$$f \cdot g = (\bar{x}_1 \bar{x}_2 \vee x_2 x_3)(x_2 \bar{x}_3 \vee \bar{x}_1 x_3)$$

$$= \bar{x}_1 \bar{x}_2 x_3 \vee \bar{x}_1 x_2 x_3$$

$$= \bar{x}_1 x_3.$$

Therefore
$$K(f \cdot g) = \begin{Bmatrix} 001 \\ 011 \\ 0x1 \end{Bmatrix}.$$

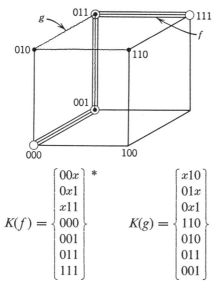

$$K(f) = \begin{Bmatrix} 00x \\ 0x1 \\ x11 \\ 000 \\ 001 \\ 011 \\ 111 \end{Bmatrix} \; * \qquad K(g) = \begin{Bmatrix} x10 \\ 01x \\ 0x1 \\ 110 \\ 010 \\ 011 \\ 001 \end{Bmatrix}$$

Figure 3.3.2   Illustration of $K(f \cdot g) = K(f) \cap K(g)$.

Also
$$K(f) \cap K(g) = \begin{Bmatrix} 0x1 \\ 011 \\ 001 \end{Bmatrix}$$

since only these cubes appear in both $K(f)$ and $K(g)$. The examples of Figure 3.3.1 can then be seen to represent the following:

For (a) $\qquad f = x_3 \lor x_1\bar{x}_2 \lor \bar{x}_1 x_2,$

where $\qquad x_3 = xx1,$

$\qquad\qquad x_1\bar{x}_2 = 10x,$

$\qquad\qquad \bar{x}_1 x_2 = 01x,$

$\qquad\qquad \overline{K(f)} = 000 \cup 110.$

For (b) $\qquad f = \bar{x}_1 \lor x_2,$

where $\qquad \bar{x}_1 = 0x,$

$\qquad\qquad x_2 = x1,$

$\qquad\qquad \overline{K(f)} = 10.$

For (c) $\qquad f = \bar{x}_1\bar{x}_3 \lor x_1\bar{x}_2\bar{x}_4 \lor x_2 x_3\bar{x}_4,$

---

* Note that the cubical complex is denoted here simply by its set of cubes and by the equal sign. We also imply the face and coface operators on these cubes. This slight abuse of terminology should cause no confusion.

where $\qquad\qquad \bar{x}_1\bar{x}_3 = 0x0x,$

$$x_1\bar{x}_2\bar{x}_4 = 10x0,$$

$$x_2 x_3 \bar{x}_4 = x110,$$

$$\overline{K(f)} = xx11 \cup 1xx1 \cup 110x \cup 001x.$$

3.4 NORMAL FORM MINIMIZATION—THE COVERING PROBLEM

In Section 3.3 we defined a cubical complex and demonstrated the correspondence between a Boolean function f and a cubical complex $K(f)$. A cubical complex may be specified by a set C of cubes of the complex such that each vertex of the complex K^0 is included in at least one of the cubes of C. Such a set C is called a *cover* of the complex K. Each cover C may be considered to define a Boolean functional expression, in fact, a disjunctive normal form expression. For example, the set K^0 is a cover and corresponds to the disjunctive canonical form of the function. Several other examples are shown in Figure 3.4.1. Here we have shown two different covers for each of the cubical complexes. What are the covers corresponding to the disjunctive canonical forms for these examples?

The rule that each vertex of a cubical complex must be included in at least one cube is analogous to the rule used in Karnaugh maps in obtaining a simplified Boolean function (Section 2.9) where each 1 entry needed to be included in at least one subcube. Although for visual interpretation we are limited to about four variables, using the 0, 1, x notation allows us to treat a problem having many variables. Every cover of a complex, then, can be thought of as representing a two-level AND-OR logical circuit (or the analogous relay network). Also by finding a simplified cover of $\overline{K(f)}$, a conjunctive normal form results if the procedure to get f given in Section 2.3 is applied to $\overline{K(f)}$. We illustrate these comments by the following example:

$$C = \begin{Bmatrix} xxxx11 \\ 1xxx0x \\ x111x1 \end{Bmatrix},$$

where C is a cover of a cubical complex $K(f)$. This cover corresponds to the function

$$(3.4.1) \qquad\qquad f = x_5 x_6 \vee x_1 \bar{x}_5 \vee x_2 x_3 x_4 x_6$$

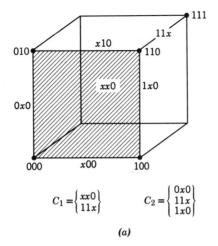

$$C_1 = \left\{ \begin{matrix} xx0 \\ 11x \end{matrix} \right\} \qquad C_2 = \left\{ \begin{matrix} 0x0 \\ 11x \\ 1x0 \end{matrix} \right\}$$

(a)

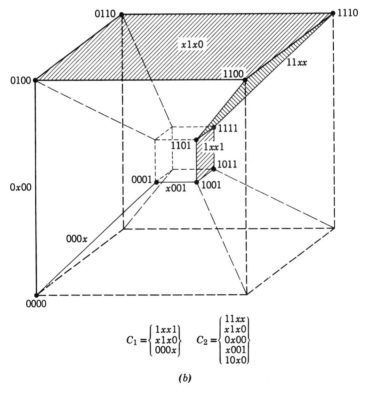

$$C_1 = \left\{ \begin{matrix} 1xx1 \\ x1x0 \\ 000x \end{matrix} \right\} \qquad C_2 = \left\{ \begin{matrix} 11xx \\ x1x0 \\ 0x00 \\ x001 \\ 10x0 \end{matrix} \right\}$$

(b)

Figure 3.4.1 (*a* and *b*) Covers for cubical complexes.

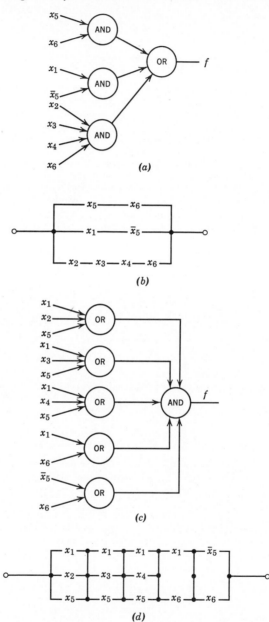

Figure 3.4.2   Switching circuits realizing Equations (3.4.1) and (3.4.2). (*a*) Two-level AND-OR logical circuit realizing (3.4.1). (*b*) Relay contact network realizing (3.4.1). (*c*) Two-level OR-AND logical circuit realizing (3.4.2). (*d*) Relay contact network realizing (3.4.2).

A cover for $\overline{K(f)}$ is

$$C' = \begin{cases} 00xx0x \\ 0x0x0x \\ 0xx00x \\ 0xxxx0 \\ xxxx10 \end{cases} .$$

[Later we shall see how a cover for $\overline{K(f)}$ can be obtained given a cover for $K(f)$.] The disjunctive normal form for $\bar{f}$ corresponding to C' is

$$\bar{f} = \bar{x}_1\bar{x}_2\bar{x}_5 \vee \bar{x}_1\bar{x}_3\bar{x}_5 \vee \bar{x}_1\bar{x}_4\bar{x}_5 \vee \bar{x}_1\bar{x}_6 \vee x_5\bar{x}_6$$

which can be transformed into the following conjunctive normal form for f.

(3.4.2) $f = (x_1 \vee x_2 \vee x_5)(x_1 \vee x_3 \vee x_5)(x_1 \vee x_4 \vee x_5)(x_1 \vee x_6)(\bar{x}_5 \vee x_6).$

The reader may check that this expression represents the same Boolean function as Equation (3.4.1). The switching circuits realizing Equations (3.4.1) and (3.4.2) are shown in Figure 3.4.2.

We can define a *cost* of an r-cube as $n - r$. The *cost of a cover* C can be defined in several ways. We consider two possibilities:

1. The cost C^a *of a cover* C is the sum of the costs of the cubes of the cover $C^a = \Sigma q_r(n - r)$, where the sum runs over all r, $0 \le r \le n$, and q_r is the number of r-cubes in C.
2. The cost C^b *of a cover* C is C^a plus the number of cubes p in the cover $C^b = C^a + p = \Sigma q_r(n - r + 1)$.

Note that for an r-cube, r of the n components are free, and $n - r$ components are bound. Thus C^a is a count on the number of letters in the formula, and C^b is a count on the number of letters plus the number of products in the normal form expression. If we consider the relay circuit, C^a is the number of contacts in the circuit, and if we consider two-level AND-OR circuits, C^a is the number of inputs to AND-elements and C^b is the number of inputs to both AND- and OR-elements, that is, the number of arrowheads, except for degenerate cases when $r = n$ and $n - 1$ or when the cover contains only one cube. The cost C^a of the cover C for $K(f)$ is thus

$$\begin{aligned} C^a &= \Sigma q_r(n - r) \\ &= 2(6 - 4) + 1(6 - 2) \\ &= 2 \cdot 2 + 1 \cdot 4 = 8, \end{aligned}$$

since there are two 4-cubes and one 2-cube in C. Note that this corresponds to the 8 appearances of letters in (3.4.1), to the 8 relay contacts in

Figure 3.4.2*b*, and to the 8 inputs to AND-elements in Figure 3.4.2*a*. The cost C^a of the cover C' for $\overline{K(f)}$ is

$$C^a = \Sigma q_r(n - r).$$
$$= 3(6 - 3) + 2(6 - 4)$$
$$= 3 \cdot 3 + 2 \cdot 2 = 13,$$

since there are three 3-cubes and two 4-cubes in C'. This cost of C^a indicates that there are 13 letter appearances in the disjunctive normal form for $\bar{f}$, and thus also for Equation (3.4.2). In addition, there are 13 relay contacts in the relay contact network of Figure 3.4.2*d* and 13 inputs to the OR-elements in the logical circuit of Figure 3.4.2*c*. The cost C^b of cover C is

$$C^b = \Sigma q_r(n - r + 1)$$
$$= 2(6 - 4 + 1) + 1(6 - 2 + 1)$$
$$= 2 \cdot 3 + 1 \cdot 5 = 11,$$

and there are exactly 11 inputs to decision elements in Figure 3.4.2*a*. Similarly, the cost C^b for cover C' is 18, where this corresponds to the 18 inputs to decision elements in Figure 3.4.2*c*.

A degenerate case, when C^a and C^b do not actually give a count of the inputs to decision elements of the corresponding logical circuit, is illustrated by cover C_1 of Figure 3.4.1*a*. Here

$$C_1 = \begin{Bmatrix} xx0 \\ 11x \end{Bmatrix},$$

so $C^a = 3$ and $C^b = 5$, but the logical circuit realizing C_1 is

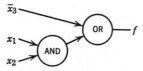

which contains only 2 inputs to AND-elements and 4 inputs to decision elements. This disparity arises from cube $xx0$ which does not require any AND-element in the circuit realization. This illustrates the degenerate case with $r = n - 1$. Why are the cases when $r = n$ and when the cover contains only one cube also considered degenerate?

The problem treated by Quine is to obtain a least cost C^a cover of a given complex K. This cover is called a *minimum cover*, and the resulting functional form is called a *minimum disjunctive normal form*. We generalize this problem by also considering least cost C^b covers and also by starting with a problem having don't care conditions, that is, a partial switching function.

To formulate the don't cares into the problem we let K be a cubical complex which contains a subcomplex L. We interpret L to be the *care* complex, and $N = K - L$ to be the *don't care* complex. Thus K is a complex containing the don't care conditions and the care conditions. Then we define a *K-cover of L* as a collection C of cubes such that *any cube of C is contained in K and each vertex of L is contained in some cube of C*. Letting $K(C)$ equal the complex defined by C, we obtain

$$L \subseteq K(C) \subseteq K.$$

We desire to obtain a K-cover of L of minimum cost, either C^a or C^b. This is called the *covering problem*, and a cover with either C^a or C^b as

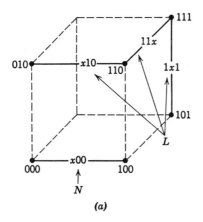

(a)

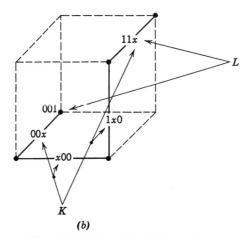

(b)

Figure 3.4.3   Some K and L complexes.

small as possible is called a *minimum cover*. As seen in the Karnaugh map a less expensive cover is usually obtained by using larger cubes. Several examples are shown in Figure 3.4.3.

In Figure 3.4.3a, L is determined by $\{x10, 1x1\}$, N by $\{x00\}$, and K is determined by $\{xx0, 1xx\}$. By using C^a, a minimum cost K-cover is $C = \{xx0, 1xx\}$, where $C^a = 2$. A minimum cost cover of the L complex (an L-cover) is $\{x10, 1x1\}$ which has cost 4. In Figure 3.4.3b, L is determined by $\{001, 11x\}$ and K by $\{00x, x00, 11x\}$. A K-cover of L is $C = \{00x, 11x\}$ with $C^a = 4$, whereas the minimum cost for an L-cover is 5. Both these examples demonstrate that the cost of a minimum K-cover of L is usually less than that of a minimum cover of L itself.

In the next sections we develop the theory and an algorithm to find minimum K-covers of L (or, in other terminology, minimum disjunctive normal forms for switching functions).

3.5 PRIME IMPLICANTS AND THE *-ALGORITHM

We assume that the statement of the covering problem is given as complexes K and L or some form that determines K and L. If some cubes are given that are of higher dimension than 0-cubes, they will be used in the algorithm rather than having to convert first to a 0-cube representation (that is, the disjunctive canonical form).

We define a cube z of K to be a *prime implicant* if $\delta_i(z) = \phi$ for each i. That is, a cube z is a prime implicant of a complex K if there exists no other cube in K which includes z. Let Z be the space of all prime implicants and Z^r be the subspace of r-dimension prime implicants. For example, the space Z of prime implicants for Figure 3.4.3a and b is $\{xx0, 1xx\}$ and $\{11x, 1x0, x00, 00x\}$, respectively. For these examples, the minimum covers are subsets of the Z. This is true in general as shown by the following theorem.

Theorem 3.5.1 If C is a minimum cover, then $C \subseteq Z$.

  PROOF. Suppose $c \in C$ and c were not a prime implicant. Then for some i

$$\delta_i(c) \neq \phi.$$

Thus, by forming a new cover by replacing c in C by $\delta_i(c)$, we obtain a cover of lower cost, using either cost C^a or C^b.

Note that this proof holds true for any cost function which increases with an increase in the number of bound components in a cover. The cost functions C^a and C^b are thus only very special cases for which the set of prime implicants includes all the cubes of any minimum cover.

The first part of the algorithm to find a minimum cover is a computation of Z. An obvious way to obtain Z is to determine all the cubes of K using the δ and ∂ operators and then to test each cube of K, using the definition of a prime implicant, to determine whether it is a prime implicant. Since there may be an extremely large number of cubes in K, this method may require a great many steps. It would be desirable to determine Z without obtaining all the cubes of K. For this purpose we define a *∗-product* (called a star-product). Since this is an operation on coordinate positions of two cubes c^r and c^s, we define the *coordinate ∗-product* by Table 3.5.1.†

Table 3.5.1 Coordinate ∗-Product

∗	0	1	x
0	0	y	0
1	y	1	1
x	0	1	x

Let $c^r = (a_1, a_2, \ldots, a_n)$ and $c^s = (b_1, b_2, \ldots, b_n)$ be cubes of a complex K. To form the *∗-product* $c^r * c^s$ form $a_i * b_i$ for $1 \leq i \leq n$. If $a_i * b_i = y$ for more than one i, $c^r * c^s = \phi$; if at most one y appears, then

$$c^r * c^s \equiv [m(a_1 * b_1), m(a_2 * b_2), \ldots, m(a_n * b_n)],$$

where $m(a_i * b_i)$ is

$$m(0) = 0,$$
$$m(1) = 1,$$
$$m(x) = m(y) = x.$$

The ∗-product of $c^r * c^s$ geometrically is the largest cube c^t (a t-cube) which has opposite $(t - 1)$-faces in c^r and c^s, respectively. If the value of $c^r * c^s$ is ϕ, no such c^t exists. The ∗-product thus has the potentiality of finding a new cube c^t which falls between cubes c^r and c^s, or which may include c^r or c^s. Figure 3.5.1 gives several illustrations of the ∗-product. Several properties of the ∗-product can be shown.

1. $c^r * c^s \equiv c^s * c^r$ commutative.
2. $c^a * (c^b * c^c) \not\equiv (c^a * c^b) * c^c$ nonassociative.
3. If $c^r \subseteq c^s$, then $c^r * c^s = c^r$.

† The ∗-product gives the same resultant as the consensus operation of Quine [6] when both these results are defined.

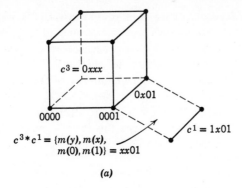

$$c^3 = 0xxx$$

$$0x01$$

$$0000 \qquad 0001$$

$$c^1 = 1x01$$

$$c^3 * c^1 = \{m(y), m(x),$$
$$m(0), m(1)\} = xx01$$

(a)

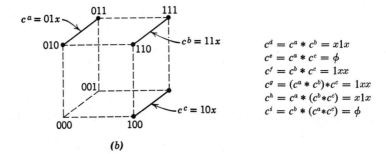

$$c^a = 01x$$

$$011 \qquad 111$$

$$010 \qquad \qquad 110 \qquad \qquad c^b = 11x$$

$$001 \qquad \qquad c^c = 10x$$

$$000 \qquad 100$$

$$c^d = c^a * c^b = x1x$$
$$c^e = c^a * c^c = \phi$$
$$c^f = c^b * c^c = 1xx$$
$$c^g = (c^a * c^b)*c^c = 1xx$$
$$c^h = c^a * (c^b*c^c) = x1x$$
$$c^i = c^b * (c^a*c^c) = \phi$$

(b)

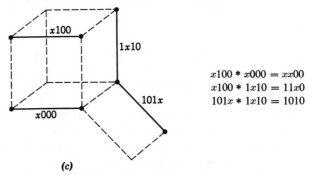

$$x100$$

$$1x10$$

$$101x$$

$$x000$$

$$x100 * x000 = xx00$$
$$x100 * 1x10 = 11x0$$
$$101x * 1x10 = 1010$$

(c)

Figure 3.5.1   Illustrations for *-product of cubes

4. If $c^r * c^s = c^t$ and $c^r \subseteq c^t$, then $\delta_i c^r \neq \phi$ for some i, some $\partial_i{}^p c^t \neq \phi$, some sequence of δ_i operations on c^r will produce c^t, and some sequence $\partial_i{}^p$ operations on c^t will produce c^r.

5. If c^{r1} and c^{r2} are opposite faces of some cube c^{r+1}, then $c^{r1} * c^{r2} = c^{r+1} = \delta_i(c^{r1})$, where i is the coordinate in which c^{r1} and c^{r2} differ.

The *-*algorithm,* which we describe now, will determine Z from some initial cover, say $\hat{C}_0$ of K. To form C_0 we remove all cubes of $\hat{C}_0$ which are faces of other cubes in $\hat{C}_0$. That is, if c_1 and $c_2 \in \hat{C}_0$ and $c_1 \subseteq c_2$, then c_1 is removed from $\hat{C}_0$. We then form $C_0 * C_0$, the *-product of each element of C_0 with each other element of C_0.

Lemma 3.5.1 $Z^0 = \{c^0 \mid c^0 * C_0 \not\supseteq \text{any 1-cube}\}$.

PROOF. Z^0 is the set of 0-cubes which are prime implicants. Since C_0 is a cover and no cube of the set on the right has a coface, $Z^0 \subseteq \{c^0 \mid c^0 * C_0 \not\supseteq \text{1-cube}\}$. Now suppose the set on the right contains some 0-cube c which does not belong to Z^0; then there must be a 1-cube d such that $\partial_i{}^p d = c$. Then $\partial_i{}^{\bar{p}} d$ must be included in the cover C_0; therefore d is a 1-cube which is included in $c^0 * C_0$.

By this lemma Z^0 is determined. We now want to form a new cover of K, delete from it the 0-cubes, and then obtain Z^1 from the new cover so that Z can be determined iteratively. We can thus form a new cover as

$$\hat{C}_1 = C_0 \cup (C_0 * C_0).$$

Some cubes of $\hat{C}_1$ may be contained in other cubes of $\hat{C}_1$, however, so we let C_1* be the cubes of $\hat{C}_1$ which are contained in cubes of $\hat{C}_1$.

$$C_1* = \{c \mid c \subset d; c, d \in \hat{C}_1\}.$$

We remove C_1* and all 0-cubes of $\hat{C}_1$ to obtain

$$C_1 = \hat{C}_1 - C_1* - \{\text{all 0-cubes of } \hat{C}_1\}.$$

Now C_1 is not, in general, a cover of K. $C_1 \cup Z^0$, however, is a cover of K. C_1 contains all the 1-cubes or cofaces of 1-cubes of K, since only 0-cubes have been removed from the cover, and the *-product forms 1-cubes from 0-cubes wherever possible. We now form $C_1 * C_1$ and see that

$$Z^1 = \{c^1 \mid c^1 * C_1 \not\supseteq \text{any 2-cube}\}.$$

We continue by forming $\hat{C}_2$ as

$$\hat{C}_2 = C_1 \cup \{C_1 * C_1\}.$$

Form C_2* as cubes of $\hat{C}_2$ contained in other cubes of $\hat{C}_2$ and obtain a C_2 as

$$C_2 = \hat{C}_2 - C_2* - \begin{Bmatrix} \text{all 0-cubes and} \\ \text{1-cubes of } \hat{C}_2 \end{Bmatrix}.$$

Now suppose that we have computed C_r and Z^r and have shown that C_r contains all r-cubes of K, $r < n$. We can then define: $\hat{C}_{r+1} = C_r \cup (C_r * C_r)$, and by forming C_{r+1}^* as all cubes of $\hat{C}_{r+1}$ which are faces of other cubes in $\hat{C}_{r+1}$ and removing all cubes of dimension r or less, we obtain

$$C_{r+1} = \hat{C}_{r+1} - C_{r+1}^* - \left\{\begin{array}{l}\text{The 0-, 1-, \ldots, } r\text{-cubes}\\\text{of } \hat{C}_{r+1}\end{array}\right\}.$$

The following two lemmas show the required induction step to prove that we can iteratively compute Z.

Lemma 3.5.2 C_{r+1} contains all $(r + 1)$-cubes of K, or cofaces of $(r + 1)$-cubes of K.

PROOF. If an $(r + 1)$-cube c^{r+1} or its cofaces are in C_r, then it is also in C_{r+1} by definition. If c^{r+1} is not in C_r, then its opposite r-faces are in C_r by hypothesis. That is, $\partial_i^1 c^{r+1} = \alpha$ and $\partial_i^0 c^{r+1} = \beta$ are contained in cubes of C_r. Let $\alpha \subseteq c^\alpha$ and $\beta \subseteq c^\beta$. Then the $*$-product gives

$$c^\alpha * c^\beta \supseteq \alpha * \beta = c^{r+1}.$$

Thus c^{r+1} or a coface of c^{r+1} is contained in $C_r * C_r$ and therefore in C_{r+1}.

Lemma 3.5.3 $Z^{r+1} = \{c^{r+1} \mid c^{r+1} * C_{r+1} \not\supseteq \text{any } (r + 2)\text{-cube}\}$.

PROOF. Let U be the set on the right-hand side. By Lemma 3.5.2, $Z^{r+1} \subseteq U$. Suppose c^{r+1} is an element of U which is not an element of Z^{r+1}. By definition of Z^{r+1} there must exist some i such that $\delta_i(c^{r+1}) = c^{r+2} \neq \phi$. Thus $\partial_i^p(c^{r+2}) = c^{r+1}$ and $\partial_i^{\bar{p}}(c^{r+2}) = \bar{c}^{r+1}$, where $\bar{c}^{r+1}$ and c^{r+1} are opposite faces of c^{r+2}. By Lemma 3.5.2, $\bar{c}^{r+1}$ is contained in some cube c^s of C_{r+1}; thus, $c^{r+1} * c^s \supseteq c^{r+2}$, and c^{r+1} is not an element of U.

The space of prime implicants Z is determined by the $*$-algorithm by iteratively finding the Z^r for all $r \leq n$,

$$Z = \bigcup_{r=0}^{n} Z^r.$$

A similar iterative construction was used to define the K^r of a complex $K(f)$. In the case of the complex if some $K^s = \phi$ for $0 \leq s \leq n$, then $K^t = \phi$ for $s \leq t \leq n$ (see Exercise 5 at the end of the Chapter). In contrast to this result, if some $Z^s = \phi$ for $0 \leq s \leq n$, we cannot say that $Z^t = \phi$ for $s \leq t \leq n$. Consider, for example, the complex shown in Figure 3.5.2. The prime implicants for this complex are $Z = \{xx0, 01x\}$. Thus $Z^0 = \phi$, $Z^1 = \{01x\}$ and $Z^2 = \{xx0\}$. The calculation of Z may be terminated before $n + 1$ steps (that is, $Z^0, Z^1, \ldots, Z^n$), however, by the following property. If $C_s = \phi$; then all $Z^t = \phi$ for $s \leq t \leq n$. This follows immediately from Lemma 3.5.2.

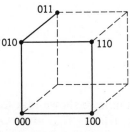

Figure 3.5.2 A cubical complex.

By assuming that C_0 for Figure 3.5.2 is given as $C_0 = \{1x0, x00, 01x\}$, we can calculate Z by the $*$-algorithm as follows:

$$C_0 = \begin{Bmatrix} 1x0 \\ x00 \\ 01x \end{Bmatrix}.$$

$$(1x0) * (x00) = 100,$$
$$(1x0) * (01x) = x10,$$
$$(x00) * (01x) = 0x0.$$

$$C_0 * C_0 = \begin{Bmatrix} 100 \\ x10 \\ 0x0 \end{Bmatrix}.$$

$$Z^0 = \phi \text{ since no 0-cubes exist in } C_0.$$

$$\hat{C}_1 = C_0 \cup (C_0 * C_0) = \begin{Bmatrix} 1x0 \\ x00 \\ 01x \\ 100 \\ x10 \\ 0x0 \end{Bmatrix}.$$

$$C_1^* = \{100\}.$$

Therefore

$$C_1 = \begin{Bmatrix} 1x0 \\ x00 \\ 01x \\ x10 \\ 0x0 \end{Bmatrix}.$$

$$C_1 * C_1 = \begin{Bmatrix} (1x0) * (x00) = 100 \\ (1x0) * (01x) = x10 \\ (1x0) * (x10) = 110 \\ (1x0) * (0x0) = xx0 \\ (x00) * (01x) = 0x0 \\ (x00) * (x10) = xx0 \\ (x00) * (0x0) = 000 \\ (01x) * (x10) = 010 \\ (01x) * (0x0) = 010 \\ (x10) * (0x0) = 010 \end{Bmatrix}.$$

$Z^1 = 01x$ since $01x$ is contained in no 2-cubes.

$$\hat{C}_2^* = C_1 \cup (C_1 * C_1).$$
$$C_2^* = \{1x0, x00, x10, 0x0, 100, x10, 110, 0x0, 000, 010\}.$$
$$C_2 = \{xx0\}.$$
$$Z^2 = \{xx0\}.$$
$$C_3 = \phi.$$

Therefore

$$Z = \{01x, xx0\}.$$

In this computation of Z we followed the precise description of the ∗-algorithm. Certain shortcuts are easily seen to be possible, however. For example, the ∗-product $(1x0) * (x00)$ is carried out in both $C_0 * C_0$ and $C_1 * C_1$, and with proper organization of the computation this would not be required. Furthermore, anytime the resultant of a ∗-product is included in one of the cubes of the cover, this resultant could be immediately discarded.

We give another example of the computation of Z and set up a tabular representation for the computation. Let the first column be the given cubes and the second column the ∗-product of the first cube with each other cube, etc.

C_0		$c_a * c_i$	$c_b * c_i$	$c_c * c_i$	$c_d * c_i$
c_a	$1xx1x$				
c_b	$0xx0x$	$yxxyx$			
c_c	$x0xx1$	$10x11$	$00x01$		
c_d	$x110x$	$111yx$	$0110x$	$xy101$	
c_e	$111x1$	11111	$y1101$	$1y1x1$	11101

$$Z^0 = \phi$$

We form another table for C_1 and continue, forming only ∗-products with the new cubes c_f, c_g, and c_h.

C_1		a	b	c	d	f	g
c_a	$1xx1x$						
c_b	$0xx0x$						
c_c	$x0xx1$						
c_d	$x110x$						
c_f	$111xx$	$1111x$	$y110x$	$1y1x1$	$1110x$		
c_g	$xx101$	$1x1y1$	$0x101$	$x0101$	$x1101$	11101	
c_h	$1x1x1$	$1x111$	$yx101$	$101x1$	11101	$111x1$	$1x101$

$$Z^1 = \phi$$

Since no new cubes are formed in the computation of $C_1 * C_1$, the algorithm stops and Z^2 and Z^3 can be obtained from the first column as

$$Z^2 = \begin{Bmatrix} x110x \\ 111xx \\ xx101 \\ 1x1x1 \end{Bmatrix},$$

$$Z^3 = \begin{Bmatrix} 1xx1x \\ 0xx0x \\ x0xx1 \end{Bmatrix},$$

and $$Z^4 = Z^5 = \phi.$$

Note that in actual practice the first table could simply be enlarged as the algorithm proceeds rather than writing out a completely new table at each step. Furthermore, during the algorithm certain rows and columns (like those for c_e) may be deleted when a new cube including the original cube is obtained.

3.6 EXTREMALS, THE <-OPERATION, AND BRANCHING

Having computed Z by the $*$-algorithm, we are then faced with the problem of selecting a subset of the cubes of Z such that it is a K-cover of L and is of minimum cost. To accomplish this selection we define extremals, give an algorithm for their computation and a branching procedure used to find a minimum cover when the set of extremals is itself not a cover. A prime implicant e of K is called an *L-extremal* if it contains a vertex d of L which is not contained in any other prime implicant of K. The vertex d is called a *distinguished vertex*. Let $E(K, L)$ denote the space of all L-externals of K. In Figure 3.4.1b complex $L = K$ is described by C_1. The cube $x1x0$ is an extremal with distinguished vertex 0110, and $1xx1$ is an extremal with distinguished vertex 1011. No other cubes are extremals here; consider, for example, the 1-cube $0x00$: vertex 0100 is contained in $x1x0$ and vertex 0000 is contained in $000x$. For the complex $K = L$ of Figure 3.5.2 the set of prime implicants Z was found to be $Z = \{01x, xx0\}$. Both these cubes are extremals since 011 is a distinguished vertex in $01x$ and 110 is a distinguished vertex for $xx0$. For the last example of Section 3.5 we found

$$Z = \left\{ \begin{array}{l} x110x \\ 111xx \\ xx101 \\ 1x1x1 \\ 1xx1x \\ 0xx0x \\ x0xx1 \end{array} \right\} .$$

The cube $0xx0x$ is an extremal with distinguished vertex 00000. Are there any other extremals for this example?

The importance of extremals is seen from the following theorem.

Theorem 3.6.1 Any minimum K-cover C of L contains $E(K, L)$.

PROOF. From Theorem 3.5.1 $C \subseteq Z$. By definition $E(K, L) \subseteq Z$ and any cube $e \in E(K, L)$ has a distinguished vertex not contained in any other cube of Z. To form a K-cover of L each distinguished vertex must be contained in the cover. Since $C \subseteq Z$, the cubes $E(K, L)$ must be used to cover the distinguished vertices, and therefore $E(K, L) \subseteq C$.

It follows from Theorem 3.6.1 that if $E(K, L)$ is a cover, it is a unique minimum cover.

The computation of $E(K, L)$ is quite straightforward if C_0 is given as a set of vertices. In such a case we need only to check to see if each vertex v of L is included in one or more cubes of Z. If v is included in only one cube $z \in Z$, then z is an extremal with distinguished vertex v; otherwise v is not a distinguished vertex. A chart of vertices versus prime implicants can be readily constructed to carry out this test for extremals (see Section 3.11). In general, however, C_0 is not given as a set of vertices and it may be inconvenient to find a representation of all vertices since the number of vertices may be very large. For example, the five coordinate example just discussed had five cubes to describe C_0, seven cubes in Z, but has 22 vertices which need to be covered.

We describe an intersection operation which will be useful in the algebraic determination of $E(K, L)$. The *coordinate intersection* is defined by Table 3.6.1.

Table 3.6.1   Coordinate Intersection

$\cap$	0	1	x
0	0	ϕ	0
1	ϕ	1	1
x	0	1	x

The *intersection* of two cubes $c^a = (a_1, a_2, \ldots, a_n)$ and $c^b = (b_1, b_2, \ldots, b_n)$ is defined as

$$c^a \cap c^b = \begin{cases} \phi & \text{if any } a_i \cap b_i = \phi \\ (a_1 \cap b_1, a_2 \cap b_2, \ldots, a_n \cap b_n) & \text{otherwise.} \end{cases}$$

For example, from Figure 3.4.1b, $x1x0 \cap 11xx = 11x0$, and $x001 \cap 0x00 = \phi$ since the last coordinate intersection $= \phi$. It is readily seen that the intersection of two cubes c^a and c^b is that cube which is common to both c^a and c^b.

We have said earlier that a set of cubes can be used to describe a complex, then the complex can be labeled $K[c_1, c_2, \ldots, c_r]$.

To determine whether or not a prime implicant z is an external we see if z can be built out of the intersections of z with the other cubes of Z.

We need consider, of course, only intersections which are not equal to ϕ, that is,

$$U(z, Z) = \{z' \mid z' \in Z \quad \text{and} \quad z' \cap z \neq \phi\}.$$

$U(z, Z)$ is called the *neighborhood* of z. $U'(z, Z) = U(z, Z) - z$ is called the *deleted neighborhood* of z.

Theorem 3.6.2 A prime implicant e is an L-extremal if and only if $K[e \cap L] \neq K[e \cap U'(e, Z) \cap L]$, and $K[e \cap L] \neq \phi$.

That is, a prime implicant is an extremal if and only if it cannot be built out of its intersections with other cubes of Z.

Before proving the theorem, let us reconsider cube $x1x0$ of Figure 3.4.1b. Let $z = x1x0$; then

$$U(z, Z) = \begin{Bmatrix} x1x0 \\ 11xx \\ 0x00 \end{Bmatrix}.$$

$$U'(z, Z) = \begin{Bmatrix} 11xx \\ 0x00 \end{Bmatrix}.$$

$$x1x0 \cap 11xx = 11x0.$$

$$x1x0 \cap 0x00 = 0100.$$

$$K[z \cap U'(z, Z)] = K[11x0, 0100].$$

$$0100 * 11x0 = y100 = x100.$$

Therefore $K[11x0, 0100] = K[11x0, x100] \neq K[x1x0]$, and $z = x1x0$ is an extremal.

PROOF. Assume e is an extremal, then e has at least one distinguished vertex d and $K[e \cap L] \neq \phi$. By definition of d, it is not contained in any other cube of Z and thus the complex $K[e \cap U'(e, Z) \cap L]$ cannot contain d. Thus $K[e \cap L] \neq K[e \cap U'(e, Z) \cap L]$. Now assume $K[e \cap L] \neq K[e \cap U'(e, Z) \cap L]$ and $K[e \cap L] \neq \phi$, then $K[e \cap L] \neq K[U'(e, Z)]$. If $K[e \cap L] \subseteq K[U'(e, Z]$, then $K[e \cap L] = K[e \cap L] \cap K[U'(e, Z)]$. So we know that $K[e \cap L] \nsubseteq K[U'(e, Z)]$. Let d be a vertex in $K[E \cap L]$ which is not in $K[U'(e, Z)]$; since $K[e \cap L] \nsubseteq K[U'(c, Z)]$ and $K[e \cap L] \neq \phi$, such a vertex must exist. Vertex d is thus a vertex of $(e \cap L)$ which is not included in any other prime implicant, thus completing the theorem.

The set of extremals $E(K, L)$ is determined by the inequality of Theorem 3.6.2., and it is noted that this inequality does not require the complex to be expressed as a set of all the vertices. If $E(K, L)$ is a K-cover of L we have completed the process and $E(K, L)$ is the unique minimum cover. $E(K, L)$ will not always be a cover, however, for as we have seen in the example of Figure 3.4.1b, $E(K, L) = \{x1x0, 1xx1\}$, which is not a cover of the complex. If $E(K, L)$ is not a K-cover of L, then $E(K, L)$ is removed from the problem (from Theorem 3.6.1 $E(K, L)$ is known to be part of the minimum K-cover), and a simpler problem of the same type results from what remains. The removal of $E(K, L)$ forms the basis for an iterative procedure for obtaining a minimum solution. To explain the iterations let us use subscripts on K, L, Z, and $E(K, L)$:

$$K = K_1 \qquad Z = Z_1,$$
$$L = L_1 \qquad E(K, L) = E_1.$$

The removal of E_1 is accomplished by

$$\hat{Z}_2 = Z_1 - E_1.$$

L_2 equals the subcomplex of L_1 not covered by E_1. To reduce the size of $\hat{Z}_2$, we introduce a *partial ordering*, denoted by $<$, between cubes of $\hat{Z}_2$, so that we can eliminate those cubes which are not maximum under the partial ordering and still obtain a minimum cover from the remaining cubes. Let u and v be cubes of $\hat{Z}_2$. We define $u < v$ if the cost of $u \geq$ cost of v and $u \cap L_2 \subseteq v \cap L_2$. If $u < v$ and $v < u$, by this definition we arbitrarily say that the cube which appears first in the list is larger, that is, $v < u$. We form Z_2 from $\hat{Z}_2$ by eliminating all nonmaximal cubes in this partial ordering.

Theorem 3.6.3 If $u, v \in \hat{Z}_2$ and $u < v$, then there exists a minimum cover not containing u.

PROOF. The cost of v is no greater than the cost of u, and v covers as much in L_2 as u.

Letting K_2 equal $K(Z_2)$, we have a pair of complexes (K_2, L_2) and we can find the set of L_2-extremals, calling this E_2, and continue. For example, if we continue with Figure 3.4.1b, we have

$$E_1 = \{x1x0, 1xx1\},$$
$$Z_1 = \{x1x0, 1xx1, 11xx, x001, 000x, 0x00\},$$
$$K_1 = L_1 = K[1xx1, x1x0, 000x].$$

Then

$$\hat{Z}_2 = \{11xx, x001, 000x, 0x00\},$$
$$L_2 = K[000x],$$
$$Z_2 = \{000x\},$$

since $000x$ is the only maximal cube under the $<$-operation and a minimum cover C is

$$C = \{x1x0, 1xx1, 000x\}.$$

The extremals in E_1 are also called first-order extremals, E_2, second-order extremals, etc., since each order of extremals reduces the problem to a smaller covering problem. The set E_1 is also often called the "core" since any minimum cover must contain E_1, and cubes of E_1 are called "essential" prime implicants. As a final example let us consider again the five coordinate example

$$Z_1 = \begin{bmatrix} x110x \\ 111xx \\ xx101 \\ 1x1x1 \\ 1xx1x \\ 0xx0x \\ x0xx1 \end{bmatrix} \begin{matrix} a \\ b \\ c \\ d \\ e \\ f \\ g \end{matrix}$$

but let this be the prime implicants for complex K, and let L_1 be the subcomplex defined by

$$\begin{pmatrix} x1101 \\ 00x11 \\ 00000 \\ 10010 \\ 10x01 \end{pmatrix}.$$

To find L-extremals we use Theorem 3.6.2.

$$U'(a, Z_1) = \begin{pmatrix} 111xx \\ xx101 \\ 1x1x1 \\ 0xx0x \end{pmatrix},$$

$$K[a \cap L] = K[\{x1101\}]$$

since $x110x \cap x1101 = x1101$ and intersections of all other cubes of L with a are empty.

$$K[a \cap L \cap U'(a, Z_1)] = K\left[\{x1101\} \cap \begin{pmatrix} 111xx \\ xx101 \\ 1x1x1 \\ 0xx0x \end{pmatrix} \right]$$

$$= K[\{11101, x1101, 01101\}]$$

$$= K[\{x1101\}].$$

Thus $K[a \cap L] = K[a \cap L \cap U'(a, Z_1)]$; so a is not an L-extremal. Similarly, b, c, and d can be found not to be L-extremals.

$$U'(e, Z_1) = \begin{pmatrix} 111xx \\ 1x1x1 \\ x0xx1 \end{pmatrix},$$

$$K[e \cap L] = K[10010],$$

$$K[e \cap L \cap U'(e, Z_1)] = K[\phi].$$

Thus $K[e \cap L] \neq K[e \cap L \cap U'(e, Z_1)]$; so e is an L-extremal. For cube f,

$$U'(f, Z_1) = \begin{pmatrix} x110x \\ xx101 \\ x0xx1 \end{pmatrix},$$

$$K[f \cap L] = K[\{01101, 00000\}].$$

Thus $K[f \cap L \cap U'(f, Z_1)] = K[01101]$ and f is also an L-extremal. For cube g,

$$U'(g, Z_1) = \begin{pmatrix} xx101 \\ 1x1x1 \\ 1xx1x \\ 0xx0x \end{pmatrix},$$

$$K[g \cap L] = K[\{00x11, 10x01\}],$$

$$K[g \cap L \cap U'(g, Z_1)] = K[10101],$$

and g is an L-extremal. This gives

$$E_1 = \begin{Bmatrix} 1xx1x \\ 0xx0x \\ x0xx1 \end{Bmatrix}$$

so that

$$\hat{Z}_2 = Z_1 - E_1 = \begin{pmatrix} x110x \\ 111xx \\ xx101 \\ 1x1x1 \end{pmatrix}$$

and L_2 is the complex not covered by E_1. For L_2 we see that of the cube $x1101$ the vertex 01101 is covered by $0xx0x$, but 11101 is not covered by $e, f,$ or g. Cubes $00x11$ and $10x01$ are covered by $x0xx1$. Vertex 00000 is covered by $0xx0x$ and vertex 10010 is covered by $1xx1x$. Thus

$$L_2 = \{11101\}.$$

Now each of the cubes of $\hat{Z}_2$ covers L_2 and each is of equal cost. Thus the $<$-operation can be applied arbitrarily to make one cube larger than all the others. For example,

$$Z_2 = \{x110x\},$$

giving $E_2 = x110x$. Thus a K cover of L is

$$E_1 \cup E_2 = \begin{Bmatrix} 1xx1x \\ 0xx0x \\ x0xx1 \\ x110x \end{Bmatrix}.$$

For some problems a cover is not obtained by finding all orders of extremals, that is, a set of prime implicants remains in which each vertex is covered by more than one prime implicant in the set. We now consider such an example for which the sets of extremals will not constitute a cover, and then describe the additional procedure called *branching* which can be used to obtain a minimum cover. Let $K = L$ as shown in Figure 3.6.1. Each element of Z_1 is maximal under the $<$-operation and thus E_1 is empty. The pair (K, L) is said to be *irreducible*. To treat this example

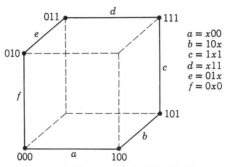

$$a = x00$$
$$b = 10x$$
$$c = 1x1$$
$$d = x11$$
$$e = 01x$$
$$f = 0x0$$

Figure 3.6.1   An irreducible (K, L).

we proceed as follows: consider cube a; either a minimum cover exists containing cube a or one not containing a (also possibly both). First let a be treated as an extremal; then $E_1 = \{a\}$ and $\hat{Z}_2 = Z_1 - E_1 = \{b, c, d, e, f\}$. Now by applying the $<$-ordering, $b < c$ and $f < e$, giving $Z_2 = \{a, c, e\}$. Both e and c are extremals of E_2 and $Z_3 = \phi$, giving the cover $C_1 = \{a, c, e\}$. Now assume that a is not contained in the cover and a is removed as in the $<$-operation. Here, $E_1 = \phi$.

$$Z_2 = \{b, c, d, e, f\},$$

but now since a is removed,

$$E_2 = \{b, f\}, \qquad \hat{Z}_3 = \{c, d, e\},$$

where $c < d$ and $e < d$, giving $Z_3 = \{d\} = E_3$. This gives a cover $C_2 = \{b, f, d\}$. Since the cost of C_1 equals the cost of C_2, either cover is a minimum.

3.7   THE EXTRACTION ALGORITHM

The problem of obtaining a cover of minimum cost can thus be solved by combining the algorithms we have just developed. We can summarize this algorithm, called the *extraction algorithm*, in the following steps.

We are given a pair of complexes (K_1, L_1), where L_1 is contained in K_1. To find a K_1-cover of L_1 having minimum cost:

1. Compute $Z_1 = Z_1(K_1)$ by the *-algorithm.
2. Find $E_1 = E_1(K_1, L_1)$ using Theorem 3.6.2.
3. Form $\hat{Z}_2 = Z_1 - E_1$.
4. Introduce the $<$-partial ordering in $\hat{Z}_2$, eliminating nonmaximal cubes to obtain Z_2.
5. Let $K_2 = K[Z_2]$ be the subcomplex of L_1 not covered by E_1.
6. If by iteration we have obtained (K_r, L_r) and the pair is reducible, compute E_r, $\hat{Z}_{r+1}$, Z_{r+1} and (K_{r+1}, L_{r+1}) as in Steps 1 through 5.
7. Proceed inductively until either $K_r = \phi$ or the pair (K_r, L_r) is irreducible. If $K_r = \phi$ and $K_{r-1} \neq \phi$, a minimum K_1-cover of L_1 is

$$C = E_1 \cup E_2 \cup \cdots \cup E_{r-1}.$$

If $K_r \neq \phi$ and (K_r, L_r) is irreducible, proceed to Step 8.

8. (K_r, L_r) is irreducible. Assume first that some $a \in Z_r$ is included in a minimum cover by letting $E_r = a$ and $\hat{Z}_{r+1} = Z_r - a$, and proceed with Step 4 to obtain a cover. Obtain another cover by assuming a is not in the cover, that is, $E_r = \phi$ and $\hat{Z}_{r+1} = Z - a$. An absolute minimum cover will be the one which has the least cost or either one if they have equal cost.

It should be noted that after applying Step 8 we may again arrive at an irreducible pair (K_s, L_s) at some later step. If so, Step 8 must also be repeated, and this can produce more than two covers, which would have to be compared to find a minimum cover.

We now apply the extraction algorithm to the example shown geometrically in Figure 3.7.1. We show only that portion of the n-cube which corresponds to prime implicants of K, and we have idealized these to give a planar representation. For this example $L = K$ and we label the cubes with letters to simplify the description.

$$K_1 = L_1 = K(a, b, \ldots, n),$$
$$Z_1 = \{a, b, \ldots, n\},$$
$$E_1 = \{a, f, h\},$$
$$\hat{Z}_2 = \{b, c, d, e, g, i, j, k, l, m, n\},$$
$$e < d; \ g < d; \ b < c,$$
$$Z_2 = \{c, d, i, j, k, l, m, n\},$$
$$E_2 = \{c\},$$
$$\hat{Z}_3 = \{d, i, j, k, l, m, n\},$$
$$d < i,$$
$$Z_3 = \{i, j, k, l, m, n\} \quad \text{and} \quad K(Z_3) \text{ is irreducible.}$$

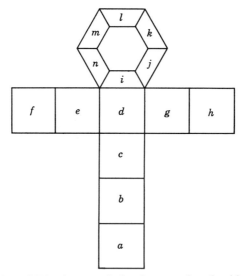

Figure 3.7.1   An example for the extraction algorithm.

Assume i is in the cover; then

$$E_3 = \{i\},$$
$$\hat{Z}_4 = \{j, k, l, m, n\},$$
$$j < k, \qquad n < m,$$
$$Z_4 = \{k, l, m\},$$
$$E_4 = \{k, m\},$$
$$\hat{Z}_5 = \{l\} \qquad L_5 = \phi.$$

Therefore a cover assuming i is in the cover is

$$C_1 = \{a, f, h, c, i, k, m\}.$$

Now at Z_3 assume i is not in the cover; then $E_3 = \phi$.

$$\hat{Z}_4 = Z_4 = \{j, k, l, m, n\},$$
$$E_4 = \{j, n\},$$
$$\hat{Z}_5 = \{k, l, m\},$$
$$k < l, \qquad m < l \qquad Z_5 = (l).$$

This cover C_2 is $\qquad C_2 = \{a, f, h, c, j, n, l\}.$

Since the cost of C_1 equals the cost of C_2, either solution is a minimum cover.

3.8   THE   #-OPERATION

In the extraction algorithm and for determining higher-order extremals we described L_r as the subcomplex of L_{r-1} not covered by E_{r-1}. This complex L_r may be easily calculated if L_1 is described by a set of vertices; then L_2 is the subset of vertices not included in E_1, etc. We have attempted to give a method which did not have to revert to the vertex representation of a complex, however, if the original representation contained cubes of higher dimension. It is quite important not to have to revert to vertices because there may be a very large number of vertices ($\leq 2^n$) required, thus making the calculations extremely lengthy. We now describe an operation which enables us to obtain L_r from L_{r-1} and E_{r-1} without reverting to vertices. This operation is a sort of subtraction operation, and will be described for any two cubes. We call this the #-*operation* (sharp operation). This operation is illustrated geometrically in Figure 3.8.1. Note that if

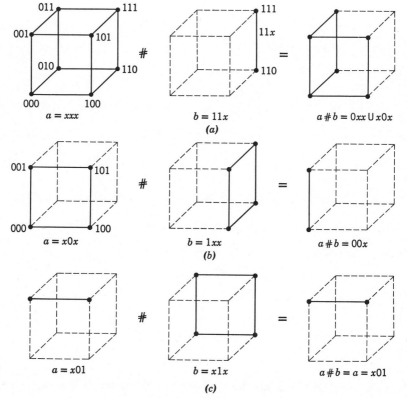

Figure 3.8.1   Illustration of #-operation.

we form $a \,\#\, b$, where a and b are cubes, we obtain the set of subcubes of a which is not included in b.

From Figure 3.8.1a we see that the $\#$-operation can produce more than one cube as a resultant. All operations on cubes up to this point produced at most one cube. Figure 3.8.1b and c show that in forming $a \,\#\, b$, cube b is not necessarily included in cube a, but $a \,\#\, b$ is included in a.

The geometric meaning of the $\#$-operation should be clear from Figure 3.8.1. To give an algebraic definition we first define a coordinate $\#$-operation as given in Table 3.8.1. Note that this operation is non-

Table 3.8.1 Coordinate $\#$-Operation $a_i \,\#\, b_i$

a_i \ b_i	0	1	x
0	z	y	z
1	y	z	z
x	1	0	z

commutative (that is, $a_i \,\#\, b_i \neq b_i \,\#\, a_i$), as can be expected from the illustrations of Figure 3.8.1.

To describe the $\#$-operation between two cubes, let $c^r = (a_1, a_2, \ldots, a_n)$ and $c^s = (b_1, b_2, \ldots, b_n)$.

$$c^r \,\#\, c^s = \begin{cases} c^r & \text{if } a_i \,\#\, b_i = y \quad \text{for any } i \\ \phi & \text{if } a_i \,\#\, b_i = z \quad \text{for all } i \\ \bigcup_i (a_1, \ldots, a_{i-1}, \alpha_i, a_{i+1}, \ldots, a_n), \text{ where} \\ a_i \,\#\, b_i = \alpha_i = 0 \quad \text{or} \quad 1 \text{ and the union runs over all such } i. \end{cases}$$

Thus for the example in Figure 3.8.1a $xxx \,\#\, 11x$ gives the coordinate result $(00z)$, so that $xxx \,\#\, 11x = 0xx \cup x0x$. Similarly, $x0x \,\#\, 1xx = 00x$, and $x01 \,\#\, x1x$ gives a coordinate result (zyz), so that $x01 \,\#\, x1x = x01$ since $c^r \,\#\, c^s = c^r$ if $a_i \,\#\, b_i = y$ for any i.

The following properties of the $\#$-operation follow immediately from the definition.

1. $c^r \,\#\, c^s = c^r$ if $c^r \cap c^s = \phi$.

2. $c^r \,\#\, c^s \subseteq c^r$.

3. $c^r \,\#\, c^s \neq c^s \,\#\, c^r$ noncommutive.

4. $(c^r \,\#\, c^s) \,\#\, c^t \neq c^r \,\#\, (c^s \,\#\, c^t)$ nonassociative.

The #-operation can also be shown to satisfy the distributive laws:

5. $$(c^r \cup c^s) \# c^t = (c^r \# c^t) \cup (c^s \# c^t),$$

and

6. $$(c^r \cap c^s) \# c^t = (c^r \# c^t) \cap (c^s \# c^t),$$

and also the following type of commutative law:

7. $$(c^r \# c^s) \# c^t = (c^r \# c^t) \# c^s.$$

We are interested in calculating L_r from L_{r-1} and E_{r-1}.

Theorem 3.8.1 Let L_{r-1} be determined by a set of cubes $\{c_1, c_2, \ldots, c_p\}$ and similarly $E_{r-1} = \{e_1, e_2, \ldots, e_q\}$; then L_r is determined by the set of cubes:

$$\{\cdots [(c_1 \# e_1) \# e_2] \cdots \# e_q\} \cup \{\cdots [(c_2 \# e_1) \# e_2] \cdots \# e_q\} \cup \cdots$$
$$\cup \{\cdots [(c_p \# e_1) \# e_2] \cdots \# e_q\}.$$

PROOF. The result of the operation $\{\cdots [(c_i \# e_1) \# e_2] \cdots \# e_q\}$ is a set of cubes from c_i that are not covered by E_{r-1}. Thus the union over $1 \leq i \leq p$ gives a cover of the subcomplex of L_{r-1} not covered by E_{r-1}.

It is also convenient to let $c^r \# C$ denote the iterated #-operation on c^r of a set of cubes represented by C. Thus L_r from Theorem 3.8.1 could be written as

$$L_r \quad \text{is determined by} \quad \bigcup_{i=1}^{p} (c_i \# E_{r-1})$$

or also as $L_{r-1} \# E_{r-1}$.

For the five coordinate example discussed earlier we had

$$L_1 = \begin{Bmatrix} x1101 \\ 00x11 \\ 00000 \\ 10010 \\ 10x01 \end{Bmatrix}$$

and

$$E_1 = \begin{Bmatrix} 1xx1x \\ 0xx0x \\ x0xx1 \end{Bmatrix} \quad \begin{matrix} e \\ f \\ g \end{matrix}$$

Using the #-operation, we now compute $L_2 = L_1 \# E_1$, setting up a table of iterative #-operations, where the circled entries are the coordinate # results. Thus from this table we see that $L_2 = 11101$. Also note that the #-computation for any pair of cubes can be terminated during the coordinate #-operation whenever a y is obtained, thereby shortening the computation. Thus, for example, $00x11 \# 1xx1x$ is immediately known to be $00x11$ when for the first coordinate $0 \# 1 = y$ is obtained.

Table 3.8.2 Iterated #-Table

E_1 L_1	$L_1 \# e$ $e = 1xx1x$	$(L_1 \# e) \# f$ $f = 0xx0x$	$(L_1 \# e \# f) \# g = L_2$ $g = x0xx1$
$x1101$	$\overline{0zzyz}$ $x1101$ $\overline{yzzzz}$	$\overline{1zzzz}$ 11101 $\overline{zzzyz}$	$\overline{zyzzz}$ 11101 $\overline{zzzzz}$
$00x11$	$00x11$ $\overline{yzzyz}$	$00x11$ $\overline{zzzzz}$	ϕ
00000	00000 $\overline{zzzzz}$	ϕ	ϕ
10010	ϕ $\overline{zzzyz}$	ϕ $\overline{yzzzz}$	ϕ $\overline{zzzzz}$
$10x01$	$10x01$	$10x01$	ϕ

The #-operation may also be used for several other purposes as illustrated by the following two lemmas. The set of extremals can be determined by the #-operation.

Lemma 3.8.1 Let $Z = (z_1, z_2, \ldots, z_p)$ be the set of prime implicants; then z_i is an L-extremal of K if and only if

$$z_i \# (Z - z_i) = \{u\},$$

where $\{u\}$ contains at least one vertex of L.

That is, deleting from z_i all those subcubes in $(Z - z_i)$ leaves at least one vertex of z_i which is in L. (Any such vertex is a distinguished vertex.) If we are given a representation for the complex $N = K - L$, the equation of Lemma 3.8.1 can be restated as

$$z_i \# (Z - z_i) \# N \neq \phi.$$

We can also determine whether two sets of cubes determine the same complex as follows.

Lemma 3.8.2 Let C_0 and C_1 be two sets of cubes; then C_0 and C_1 are covers for the same complex if and only if

$$C_0 \# C_1 = C_1 \# C_0 = \phi.$$

Here $C_0 \# C_1 = \phi$ means that any vertex in C_0 is also in C_1; and the converse statement holds for $C_1 \# C_0 = \phi$.

3.9   THE LOCAL EXTRACTION ALGORITHM

This algorithm, like the extraction algorithm, is used to obtain a K-cover of L, where covers of K and L are given. The method differs from the extraction algorithm in that it does not require the complete set Z of prime implicants to be computed as a preliminary step in the algorithm. In addition, this method requires only a local test to find one extremal at a time, rather than having to test for extremals with the complete list of prime implicants. We give only a very brief explanation of this algorithm.

In the local extraction algorithm, rather than starting with the pair of complexes (K_1, L_1), we start with the pair (K_1/N_1), where $N_1 = K_1 \# L_1$, and where K_1 is given in terms of a cover C_0 and N_1 is given by a cover D_0. We read (K_1/N_1) as K_1 modulo N_1. To find a cover we want a (K_1/N_1)-cover; that is, a cover C of cubes of K_1 which covers each vertex of K_1 which is not in N_1.

We start the algorithm by finding a K_1-prime implicant cover of K_1; call it C_1, and an N_1-prime implicant cover of N_1; call this D_1. Since we are given C_0 and D_0, we can obtain C_1 and D_1 by a calculation which replaces each cube c^r in C_0 with a K_1-prime implicant containing c^r; and similarly replacing each cube d^r in D_0 with an N_1-prime implicant containing d^r. To accomplish this we let $c^r = (c_1, c_2, \ldots, c_n)$ and we let c_i be the first non-x component. Form $c^{r+1} = (c_1, c_2, \ldots, c_{i-1}, x, c_{i+1}, \ldots, c_n)$ and $\bar{c}^r = (c_1, c_2, \ldots, c_{i-1}, \alpha, c_{i+1}, \ldots, c_n)$, where $\alpha = 0$ if $c_i = 1$ and $\alpha = 1$ if $c_i = 0$. We then check to see if c^{r+1} is in K_1. This can be done by the $\#$-operation.

Lemma 3.9.1 $\bar{c}^r \# (C_0 - c^r) = \phi$ if and only if c^{r+1} is in K_1.

If c^{r+1} is in K_1, c^r is replaced with c^{r+1} and the operation is repeated on the next non-x coordinate of c^{r+1}. If c^{r+1} is not in K_1, we try the same operation on the next succeeding non-x coordinate of c^r. This process of expanding c^r is continued until all non-x coordinates have been tested. The resultant cube z is the prime implicant which replaces c^r. That the resultant cube is a prime implicant follows directly from the definition of prime implicant, since $\delta_i(z) = \phi$ for each i. After applying this to each c^r of C_0 and similarly to each d^r of D_0, we obtain the respective prime implicant covers C_1 and D_1 where

$$C_1 \subseteq Z(K_1) \quad \text{and} \quad D_1 \subseteq Z(N_1).$$

From C_1 and D_1 we can find extremals for our problem; that is, a (K_1/N_1)-extremal is a prime implicant of K_1 which contains a vertex of K_1

not contained in N_1, where this vertex is contained in no other prime implicant of K_1. This can be seen from Lemma 3.9.2.

Lemma 3.9.2 If C is a (K_1/N_1)-cover of K_1-prime implicants, then C contains every (K_1/N_1)-extremal.

This lemma follows from the fact that each vertex of K_1 not in N_1 must be covered, and in a prime implicant cover only one prime implicant is available to cover a distinguished vertex. Now since C_1 contains all (K_1/N_1)-extremals, we need a method for finding them. This is shown in Lemma 3.9.3.

Lemma 3.9.3 For complexes (K_1/N_1) and prime implicant covers C_1 of K_1 and D_1 of N_1, a cube e of C_1 is a (K_1/N_1)-extremal if and only if

$$e \nsubseteq K\{[(C_1 - e) \cup D_1] * e\}.$$

PROOF. $[(C_1 - e) \cup D_1]$ covers all the vertices of K_1 except possibly some vertices of e not in N_1. Now if $\{[(C_1 - e) \cup D_1] * e\}$ contains all the vertices of e, then e has no distinguished vertex and e is not an extremal. Otherwise e is an extremal.

Thus we can find an extremal e, if any exists, and using this we can iterate, similar to the method used in the extraction algorithm. Let

$$\hat{C}_2 = C_1 - e,$$
$$\hat{D}_2 = D_1 \cup e.$$

Let C_2 be the subset of $\hat{C}_2$ not covered by $\hat{D}_2$, and D_2 be the subset of $\hat{D}_2$ in which each element of D_2 has a nonempty *-product with at least one element of C_2. By these definitions those don't care conditions in $\hat{D}_2$ which are too far distant to interact with any cubes in C_2 have been eliminated as well as those parts of $\hat{C}_2$ covered by $\hat{D}_2$. We now wish to define a $<$-operation and use this in the vicinity of e to find other extremals. We compute the "periphery" of e, $P = P(e, C_2 \cup D_2)$, which consists of all prime implicants determined by $C_2 \cup D_2$ that have a nonempty intersection with e. We can compute $P(e, C_2 \cup D_2)$ by the following formula. Let

$$G(e) = \{p \mid p = e \cap (C_2 \cup D_2) \neq \phi\};$$
then
$$P(e, C_2 \cup D_2) = Z(G),$$
where
$Z(G)$ is computed by the *-algorithm.

Then we define $\tilde{P}(e) = P - D_2$, where this means that cubes that appear in both P and D are eliminated from P to form $\tilde{P}(e)$. Now for cube $u \in \tilde{P}(e)$ we find a maximal cube v, where $v \in \tilde{P}(e)$, such that $v > u$ with respect to (K_2/N_2), and $K_2 = K(C_2)$, and $N_2 = K(D_2)$. Now we calculate $P(v)$, the periphery of v, and let $\tilde{P}(\overset{>}{v})$ be the subset of $\tilde{P}(v)$ which are maximal in their own peripheries. Then if v is not contained in $\tilde{P}(\overset{>}{v})$, it is an extremal in the sense that some minimum cover contains v.

Consider the example in Figure 3.9.1. Taking cube e, we form

$$K\{[(C_1 - e) \cup D_1] * e\} =$$
$$K\{(a, b, d, \alpha) * e\} = K(\delta, \alpha).$$

Since $e \nsubseteq K(\delta, \alpha),$ e is an extremal.

Then
$$\hat{C}_2 = \{a, b, d\},$$
$$\hat{D}_2 = \{a, \alpha, \gamma, e\},$$
$$C_2 = \{b, d\},$$
$$D_2 = \{a, \alpha, \gamma, e\},$$
$$G(e) = \{b, d, a, \alpha, e\},$$
$$P(e) = \{a, b, c, d, e\},$$
$$\tilde{P}(e) = \{b, c, d\},$$
$$c > b$$
$$P(c) = \{a, b, c, d, e\},$$
$$\tilde{P}(c) = \{b, d\},$$
$$\tilde{P}(\overset{>}{c}) = \{d\}.$$

Therefore c is an extremal and we go on to explain the next steps.

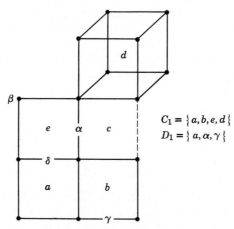

Figure 3.9.1   Example for local extraction algorithm.

If v is an extremal, as we found c to be in the preceding example, we form

$$\hat{C}_3 = C_2 - v,$$
$$\hat{D}_3 = D_2 \cup v,$$

and proceed as we did for $\hat{C}_2$ and $\hat{D}_2$.

If v is not an extremal, then we test another maximal cube in $\tilde{P}(e)$ until an extremal is found or until all maximal cubes in $\tilde{P}(e)$ have been tested. In the latter case we return to C_2 and test for more extremals inductively. Finally, if C_2 has no further extremals, we use a local branching operation. Before going on with the description of this branching, however, let us return to our example of Figure 3.9.1. We have seen that c is an extremal; thus

$$\hat{C}_3 = C_2 - c = \{b, \alpha\},$$
$$\hat{D}_3 = \{a, \alpha, \gamma, e, c\},$$
$$C_3 = \{d\},$$
$$D_3 = \{a, \alpha, e, c\},$$
$$G(c) = \{a, \alpha, d, e, c\},$$
$$P(c) = \{a, e, c, d\},$$
$$\tilde{P}(c) = P(c) - D_3 = \{d\},$$
$$d \text{ is maximal,}$$
$$P(d) = \{e, c, d\},$$
$$\tilde{P}(d) = \phi; \text{ therefore } d \text{ is an extremal.}$$

Thus a minimal (K_1/N_1)-cover is $\{e, c, d\}$.

The following is the final step of the local extraction algorithm. Here we have arrived at a condition C_r and D_r where no extremals exist in C_r. Let $u \in C_r$, where if u is maximal we call it z, but if u is not maximal, let z be a maximal element greater than u in the periphery of u. We then branch, considering the two possibilities: (1) that z is contained in the minimum cover and (2) that z is not contained in the minimum cover.

For (1) we let

$$\hat{C}_{r+1} = C_r - z,$$
$$\hat{D}_{r+1} = D_r \cup z,$$

consider z as an extremal, and continue as for $\hat{C}_2$ and $\hat{D}_2$.

For (2) we let

$$\hat{C}_{r+1} = C_r - z,$$
$$\hat{D}_{r+1} = D_r,$$

and

$$\hat{U}_{r+1} = U_r \cup z,$$

where U_s is the set of prime implicants deleted from $K(C_s \cup D_s)$. Note that at this step $U_r = \phi$. Construct C_{r+1} and D_{r+1} as previously done for C_2 and D_2, and let U_{r+1} be the subset of elements of $\hat{U}_{r+1}$ whose $*$-product with C_{r+1} is not empty. Now we proceed as before, but in this case we let $P = P[v, (C_{r+1} - v) \cup D_{r+1} \cup U_{r+1}]$ for the periphery of v and let $\tilde{P}(\vec{v}) = P - D_{r+1} - U_{r+1} - \{$nonmaximal elements in $P\}$, and as before v is an extremal if and only if $v \nsubseteq K[\tilde{P}(\vec{v})]$.

Although added calculation is required in the local extraction algorithm, because of computing peripheries and also because a given prime implicant may have to be computed more than once during the course of the algorithm, these disadvantages may be outweighted in some problems by the advantage that we are able to get away from dealing with the complete list of Z during any single step of the algorithm.

3.10   APPROXIMATE MINIMUM COVERS

As in many combinatorial problems, it is theoretically trivial to find a minimum cover for any given cubical complex K (or a K-cover of L for a pair of cubical complexes K and L, where $L \subseteq K$), since we simply have to examine only a finite number of possible covers. The mechanics of searching through all the possibilities, however, can become extremely lengthy since there may be a very large number of possibilities. By using the theorems and techniques of the extraction algorithm certain covers are eliminated, thus reducing the number of possibilities which need to be examined.

Several difficulties can arise in the extraction algorithm, however. One of these difficulties is simply when the set Z of prime implicants becomes very large, then the test for extremals becomes lengthy because Z has many elements. The local extraction algorithm is an attempt to circumvent this difficulty by dealing with prime implicant covers rather than a complete set Z of prime implicants.

In the local extraction algorithm, however, we calculate the peripheries of the prime implicants in the cover in an attempt to find extremals. The calculations required to obtain the peripheries may become extensive for certain problems, and then these calculations may offset the advantage of not requiring the complete Z to be used in the calculation.

Another difficulty occurs when a cubical complex has no (or very few) cubes that are extremals and results in many levels of branching being required to obtain a cover. Then the extraction algorithm reverts to searching through many possible solutions by iterative branching. It has been shown that the problem of finding a minimum cover can be stated as an integer programming problem; thus an alternative to branching is to find an integer solution to a set of linear inequalities. This approach will not be described here, for it would require introducing a great deal of material not directly connected with the covering problem. It is not immediately clear which of these two techniques (branching or integer programming) is most efficient, although it can be shown that that one approach obtains trial solutions in a different order from the other. Further investigation of this part of the covering problem and statistics for comparing different algorithms for the covering problem would be of interest.

A class of examples which have many prime implicants and require several branching steps illustrates the difficulties we have mentioned. Let $K = L$ be a cubical complex with $n = 3k$ coordinates $k = 1, 2, \ldots$ such that K is defined by the set of all cubes in which each cube has exactly k coordinates equal to 1, exactly k coordinates equal to 0, and exactly k coordinates equal to x. This set of cubes can be seen to be the set Z of prime implicants; also K has no extremals. Thus for this class of examples K has

$$\begin{Bmatrix} 3k \\ k \end{Bmatrix} \cdot \begin{Bmatrix} 2k \\ k \end{Bmatrix} = \frac{(3k)!}{(k!)^3} \qquad \text{prime implicants}$$

Table 3.10.1 shows the number of prime implicants for several of these

Table 3.10.1 Number of Prime Implicants in a Special Class of Boolean Functions

n	Number of prime implicants
3	6
6	90
9	1,680
12	34,650

functions, readily indicating the difficulties of finding minimum covers for such functions.

Quite often it may not be necessary to obtain a minimum cover, either if the problem causes one of the difficulties mentioned previously or if the cost of the switching circuit is not of primary concern. Certain very simple techniques may then be used to find an "approximate minimum cover."

In this section we describe one algorithm to obtain an approximate minimum cover. This algorithm is extremely simple in its approach and may at times not give a very satisfactory solution; various refinements in the algorithm however, can be made to improve the solution, and these follow the methods described for the extraction and local extraction algorithms.

We start with covers C_0 and D_0 of complexes K_1 and N_1 respectively. The cubes of C_0 are expanded into prime implicants as described in the local extraction algorithm to form C_1. Let $D_0 = D_1$. We wish to find a (K_1/N_1)-cover which consists of a subset of the cubes in C_1. Thus we next check to find if any cube f of C_1 covers some vertex in K not covered by any other cube in C_1 and also not included in N_1. A cube f is of this type if

$$f \mathbin{\#} (C_1 - f) \mathbin{\#} D_1 \neq \phi.$$

Let F_1 indicate all such cubes f of C_1. (Note that F_1 includes all the first-order extremals of L_1.) Then form

$$C_2 = C_1 - F_1,$$
$$D_2 = D_1 \cup F_1,$$
$$A_2 = F_1,$$

where A_i is a partial K_1-cover of L_1. Arrange C_2 in a list such that the cubes of least cost appear first, etc. Now iteratively test the cubes in the list of C_2 to see if: For $c^r \in C_2$

$$c^r \mathbin{\#} D_2 = \phi.$$

If $c^r \mathbin{\#} D_2 = \phi$, then discard c^r, but if not, form

$$C_3 = C_2 - c^r$$
$$D_3 = D_2 \cup c^r$$
$$A_3 = A_2 \cup c^r$$

Now proceed with these new C_3, D_3, and A_3 as before, until finally A_r constitutes a (K_1/N_1)-cover. This A_r is taken as an approximate minimum cover.

As an example of this method for obtaining an approximate minimum K_1-cover of L_1 let

$$C_0 = \begin{Bmatrix} xx010 \\ x1111 \\ xx001 \\ 00x11 \\ x0x00 \\ 10x11 \end{Bmatrix}$$

and

$$D_0 = D_1 = \begin{Bmatrix} x0011 \\ x1001 \\ 11010 \\ 10100 \end{Bmatrix}$$

be covers for K_1 and N_1 respectively. We wish to replace each cube in C_0 with a prime implicant. Taking cube $xx010$, we test to see if $xxx10 \subseteq K_1$ using Lemma 3.9.1, that is, computing

$$xx110 \mathbin{\#} \begin{pmatrix} x1111 \\ x0x00 \\ 00x11 \\ xx001 \\ 10x11 \end{pmatrix} = xx110 \neq \phi$$

so that $xxx10 \nsubseteq K_1$, and thus $xx010$ cannot be replaced by $xxx10$. Similarly, we find that $xx010$ cannot be replaced by $xx0x0$ or $xx01x$; thus $xx010$ is a prime implicant. For cube $x1111$ we form $xx111$ and test

$$x0111 \mathbin{\#} \begin{pmatrix} xx010 \\ x0x00 \\ 00x11 \\ xx001 \\ 10x11 \end{pmatrix}.$$

In this case $x0111 \mathbin{\#} 00x11 = 10111$ and $10111 \mathbin{\#} 10x11 = \phi$ so that $xx111 \subseteq K_1$, and we replace $x1111$ with $xx111$. Continuing this process on each cube of C_0, we obtain the prime implicant cover

$$C_1 = \begin{cases} xx010 \\ xx111 \\ xx001 \\ x0x11 \\ x0x00 \end{cases}.$$

Now we wish to determine F_1. Letting $f = xx010$, we form $f \mathbin{\#} (C_1 - f) \mathbin{\#} D_1$.

$$f \mathbin{\#} (C_1 - f) = (xx010) \mathbin{\#} \begin{pmatrix} xx111 \\ xx001 \\ x0x11 \\ x0x00 \end{pmatrix} = xx010$$

Then

$$[f \mathbin{\#} (C_1 - f)] \mathbin{\#} D_1 = (xx010) \mathbin{\#} \begin{pmatrix} x0011 \\ x1001 \\ 11010 \\ 10100 \end{pmatrix} = \begin{Bmatrix} 0x010 \\ x0010 \end{Bmatrix} \neq \phi.$$

Thus $xx010 \in F_1$. Similarly, the other cubes of F_1 can be determined, giving

$$F_1 = \begin{cases} xx010 \\ xx111 \\ xx001 \\ x0x00 \end{cases} = A_2.$$

Thus $C_2 = C_1 - F_1 = \{x0x11\}$.

$$D_2 = D_1 \cup F_1 = \begin{Bmatrix} x0011 \\ xx001 \\ xx010 \\ x0x00 \\ xx111 \end{Bmatrix}.$$

Since C_2 contains only one cube here, we simply have to test for $(x0x11) \#$ D_2. This is

$$x0x11 \# \begin{Bmatrix} x0011 \\ xx001 \\ xx010 \\ x0x00 \\ xx111 \end{Bmatrix} = \phi$$

so $x0x11$ is discarded and

$$A_2 = \begin{Bmatrix} xx010 \\ xx111 \\ xx001 \\ x0x00 \end{Bmatrix}$$

is an approximate minimum cover.

As can be checked by the reader, this cover is not a minimum cover since the prime implicant $x00xx$ is not obtained in the process of transforming C_0 to C_1. A minimum cover for this problem is

$$C_{min} = \begin{Bmatrix} x00xx \\ x0x00 \\ xx010 \\ xx111 \end{Bmatrix},$$

which has a cost one less than A_2.

3.11   QUINE-McCLUSKEY MINIMIZATION CHART METHODS

In both the determination of the prime implicants and finding a minimum cover, judicious organization of the calculations leads to considerable simplification of the procedures. When K and L are both represented by sets of vertices, an organization in the form of charts leads to relatively straightforward procedures for finding the prime implicants and the extremals of a problem. We shall briefly discuss these chart methods in this section. Given two r-cubes of a complex, they can be combined to form a $(r + 1)$-cube in the complex if and only if their components are exactly the same except for differing in exactly one bound component. This, of course, is directly analogous to the Boolean identity

$Ax \vee A\bar{x} = A$, where A is a product term of variables other than x. Since each prime implicant corresponds to a cube of the cubical complex K which is not included in any other cube of the complex, successive combining of cubes in this way will lead to the set of prime implicants. In addition, all the cubes of K, that is, $K^0, K^1, \ldots$, will be obtained if we start with K described by vertices, and all possible such combinations are successively generated. Those cubes not included in any other cubes are then the set of all prime implicants. (Note that these results follow directly from the discussion in Section 3.3 and the definition of prime implicants.)

Starting with K^0 we see that combining can only occur between a pair of vertices if one vertex of the pair has exactly one more 1 than the other vertex of the pair. (Other pairs differ in two or more components.) Thus we may place vertices into groups where vertices in each group have exactly the same number of 1's; and we need consider only combining pairs of vertices, one from each group, where the number of 1's of the groups differ by only one. By placing these groups in a column, where the number of 1's increase as we proceed down the column, we need to combine only between adjacent groups in the column. Once the set of all r-cubes of K, (that is, K^r) has been obtained, we may again form groups of r-cubes where each r-cube in a group contains the same numbers of 1's as any other r-cube in the same group. These groups may then be arranged in a column where the number of 1's increases as we proceed down the column. As for vertices, combining will again occur only between adjacent groups. An example using this organization is shown in Figure 3.11.1, where for any column, cubes in the same group appear between horizontal rules.

In this procedure, in proceeding from K^i to K^{i+1}, those cubes in K^i which combine to form a cube in K^{i+1} can have a check ($\sqrt{}$) placed beside them. Such a cube of K^i is then included in the cube formed for K^{i+1} and thus this cube of K^i is not a prime implicant. These check marks are shown in Figure 3.11.1. At the termination of the procedure, those cubes that are not checked are not included in any other cube of K and are thus prime implicants. For our example we obtain

$$Z = \begin{Bmatrix} x0x00 \\ xx001 \\ xx010 \\ x0x11 \\ xx111 \\ x00xx \end{Bmatrix}.$$

Now that Z is determined, the next step is to find the *L*-extremals of K.

K^0	K^1	K^2	K^3
00000 √			
00001 √	0000x √	000xx √	x00xx
00010 √	000x0 √	x000x √	
00100 √	00x00 √	x00x0 √	
10000 √	x0000 √	x0x00	
00011 √	000x1 √	x00x1 √	
01001 √	0x001 √	xx001	
10001 √	x0001 √	x001x √	
01010 √	0001x √	xx010	
10010 √	0x010 √	100xx √	
10100 √	x0010 √	x0x11	
00111 √	x0100 √	xx111	
10011 √	1000x √		
11001 √	100x0 √		
11010 √	10x00 √		
01111 √	00x11 √		
10111 √	x0011 √		
11111 √	x1001 √		
	100x1 √		
	1x001 √		
	x1010 √		
	1001x √		
	1x010 √		
	0x111 √		
	x0111 √		
	10x11 √		
	x1111 √		
	1x111 √		

Figure 3.11.1   Chart to determine prime implicants.

Z \ L^0	00000	00001	00010	00100	10000	10001	01010	10010	00111	01111	10111	11111
x0x00	x			ⓧ	x							
xx001		x				x						
xx010			x				ⓧ	x				
x0x11									x		x	
xx111									x	ⓧ	x	ⓧ
x00xx	x	x	x		x	x		x				

Figure 3.11.2   Prime implicant chart.

Assume L is represented by the vertices L^0, as shown in the following for our example.

$$L^0 = \begin{cases} 00000 \\ 00001 \\ 00010 \\ 00100 \\ 10000 \\ 10001 \\ 01010 \\ 10010 \\ 00111 \\ 01111 \\ 10111 \\ 11111 \end{cases}.$$

A table having one row per prime implicant and one column per vertex in L^0 can be formed where an x is placed in the ith row, jth column entry in this table if and only if the prime implicant of the ith row covers (or includes) the vertex of the jth column. This table is called a *prime implicant chart*, as shown in Figure 3.11.2.

The rows having x's in any column of the chart indicate those prime implicants which cover the vertex indicated by the column. Thus prime implicants $x0x00$ and $x00xx$ cover vertex 00000 as indicated by the first column. Any column having only one x represents a distinguished vertex, and the prime implicant represented by the row for such an x is thereby an extremal of E_1. In our example the x's indicating elements of E_1 are encircled, and we find

$$E_1 = \begin{cases} x0x00 \\ xx010 \\ xx111 \end{cases}.$$

All rows representing elements of E_1 and resulting columns with x's in these rows may now be crossed out, since only those vertices of L^0 not yet covered and those prime implicants not as yet required in a minimum cover need to be considered further. For clarity our table is redrawn, with these rows and columns eliminated, in Figure 3.11.3. Now it is seen

Z \\ L	00001	10001
$xx001$	x	x
$x0x11$		
$x00xx$	x	x

Figure 3.11.3   Prime implicant chart with E_1 eliminated.

that $x0x11$ does not cover any of the remaining vertices of L and can thus be eliminated. (This could have been seen from Figure 3.11.2 in that $x0x11 < xx111$ since the cost of $x0x11$ is equal to that of $xx111$, but $xx111$ covers more vertices of L than $x0x11$.) Now vertices 00001 and 10001 need to be covered. Cubes $x00xx$ and $xx001$ cover both these vertices, but since the cost of $x00xx$ is less than that of $xx001$, applying the $<$-operation eliminates $xx001$ so that

$$E_2 = x00xx,$$

giving the minimum cover

$$C_{\min} = E_1 \cup E_2 = \begin{pmatrix} x0x00 \\ xx010 \\ xx111 \\ x00xx \end{pmatrix}.$$

As in the extraction algorithm, successive order extremals can be found by simple manipulations of this chart. It is possible that successive elimination of rows and columns (using the $<$-operation as indicated) terminates before a cover is determined. The remainder of the cover can then be found by a procedure analogous to branching, that is, picking a prime implicant representing some remaining row and then proceeding as before, using both the assumption that this prime implicant is, or is not, in a minimum cover.

These chart methods are extremely useful for calculating minimum covers by hand when the number of vertices in K and L is not so large as to make the techniques cumbersome. Furthermore, the theory of minimization can be stated or derived as rules of manipulation on the charts. Chart methods corresponding to the cubical complex methods which do not revert to vertices are also possible to develop, but we shall not discuss these here.

Exercises

1. We have discussed the one-to-one correspondence between a Boolean functional expression and a series-parallel two-terminal relay contact network. Develop a similar one-to-one correspondence for logical diagrams using AND-, OR-, and NOT-elements. (*Hint.* Do not restrict yourself to two inputs for each of the AND- and OR-elements.)
2. Corresponding to a disjunctive normal form, we obtained a two-level AND-OR logical circuit. Produce an analogous result for the conjunctive normal form.

   Give the two-level AND-OR logical circuits and the analogous conjunctive normal form circuits for the following functions. (Try to use as few total arrowheads as possible.)

   (a) $f = (a \oplus b)c \vee \bar{a}\bar{b}$.
   (b) $f = a(b \vee \bar{c}) \vee \bar{b}(\bar{a} \vee a\bar{c}) \vee a\bar{b}c$.

3. Are the following logical circuits combinational? Show why, and if they are combinational, give the output functions.

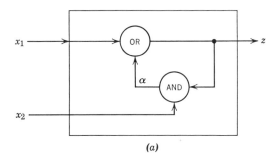

(a)

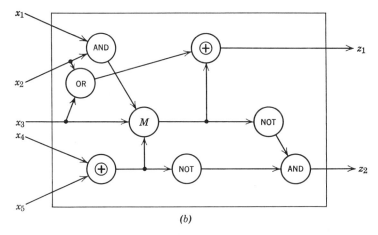

(b)

4. Give the cubical representation of $K(f)$ for the following functions, using the 0, 1, x notation. Give K^0, K^1, ...

   (a) $f = (a \oplus b)c \vee \bar{a}\bar{b}$.
   (b) $f = a(b \vee \bar{c}) \vee \bar{b}(\bar{a} \vee a\bar{c}) \vee a\bar{b}c$.
   (c) $f = abc \vee abd \vee abe \vee acd \vee ace \vee ade \vee bcd \vee bce \vee bde \vee cde$.

5. Prove that for any Boolean function f if $K^r(f) = \phi$ (that is, there are no r-cubes), then $K^{r+1}(f) = \phi$; $0 \le r \le n - 1$.

6. Find a cover having cost $C^a \le 21$ for the complex determined by the following set of cubes.

$$
C_0 = \begin{cases}
xx1000 \\
x00100 \\
000x00 \\
0x0010 \\
00010x \\
0001x1 \\
xx0000
\end{cases}
$$

Determine the costs C^a and C^b of the cover.

7. Calculate Z for the C_0 given in Exercise 6.
8. Prove the property

$$\text{If } c^r \subseteq c^s \text{ then } c^r * c^s = c^r.$$

9. Given a complex K determined by

$$\begin{pmatrix} 0110 \\ 1010 \\ xx0x \\ 00xx \\ 11xx \end{pmatrix}$$

and a subcomplex L of K determined by

$$\begin{pmatrix} 000x \\ 00x1 \\ x000 \\ 1x00 \\ 11x0 \end{pmatrix}$$

Represent each of these two complexes on a 4-cube and give a K-cover of L which uses only two cubes.

10. Find a minimum cost K-cover of L for the following:

   (a)

a	b	c	d
e	f	g	h
i	j	k	l
m	n	o	p
q	r	s	t

$$K = L$$

The cubical complex is represented by this figure where a through t are prime implicants. Give a subset of $\{a, \ldots, t\}$ which is a minimum cover.

   (b)

L is determined by

$$\begin{pmatrix} 1111x \\ 01x11 \\ 0010x \\ x0100 \\ x1010 \\ 110x0 \\ 1x010 \end{pmatrix}.$$

$N = K - L$ is determined by

$$\begin{pmatrix} 01001 \\ 011x0 \\ 1x101 \\ 10000 \\ 10011 \end{pmatrix}.$$

(c)

$$L = \begin{Bmatrix} 00x00 \\ 1110x \\ 0x101 \\ x1100 \\ 1x00x \\ 11x01 \\ 0000x \end{Bmatrix}$$

$$N = \begin{Bmatrix} 1x01x \\ 0x11x \end{Bmatrix}$$

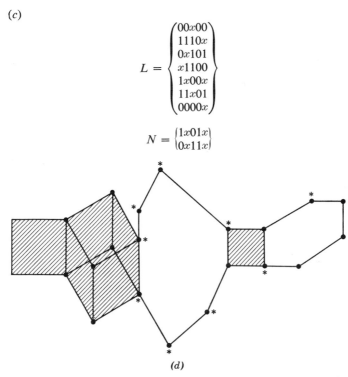

(d)

Vertices of L are represented with * and are a subset of the vertices of K. All the prime implicants of K are shown.

11. For the complex shown below, where all prime implicants are shown, find *all* minimum cost covers for the complex, assuming that all 1-cubes have equal cost and 0-cubes have a higher cost that 1-cubes.

12. We are given a character recognition problem to find four two-level AND-OR circuits, call them f_1, f_0, f_H, and f_B, which are equal to 1 if the characters 1, 0, H, or blank are being read, respectively, and are 0 otherwise. The four characters are stylized on three by four boards, as shown here and on next page.

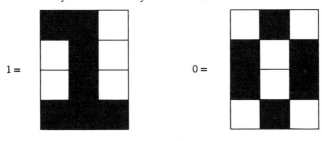

1 =   0 =

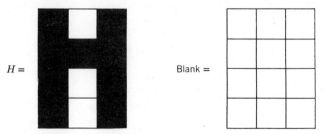

$H =$ Blank =

The characters are sensed by seven variables as shown below.

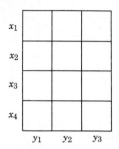

y_1 y_2 y_3

x_i—reads row i $(1 \leq i \leq 4)$ and equals 1 if two or more squares in row i are black; otherwise x_i equals 0.

y_j—reads column j $(1 \leq j \leq 3)$ and equals 1 if three or more squares in column j are black; otherwise y_j equals 0.

To allow for error in characters and sensing, we *demand* that the correct character be indicated on f_1, f_0, f_H, f_B, not only when all squares are correct but also when exactly one arbitrary square is allowed to change from black to white, or white to black.

Optional subquestion:
   Can we allow two arbitrary squares to change and still obtain functions f_1, f_0, f_H, and f_B to give correct character sensing?

13. Prove the following properties for the #-operation.
   (a) $(c^r \cup c^s) \# c^t = (c^r \# c^t) \cup (c^s \# c^t)$
   (b) $(c^r \# c^s) \# c^t = (c^r \# c^t) \# c^s$.

14. Assume we wish to convert from the 8-4-2-1 representation of decimal digits to the excess-3 representation as shown in the table at the top of page 193.
   (a) Find covers C_{y_1}, C_{y_2}, C_{y_3}, and C_{y_4} for the cubical complexes for y_1, y_2, y_3, and y_4 in terms of the input variables x_1, x_2, x_3, and x_4. Also find a cover for the cubical complex representing the "don't care" conditions.
   (b) Can you find a set Y having two variables which can be used to form simple disjoint decompositions for all the excess-3 digit conditions y_1, y_2, y_3, and y_4?

x_1	x_2	x_3	x_4	Decimal Digit	y_1	y_2	y_3	y_4
8	4	2	1					
0	0	0	0	0	0	0	1	1
0	0	0	1	1	0	1	0	0
0	0	1	0	2	0	1	0	1
0	0	1	1	3	0	1	1	0
0	1	0	0	4	0	1	1	1
0	1	0	1	5	1	0	0	0
0	1	1	0	6	1	0	0	1
0	1	1	1	7	1	0	1	0
1	0	0	0	8	1	0	1	1
1	0	0	1	9	1	1	0	0

8-4-2-1 Representation   Excess-3 Representation

(Note that in excess-3 representation by complementing each digit the 9's complement is obtained, that is $\bar{0}\,\bar{1}\,\bar{1}\,\bar{1} = 1\,0\,0\,0$ or $\bar{4} = 5$, etc.)

15. Prove that every prime implicant of a unate function is an extremal.

16. Assume that a binary adder is to be designed such that each stage of the adder has two digit position inputs a_{i+1}, b_{i+1}, and a_i, b_i, and a single carry input from the next least significant stage c_i, and has outputs for two sum digits, s_{i+1} and s_i, and one carry digit output c_{i+2} as shown in the following diagram.

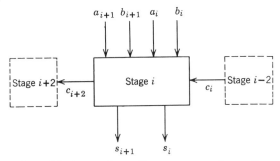

(a) Give the cubical complexes for s_{i+1}, s_i, and c_{i+2} for variables a_{i+1}, b_{i+1}, a_i, b_i, and c_i.

(b) Find minimum AND-OR-circuits for each of the three outputs s_{i+1}, s_i, and c_{i+2}.

17. Using cubical complexes find minimum covers for the following Exercises in Chapter 2: 8, 9, 12, 15(c), and 18(a).

18. Given the following covers for cubical complexes:

$$L \text{ determined by } \begin{Bmatrix} x100 \\ 1x10 \\ 0111 \end{Bmatrix},$$

$$N \text{ determined by } \begin{Bmatrix} x000 \\ x101 \\ 1011 \\ 0110 \end{Bmatrix},$$

and K determined by $L \cup N$,

(a) find the set of prime implicants $Z(K)$.

(b) find a minimum cost K-cover of L, where the cost of the cover is the sum of that of the cubes in the cover, and the cost of the various size cubes is given by the following table.

Cube Size	Cube Cost
0-cube	5
1-cube	5
2-cube	4
3-cube	3
4-cube	1

19. Assume that a prime implicant cover C is given for a cubical complex K. Develop an algorithm for converting C into a prime implicant cover for the complementary complex $\bar{K}$.

20. Given cubical complexes K_1, L_1, and N_1, where

$$K_1 \supseteq L_1,$$
$$K_1 \supseteq N_1,$$
$$N_1 = K_1 - L_1.$$

Let C_1 be a cover for K_1, D_1 be a cover for N_1, and B_1 be a cover for L_1. Given an arbitrary cube c, with the same number of coordinates as the cubes in K_1, L_1, and N_1, determine if

$$c \cap B_1 = (c \cap C_1) \# D_1$$

either by proving this to be true or by giving a counterexample.

21. In the covering problem for cubical complexes for a K-cover of L, discussed in this chapter, the cost of an r-cube having n coordinates is $n - r$. Consider a variation of the covering problem in which the cost associated with the appearance of an inverted variable is α times the cost associated with the appearance of a noninverted variable. The variables and inverted variables appear in terms of the disjunctive normal form. Let $\alpha > 1$, indicating that there is an extra cost in the AND-circuits for those inputs which use inverted variables.

(a) Define the cost function for cubes of the complex for this new cost criterion on variable appearances and give formulas for two cost criterion for a cover, where

(i) Cost C^α for a cover C is the sum of the costs of the cubes in C.

(ii) Cost C^β is the sum of the costs of the cubes in C plus β times the number of cubes in C, where $0 < \beta \leq 1$.

(b) Either

(i) Prove that the extraction algorithm can be used to obtain a minimum cost C^α cover using this new cost criterion in the algorithm, or

(ii) give an example where the extraction algorithm does not produce a minimum cost C^α cover.

(*c*) Give a cost criterion for the cubes of a cover *C* for which the following theorem would not be true, and give an example demonstrating the contradiction.

Theorem. If *C* is a minimum cost *K*-cover of *L*, then each cube of *C* is a prime implicant of complex *K*.

REFERENCE NOTATIONS

A precise formulation of switching networks using a restricted variety of gate-type elements is given by Burks and Wright in [3]. The normal form minimization problem was first studied by Quine [13, 14]. Considerable attention has since been given to this basic switching theory problem [1, 2, 5–7, 9, 10, 15–18]. The cubical complex approach given in Sections 3.3 and 3.5 through 3.9 is primarily based on the work of Roth [15–17]. A somewhat similar approach is given in [18]. The brief description in Section 3.11 can be studied further by looking at McCluskey's original paper [10], which is quite easy to read, or by referring to descriptions of this work in any of many books, for example, in [4, 11]. An "irredundant cover" of a complex has the property that if any cube is eliminated from the cover, the resulting set of cubes is no longer a cover. Minimum covers are, of course, irredundant. Irredundant covers are studied in [8] and [12]. Attempts to expand map methods to many variables are presented in [1] and [2]. In [7] Boolean functional forms are described which give a very large number of prime implicants, similar to those discussed in Table 3.10.1. In [6] the use of linear programming as an alternative to branching is examined, and in [9] a technique is given for finding minimum covers for the special case when the N_1 complex is extensive.

REFERENCES

1. Arthur, M. E., "Geometric Mapping of Switching Functions," *IRE Transactions on Electronic Computers*, Vol. EC-10, No. 4, pp. 631–637, December 1961.
2. Booth, T. M., "The Vertex-Frame Method for Obtaining Minimal Proposition-Letter Formulas," *IRE Transactions on Electronic Computers*, Vol. EC-11, No. 2, pp. 144–154, April 1962.
3. Burks, A. W. and J. B. Wright, "Theory of Logical Nets," *Proceedings of the IRE* pp. 1357–1365, October 1953.
4. Caldwell, S. H., *Switching Circuits and Logical Design*, Chapter 5, John Wiley and Sons, 1958.
5. Chu, J. T., "A Generalization of a Theorem of Quine for Simplifying Truth Functions," *IRE Transactions on Electronic Computers*, Vol. EC-10, No. 2, pp. 165–168, June 1961.
6. Cobham, A., R. Fridshal, and T. H. North, "An Application of Linear Programming to the Minimization of Boolean Functions," *Proceedings of the Second Annual Symposium on Switching Circuit Theory and Logical Design*, AIEE, pp. 3–9, September 1961.
7. Dunham, B. and R. Fridshal, "The Problem of Simplifying Logical Expressions," *Journal of Symbolic Logic*, Vol. 24, No. 1, pp. 17–19, March 1959.
8. Gazale, M. J., "Irredundant Disjunctive and Conjunctive Forms of a Boolean Function," *IBMJ*, Vol. 1, pp. 171–176, April 1957.
9. McCluskey, E. J., Jr., "Minimal Sums for Boolean Functions Having Many Unspecified Fundamental Products," *Proceedings of the Second Annual Symposium on Switching Circuit Theory and Logical Design*, AIEE, pp. 10–17, September 1961.

10. McCluskey, E. J., Jr., "Minimization of Boolean Functions," *B.S.T.J.*, Vol. 35, No. 6, pp. 1417–1444, November 1956.
11. McCluskey, E. J., Jr., and T. C. Bartee, editors, *A Survey of Switching Circuit Theory*, McGraw-Hill Book Co., New York, 1962.
12. Mott, T. H., Jr., "Determination of the Irredundant Normal Forms of a Truth Function by Iterated Consensus of the Prime Implicants," *IRE Transactions on Electronic Computers*, Vol. EC-9, No. 2, pp. 245–252, June 1960.
13. Quine, W. V., "The Problem of Simplifying Truth Functions," *American Mathematical Monthly*, Vol. LIX, No. 8, pp. 521–531, October 1952.
14. Quine, W. V., "A Way to Simplify Truth Functions," *American Mathematical Monthly*, Vol. LXII, No. 9, pp. 627–631, November 1955.
15. Roth, J. P., "Algebraic Topological Methods for the Synthesis of Switching Systems in *n*-variables," *The Institute for Advanced Study*, Princeton, New Jersey, ECP56-02, April 1956.
16. Roth, J. P., "Algebraic Topological Methods for the Synthesis of Switching Systems, I" *Transactions of the American Mathematical Society*, Vol. 88, No. 2, pp. 301–326, July, 1958.
17. Roth, J. P., "Algebraic Topological Methods in Synthesis," *Proceedings of an International Symposium on the Theory of Switching*, April 2–5, 1957, in *Annals of Computation Laboratory of Harvard University*, Vol. 29, pp. 57–73, 1959.
18. Urbano, R. H. and R. K. Mueller, "A Topological Method for the Determination of the Minimal Forms of a Boolean Function," *IRE Transactions on Electronic Computers*, Vol. EC-5, No. 3, pp. 126–132, September 1956.

4

Multiple Output and Multilevel Combinational Circuits

4.1 INTRODUCTION

In Chapter 3 we described several algorithms for determining a minimum cost cover for cubical complexes and saw how this cover corresponds to a minimum cost two-level combinational circuit with one output. Although restricting the form of combinational circuits to two-level AND-OR circuits or two-level OR-AND circuits has enabled us to give relatively precise formulations and straightforward algorithms for finding minimum cost two-level circuits, from another viewpoint this restriction may be some-what undesirable. There may be some forms of combinational circuits that use other types of decision elements, or more than two-levels, which realize the desired switching functions, where these other forms may be less costly (for example, by requiring fewer decision elements or relay contacts) than a circuit which results from a minimum cover. In this chapter we discuss techniques for designing these other forms of com-binational circuits using decision elements, and in Chapter 5 we discuss techniques which pertain to the design of more general forms of relay contact networks. In Sections 4.2 and 4.3 we show how the techniques of Chapter 3 can be extended to treat combinational circuits having more than one output, and in Sections 4.4 and 4.6 we consider several methods of obtaining circuit structures having more than two levels.

Two methods for treating multiple output problems are given. The first method transforms the problem into a single output problem, which can be treated by the methods of Chapter 3 and then reinterpreted into its multiple output form. The second method assigns designating tags to each output; by correct interpretation of these tags, in conjunction with the minimum cover techniques for each output, a minimum multiple output form is obtained.

Finally, techniques to obtain nonnormal form circuits are discussed, which factor a cover of a complex, give a decomposition of a cubical complex, and give a rather general form of logical diagram (Boolean graph) by special iterative decomposition techniques.

As we discuss these techniques it will become apparent that the techniques can become considerably more complex and that considerably less is known about the design of general multilevel circuits than that for two-level circuits. There are several reasons for this. First, it is somewhat difficult to formulate meaningful models and design criteria for multilevel combinational circuits, and second, there are often a great variety of circuit forms possible for realizing a given circuit requirement.

4.2 MULTIPLE OUTPUT MINIMIZATION—A TRANSFORMATION METHOD

In the minimization algorithms described in Chapter 3 we considered methods for finding a minimum cost cover for a cubical complex. This could then be used to obtain a minimum two-level AND-OR circuit using the n-variables as inputs and having a single output. In this section we consider methods for treating multiple output problems to be realized by AND-OR circuits. We could, of course, treat a multiple output problem having m-outputs as m separate single output problems and find m separate minimum cost AND-OR circuits. With such an approach, however, we completely overlook the possibility of using the same elements as part of a circuit for realizing more than one of the outputs, and it is essentially this feature that can create a large saving in circuitry.

To demonstrate this, consider the following problem. A circuit with three inputs x_1, x_2, and x_3 is to be designed having three outputs z_1, z_2, and z_3, where the output conditions are described, respectively, by the covers C_1, C_2, C_3 as follows:

$$C_1 = \begin{Bmatrix} x00 \\ 1x1 \end{Bmatrix},$$

$$C_2 = \begin{Bmatrix} 0x1 \\ x10 \end{Bmatrix},$$

$$C_3 = \begin{Bmatrix} x01 \\ 11x \\ 0x0 \end{Bmatrix},$$

Each one is a minimum cover and thus a circuit satisfying the design requirements could be obtained by forming a two-level AND-OR circuit for each cover. This circuit would require a total of seven 2-input AND-elements, two 2-input OR-elements, and one 3-input OR-element. Another cover for output z_3, however, is

$$C_3' = \begin{Bmatrix} 00x \\ 1x1 \\ x10 \end{Bmatrix},$$

and if this cover is used for z_3, the cube $1x1$ is seen to appear in both C_1 and C_3'; thus a single AND-element representing the cube $1x1$ can be used in both the circuit for z_1 and z_3. Similarly, a single AND-element representing cube $x10$ can be used in the z_2 and z_3 circuits. The resulting multiple output circuit is shown in Figure 4.2.1, and it requires only five AND-elements and three OR-elements.

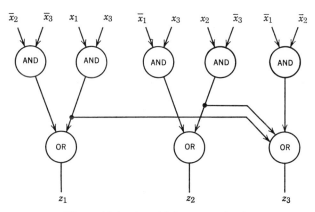

Figure 4.2.1   A multiple output circuit.

The first method we consider for these problems is due to D. E. Muller. It consists of transforming an n-input m-output problem into an $(n + m)$-input single output problem, which on minimizing the single output problem produces a simultaneous minimization of polynomials for the multiple output problem.

We assume that the circuit requirements are given in terms of Boolean functions. Assume that the multiple output problem has n-input variables and m-outputs. Each output may then be expressed as a Boolean function of n-inputs.

(4.2.1)

$$\begin{cases} z_1 = z_1(x_1, x_2, \ldots, x_n) \\ z_2 = z_2(x_1, x_2, \ldots, x_n) \\ \quad \cdot \\ \quad \cdot \\ \quad \cdot \\ z_m = z_m(x_1, x_2, \ldots, x_n). \end{cases}$$

The don't care conditions can be expressed as another function:

(4.2.2) $$g(x_1, x_2, \ldots, x_n) = 0.$$

Note that, in general, the don't care conditions could be different for each z_i function, but we consider here only the special case of a common set of don't care conditions for all the z_i.

We desire to obtain a specific type of minimum representation of (4.2.1) subject to the subsidiary don't care condition (4.2.2). This minimum representation in the case that $m = 1$ is a minimum disjunctive normal form (also called a minimum ∨-polynomial or a minimum cover when using cubical complexes). We now consider constructing the z_i out of polynomials, such that

(4.2.3) $$z_i = \bigvee_{j_i=0} M_{j_1 j_2 \cdots j_m},$$

where the $M_{j_1 j_2 \cdots j_m}$ are ∨-polynomials and $M_{j_1 j_2 \cdots j_m}$ is used in forming the function z_i if $j_i = 0$, and $M_{j_1 j_2 \cdots j_m}$ is not used in z_i if $j_i = 1$. The ∨ symbol signifies the ∨-operation between polynomials. The ∨-polynomials for the $M_{j_1 j_2 j_3}$'s of our example of Figure 4.2.1 are particularly simple. They are

$M_{000} = \phi,$ since no terms are common to all three outputs.

$M_{001} = \phi$

$M_{010} = x_1 x_3,$ since $x_1 x_3$ is used in both outputs z_1 and z_3.

$M_{011} = \bar{x}_2 \bar{x}_3,$

$M_{100} = x_2 \bar{x}_3,$

$M_{101} = \bar{x}_1 x_3,$

and

$M_{110} = \bar{x}_1 \bar{x}_2.$

By using (4.2.3), this gives

$$z_1 = M_{000} \vee M_{001} \vee M_{010} \vee M_{011} = x_1 x_3 \vee \bar{x}_2 \bar{x}_3,$$

$$z_2 = M_{000} \vee M_{001} \vee M_{100} \vee M_{101} = x_2 \bar{x}_3 \vee \bar{x}_1 x_3,$$

and

$$z_3 = M_{000} \vee M_{010} \vee M_{100} \vee M_{110} = x_1 x_3 \vee x_2 \bar{x}_3 \vee \bar{x}_1 \bar{x}_2,$$

which can be checked against the covers C_1, C_2, and C_3'. Note that in constructing the z_i circuits the $M_{j_1 j_2 \cdots j_m}$ polynomials are constructed first, and then these polynomials are interconnected to form the z_i circuits. (In our simple example, however, each $M_{j_1 j_2 \cdots j_m}$ was either empty or a single product term.)

We thus consider reduction of the switching circuits for the z_i outputs in two parts.

1. The problem of simultaneously minimizing the set of $M_{j_1 j_2 \cdots j_m}$ polynomials.

2. The problem of minimizing the connectives represented by the $\vee$ in (4.2.3).

Part (1) is solved by transforming the z_i into a single output problem, as we shall show subsequently. Note, however, that the z_i expressions as obtained from (4.2.3) will not, in general, be minimum $\vee$-polynomials. For example, some term t_1 of z_i may be included in some term t_2 in z_i, where t_1 and t_2 appeared in different $M_{j_1 j_2 \cdots j_m}$ polynomials of z_i; this we shall show later.

We now introduce m coding variables $y_1, y_2, \ldots, y_m$ and form a single function F from the z_i as follows:

$$(4.2.4) \qquad F = \bigvee_{i=1}^{n} \bar{y}_i z_i(x_1, x_2, \ldots, x_n).$$

The m imaginary inputs $y_1, y_2, \ldots, y_m$ are restricted by the conditions

$$(4.2.5) \qquad \bar{y}_i \bar{y}_j = 0 \quad \text{when} \quad i \neq j \quad \text{and} \quad y_1 y_2 \cdots y_m = 0.$$

Equations (4.2.2) and (4.2.5) can be combined into a single don't care expression,

$$(4.2.6) \qquad G = g(x_1, x_2, \ldots, x_n) \vee y_1 y_2 \cdots y_m \vee \bigvee_{i \neq j} \bar{y}_i \bar{y}_j = 0.$$

The function F can then be minimized subject to the don't care conditions G. We will see later how these can be expressed as complexes for our minimization algorithms. Let us assume now, however, that P is the minimized $\vee$-polynomial for F, where P is obtained by one of the methods discussed in Chapter 3. The y_i variables may appear either complemented or uncomplemented. From (4.2.5) it can be seen that a complemented y_i variable may be replaced by

$$(4.2.7) \qquad \bar{y}_i = y_1 y_2 \cdots y_{i-1} y_{i+1} \cdots y_m.$$

This relation can be shown as follows. Since $\bar{y}_i y_j = 0$ for $i \neq j$, we have

$$(\bar{y}_1 \vee \bar{y}_2 \vee \cdots \vee \bar{y}_{i-1} \vee \bar{y}_{i+1} \vee \cdots \vee \bar{y}_m) \bar{y}_i = 0$$

and from $y_1 y_2 \cdots y_m = 0$ we have $(y_1 y_2 \cdots y_{i-1} y_{i+1} \cdots y_m) y_i = 0$. Thus

$$\overline{(y_1 y_2 \cdots y_{i-1} y_{i+1} \cdots y_m)} \bar{y}_i \vee (y_1 y_2 \cdots y_{i-1} y_{i+1} \cdots y_m) y_i =\,\cdot 0$$

or

$$\bar{y}_i \oplus (y_1 y_2 \cdots y_{i-1} y_{i+1} \cdots y_m) = 0,$$

giving the result of Equation (4.2.7).

After replacing each $\bar{y}_i$ with (4.2.7), P may be written as

(4.2.8) $$F = P = \bigvee (y_1)_{j_1}(y_2)_{j_2} \cdots (y_m)_{j_m} M_{j_1 j_2 \cdots j_m},$$

where $M_{j_1 j_2 \cdots j_m}$ is a polynomial involving $x_1, x_2, \ldots, x_n$ and the notation $(y_i)_{j_i}$ is defined by

$$(y_i)_{j_i} = 1 \qquad \text{if} \quad j_i = 0,$$
$$(y_i)_{j_i} = y_i \qquad \text{if} \quad j_i = 1.$$

Thus $M_{j_1 j_2 \cdots j_m}$ is a polynomial derived from P by combining all terms having the same $(y_1)_{j_1}(y_2)_{j_2} \cdots (y_m)_{j_m}$ factor. Referring back to Equation (4.2.3), the $M_{j_1 j_2 \cdots j_m}$ are placed in this equation to obtain each of the output functions $z_1, z_2, \ldots, z_m$.

With this sort of formation for the $M_{j_1 j_2 \cdots j_m}$ polynomials, the following theorem holds.

Theorem 4.2.1   The $M_{j_1 j_2 \cdots j_m}$ are simultaneously minimized.

PROOF. If Equation (4.2.3) were not minimized by the foregoing procedure of defining the single function F and finding a minimum $\vee$-polynomial P for F, a simpler set of $M_{j_1 j_2 \cdots j_m}$ exists which satisfies (4.2.3). This simpler set could then be used to form F in (4.2.4). Then by expanding this form of F by (4.2.5) and (4.2.7) to eliminate all $\bar{y}_i$'s, a simpler expression of the form of (4.2.8) would be obtained. The expression for (4.2.8) was assumed minimized, however, and hence no simpler expression can exist. Thus the theorem is proved.

The type of circuit obtained from this treatment of multiple output circuits is illustrated in Figure 4.2.2.

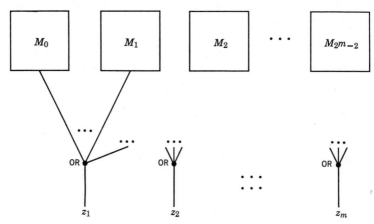

Figure 4.2.2   A multiple output circuit.

The M_j represent the $2^m - 1$ two-level AND-OR-circuits for the $M_{j_1 j_2 \cdots j_m}$ polynomials, where $j_1 j_2 \cdots j_m$ is considered as a binary number ranging from 0 to $2^m - 2$. The z_i is formed by attaching each $M_{j_1 j_2 \ldots j_m}$ with $j_i = 0$ to the z_i output node.

Since we have not considered Part (2) of the minimization problem, as yet, the cost of the OR-circuits at each output node must be considered to be zero.

The method of transforming the multiple output problem to a minimization problem of a single switching function to obtain Part (1) minimization is thus completely described. We now give a more detailed explanation of the minimization of F subject to G using cubical complexes. For this purpose we describe the following method for obtaining the cubical complex representation for F and G, using the imaginary y_i inputs to expand the number of coordinates in each cube of z_i and g from n to $n + m$ coordinates.

1. For each cube representing each z_i, m coordinates are appended to the left of the cube, such that the ith coordinate is made x, and the other $m - 1$ coordinates are made 1's. This corresponds to Equation (4.2.4), where Equation (4.2.7) is used to represent $\bar{y}_i$.

2. For each cube in g, m coordinates (each an x) are appended to the left of the cube.

3. A cover for $L(F)$ is represented by the set of all modified z_i cubes.

4. A cover for $N(G)$ is represented by all the cubes formed by (2) plus the cubes needed to represent $y_1 y_2 \cdots y_m \vee \bigvee_{i \neq j} \bar{y}_i \bar{y}_j$. The cube representing $y_1 y_2 \cdots y_m$ has the first m coordinates equal to 1 and the remaining n coordinates equal to x. $\bigvee_{i \neq j} \bar{y}_i \bar{y}_j$ requires $[m(m-1)]/2$ cubes. The coordinates of each of these cubes are all x's except those of the pair of ith and jth which are set equal to 0.

For our previous three output example defined by C_1, C_2, C_3 we obtain the following covers for $L(F)$ and $N(G)$.

$$
L(F) = \left\{
\begin{array}{l}
x11x00 \\
x111x1 \\
1x10x1 \\
1x1x10 \\
11xx01 \\
11x11x \\
11x0x0
\end{array}
\right\},
$$

$$
N(G) = \left\{
\begin{array}{l}
111xxx \\
00xxxx \\
0x0xxx \\
x00xxx
\end{array}
\right\}.
$$

With the covers for $L(F)$ and $N(G)$ thus defined, the extraction algorithm can be used to find a minimum cost cover for F. The result for F is a set of cubes each having $n + m$ coordinates. Let a cube c of the cover be represented as $(c_1, c_2, \ldots, c_m, c_{m+1}, \ldots, c_{m+n})$. The $c_1, c_2, \ldots, c_m$ in each cube determine the $M_{j_1 j_2 \cdots j_m}$ which has $(c_{m+1}, c_{m+2}, \ldots, c_{m+n})$ as a cube of its complex. This is determined as follows.

5. If $c_1 = c_2 = \cdots = c_m = x$, place $(c_{m+1}, \ldots, c_{m+n})$ into the list for $M_{00 \cdots 0}$.

6. If the c_i, $1 \le i \le m$ are a mixture of 0's and x's, place $(c_{m+1}, \ldots, c_{m+n})$ into the list for $M_{j_1 j_2 \cdots j_m}$, where

$$j_i = 0 \quad \text{if} \quad c_i = 0$$

and

$$j_i = 1 \quad \text{if} \quad c_i = x.$$

7. If the c_i, $1 \le i \le m$ are a mixture of 1's and x's, place $(c_{m+1}, \ldots, c_{m+n})$ into the list for $M_{j_1 j_2 \cdots j_m}$, where

$$j_i = 0 \quad \text{if} \quad c_i = x$$

and

$$j_i = 1 \quad \text{if} \quad c_i = 1.$$

It can be shown that the coordinates c_i, $1 \le i \le m$ for any cube will never be a mixture of 0's and 1's in the minimum form for F (see Exercise 1).

For our example a minimum cover is

$$\begin{pmatrix} 0xxx00 \\ x1x1x1 \\ x0x0x1 \\ 1xxx10 \\ xx000x \end{pmatrix}$$

and under the interpretation given in (5), (6), and (7) the $M_{j_1 j_2 j_3}$ given earlier can be obtained.

We now consider methods of computing the cost of the cubes and circuits for multiple output circuits. We have cubes with $m + n$ coordinates.

If the cost can be represented by the number of input lines to the AND-elements, let us compute the cost of a cube $(c_1, c_2, \ldots, c_{m+n})$, ignoring the $(c_1, c_2, \ldots, c_m)$ part of the cube. The minimum cost circuit under this criterion will then be the desired circuit. To be precise, we should consider a cube having only one non-x coordinate in the $(c_{m+1}, \ldots, c_{m+n})$ part of the cube to have cost 0 rather than cost 1; we ignore this special case in our discussion.

If the cost is the number of input and output lines of the AND-elements, the cost of a cube $(c_1, c_2, \ldots, c_m, c_{m+1}, \ldots, c_{m+n})$ is computed as the number of 0's and 1's in $(c_{m+1}, \ldots, c_{m+n})$ plus the number of x's in $(c_1, \ldots, c_m)$, where $(c_1, \ldots, c_m)$ is composed of only 1's and x's. Any cube $(c_1, \ldots, c_m)$ having 0's and x's is changed, replacing 0's with x's and x's with 1's. This change is allowable by the peculiar nature of the don't care conditions introduced by the multiple output coding.

A minimum cost circuit under the assumption that the cost is the number of input and output lines of the AND-elements can be found by the following procedure. The prime implicants are produced as usual. All cubes are made to have only 1's and x's in the first m coordinates. For each prime implicant having r x's in the first m coordinates, $1 \leq r \leq m, (2^r - 2)$, additional cubes are added which have the same $(c_{m+1}, \ldots, c_{m+n})$ coordinates, but have all possible combinations of $r - 1$, x's through one x in the original r coordinates having x's in $(c_1, \ldots, c_m)$. For example, if $(c_1, c_2, \ldots, c_m) = (xx x 1)$ for some prime implicant, then the six additional cubes added to the list have $(c_1, c_2, \ldots, c_m)$ coordinates $(xx11)$, $(x1x1)$, $(1xx1)$, $(1x11)$, $(11x1)$, and $(x111)$. Minimization may now be accomplished by considering this expanded list as prime implicants and not performing the $<$-operation on the $(c_1, c_2, \ldots, c_m)$ parts of the cubes. The resulting circuit will have a minimum number of input and output lines on the AND-elements. This condition is identical to having a minimum sum of inputs to the AND-elements plus inputs to the OR-elements, since each output of an AND-element is an input to an OR-element.

Unfortunately, the procedure described in the last paragraph for a minimum number of inputs to AND- and OR-elements greatly increases the number of prime implicants, making it somewhat impractical for large problems. If one is satisfied with an approximate solution, then he can minimize using a cost as only inputs to the AND-elements (that is, the number of 0's and 1's in the $(c_{m+1}, \ldots, c_{m+n})$ part of the cubes), and then later remove any redundant output lines of the AND-elements. This is discussed briefly in the next two examples.

Consider the two output example.

$$z_1 = \bar{x}_1 \vee \bar{x}_2,$$
$$z_2 = x_1 x_2 \vee \bar{x}_1 \bar{x}_2.$$

The cubical complexes for these two functions can be represented by the covers

$$K(z_1) = \begin{Bmatrix} 0x \\ x0 \end{Bmatrix},$$

$$K(z_2) = \begin{Bmatrix} 11 \\ 00 \end{Bmatrix}.$$

The functions F and G are then represented by

$$L(F) = \begin{pmatrix} x1x0 \\ x10x \\ 1x00 \\ 1x11 \end{pmatrix}$$

and

$$N(G) = \begin{pmatrix} 11xx \\ 00xx \end{pmatrix},$$

where

$$K = L \cup N.$$

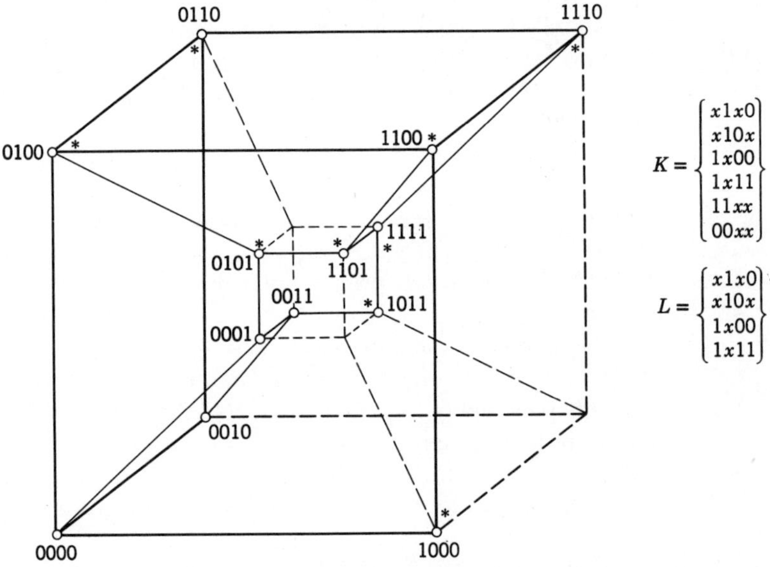

Figure 4.2.3   Cubical complex for multiple output problem.

The complexes K and L are shown on the 4-cube in Figure 4.2.3, where the vertices of L are indicated by an *. By using the *-algorithm the set of prime implicants Z is found to be

$$Z = \begin{cases} xx00 \\ 0xx0 \\ 0x0x \\ 00xx \\ x1x0 \\ x10x \\ x011 \\ 1x11 \\ 11xx \end{cases}.$$

A minimum K-cover of L is then

$$C = \begin{cases} xx00 \\ x1x0 \\ x10x \\ 1x11 \end{cases}.$$

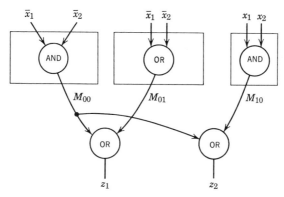

Figure 4.2.4   Multiple output circuit.

By decoding the first two coordinates to get M_{00}, M_{01}, and M_{10}, we obtain

$$M_{00} = \{00\},$$

$$M_{01} = \begin{cases} x0 \\ 0x \end{cases},$$

$$M_{10} = \{11\}.$$

This gives z_1 and z_2 as

$$z_1 = M_{00} \lor M_{01} = \bar{x}_1\bar{x}_2 \lor \bar{x}_1 \lor \bar{x}_2,$$

$$z_2 = M_{00} \lor M_{10} = \bar{x}_1\bar{x}_2 \lor x_1x_2.$$

A resulting circuit configuration is shown in Figure 4.2.4. It was mentioned earlier that certain terms in M polynomials may be redundant for certain outputs. This example demonstrates this. Here the term $\bar{x}_1\bar{x}_2$ is included in $\bar{x}_1$ and thus $M_{00} = \bar{x}_1\bar{x}_2$ is redundant for z_1 and could be eliminated, giving the equations

$$z_1 = \bar{x}_1 \lor \bar{x}_2$$

and

$$z_2 = x_1x_2 \lor \bar{x}_1\bar{x}_2.$$

The resulting circuit is shown in Figure 4.2.5.

As seen in this example, the transformation from a multiple output to a single output problem creates many extra prime implicants. It also produces a problem in which no prime implicants are extremals, thus forcing us to use branching at the outset when looking for a minimum cover. It can be readily verified, however, that the prime implicants occur

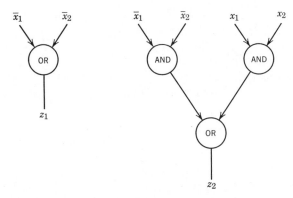

Figure 4.2.5   Multiple output circuit with redundant term removed from z_1.

in pairs for those prime implicants in which the first m coordinates are not all x's and which are not elements of the complex formed by G. Thus, if $c = (c_1, \ldots, c_m, c_{m+1}, \ldots, c_{m+n})$ is a prime implicant not included in G and if c_i for $1 \leq i \leq m$ is a mixture of 0's and x's, there is another prime implicant $d = (d_1, \ldots, d_m, d_{m+1}, \ldots, d_{m+n})$, where (c, d) form a pair, in which $d_{m+i} = c_{m+i}$ for $1 \leq i \leq n$ and $d_j = 1$ if $c_j = x$ and $d_j = x$ if $c_j = 0$ for $1 \leq j \leq m$. In our example these pairs are $[(0xx0), (x1x0)]$; $[(0x0x), (x10x)]$; and $[(x011), (1x11)]$. For finding minimum M polynomials, one prime implicant from each of these pairs may be eliminated from Z, since this cannot affect the form of the M polynomials. This reduction in the number of prime implicants which need to be considered simplifies materially the problem of finding a minimum cover for F because both fewer cubes have to be considered and some extremals may also occur after this reduction.

The example just considered does not show how AND-elements can be used for more than one output; that is, the circuit of Figure 4.2.5 could have been obtained simply by treating each output separately as a single output problem. Our three output example, however, of Figure 4.2.1 did show the sharing of several AND-elements with several outputs. Our next example shows more clearly how the sharing of circuitry occurs in the M polynomials. Let us consider a three output problem of three inputs in which

$$L_1 = \left\{ \begin{matrix} 1x1 \\ x00 \end{matrix} \right\},$$

$$L_2 = \left\{ \begin{matrix} 01x \\ x00 \\ 10x \end{matrix} \right\},$$

and

$$L_3 = \left\{ \begin{matrix} 01x \\ xx1 \end{matrix} \right\},$$

define the three outputs z_1, z_2, z_3, respectively (there are no don't cares for the problem). Using the multiple output coding, we get F and G as

$$F = \left\{ \begin{matrix} x111x1 \\ x11x00 \\ 1x101x \\ 1x1x00 \\ 1x110x \\ 11x01x \\ 11xxx1 \end{matrix} \right\}$$

and

$$G = \left\{ \begin{matrix} 111xxx \\ 00xxxx \\ 0x0xxx \\ x00xxx \end{matrix} \right\},$$

Using the extraction algorithm on F (after considerable calculation), a minimum cover C can be obtained, where

$$C = \left\{ \begin{matrix} xx0xx1 \\ 1xx01x \\ xx1x00 \\ xx110x \\ x1x1x1 \end{matrix} \right\}.$$

This is then decoded to give the M polynomials as sets of cubes

$$M_{000} = \phi,$$
$$M_{001} = \{x00, 10x\},$$
$$M_{010} = \{1x1\},$$
$$M_{011} = \phi,$$
$$M_{100} = \{01x\},$$
$$M_{101} = \phi,$$
$$M_{110} = \{xx1\}.$$

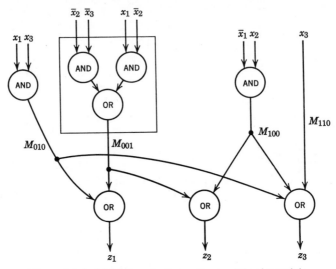

Figure 4.2.6   Multiple output circuit using M-polynomials.

The resulting circuit is shown in Figure 4.2.6.   A three-level circuit, AND followed by OR followed by OR, is seen to result from this formulation of the problem, where the M polynomials, by Theorem 4.2.1, have been simultaneously minimized.   We can modify slightly this circuit by using only one level of AND-elements which directly feed into the output OR-elements.   Thus the circuit of Figure 4.2.6 is modified to that of Figure 4.2.7.   Notice here that the $x_1\bar{x}_2$ leading into the OR-element for z_1, which is shown dotted, can be eliminated since $x_1\bar{x}_2 = x_1\bar{x}_2\bar{x}_3 \vee x_1\bar{x}_2 x_3$, where the

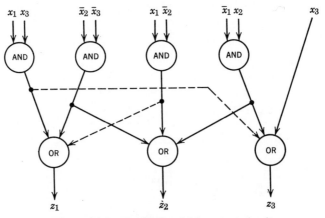

Figure 4.2.7   Modified multiple output circuit.

term $x_1\bar{x}_2\bar{x}_3$ will make the $\bar{x}_2\bar{x}_3$ AND-element have an output of 1 so that $z_1 = 1$, and the term $x_1\bar{x}_2x_3$ will make the x_1x_3 AND-element have an output of 1 so that $z_1 = 1$. Similarly, the x_1x_3 leading into the OR-circuit for z_3 can be eliminated, since $x_3 \vee x_1x_3 = x_3$. With this simplification we see that the number of input arrowheads in the circuit is fifteen. If a separate minimum AND-OR circuit were made for each output, the total number of input arrowheads would be nineteen as can be checked by the reader.

4.3 MULTIPLE OUTPUT MINIMIZATION—A TAG METHOD

We now wish to discuss a second method to obtain multiple output circuits. This method uses m tag variables for the cubes, one for each output, similar to the first method, but here we do not directly transform the problem into a single output problem nor do we introduce extra don't care cubes by the tag process. Let the output functions $z_1, z_2, \ldots, z_m$ be represented by a set of complexes $L_1, L_2, \ldots, L_m$, respectively, where each of these complexes is described by a cover of its respective complex, and let N be the don't care complex, also represented by a set of cubes. We assume that the don't care conditions are alike for each output, as defined by N. With only minor complications we can consider different don't care complexes for each output, but we shall not discuss this here.

The first step of this method is to form all intersection complexes from the L's, that is, $L_1 \cap L_2$, $L_1 \cap L_3$, $\ldots$, $L_{m-1} \cap L_m$, $L_1 \cap L_2 \cap L_3$, $\ldots$, $L_1 \cap L_2 \cap \cdots \cap L_m$. This is done by intersecting the respective covers to get a cover of the desired intersection complex. We now tag each cube with m coordinates on the left such that the tag entries are $x11 \cdots 1$ for cubes in L_1, $1x11 \cdots 1$ for cubes in L_2, $x1x1 \cdots 1$ for cubes in $L_1 \cap L_3$, and $xx \cdots x$ for cubes in $L_1 \cap L_2 \cap \cdots \cap L_m$. That is, if L_j appears for the symbolic representation of the complex for the cube being considered, then the jth coordinate in the tag is set equal to x; otherwise it is set equal to 1. Cubes in N are assigned a tag $xx \cdots x$. We may interpret the ith tag coordinate x as meaning that the cube is a cube of the K_i complex; and the ith tag coordinate of 1 as meaning that the cube is *not* a cube of the K_i complex, where $K_i = L_i \cup N$.

The next step is to consider the set of all the tagged cubes as a cover of a complex K and to determine the prime implicants Z of K, say, by the *-algorithm. A subset of Z is called the set of *multiple output prime implicants*, denoted by $(Z)^m$, where $(Z)^m$ are all cubes of Z except those having all 1's in the first m coordinates. Of course, we are not interested in cubes having all 1's in the first m coordinates because under our interpretation they are not associated with any of the outputs.

Before continuing, let us find the multiple output prime implicants for the last example of Section 4.2. The covers for the respective complexes are

$$L_1 = \begin{Bmatrix} 1x1 \\ x00 \end{Bmatrix},$$

$$L_2 = \begin{Bmatrix} 01x \\ x00 \\ 10x \end{Bmatrix},$$

$$L_3 = \begin{Bmatrix} 01x \\ xx1 \end{Bmatrix},$$

$$N = \phi$$

$$L_1 \cap L_2 = \begin{Bmatrix} 101 \\ x00 \\ 100 \end{Bmatrix} \quad \text{or} \quad \begin{Bmatrix} 10x \\ x00 \end{Bmatrix},$$

$$L_1 \cap L_3 = \{1x1\},$$

$$L_2 \cap L_3 = \begin{Bmatrix} 01x \\ 101 \end{Bmatrix},$$

$$L_1 \cap L_2 \cap L_3 = \{101\}.$$

Tagging each of these cubes gives us the set of cubes

$$K = \begin{Bmatrix} x11\ 1x1 \\ x11\ x00 \\ 1x1\ 01x \\ 1x1\ x00 \\ 1x1\ 10x \\ 11x\ 01x \\ 11x\ xx1 \\ xx1\ 10x \\ xx1\ x00 \\ x1x\ 1x1 \\ 1xx\ 01x \\ 1xx\ 101 \\ xxx\ 101 \end{Bmatrix}$$

which on eliminating any cube that is included in some other cube of the set gives

$$K = \begin{Bmatrix} 11x\ xx1 \\ xx1\ 10x \\ xx1\ x00 \\ x1x\ 1x1 \\ 1xx\ 01x \\ xxx\ 101 \end{Bmatrix}.$$

The *-algorithm applied to this set of cubes gives the set of prime implicants

$$Z = \begin{cases} 11x\,xx1 \\ xx1\ 10x \\ xx1\ x00 \\ x1x\ 1x1 \\ 1xx\ 01x \\ xxx\ 101 \\ 1x1\ 0x0 \\ 111\ x0x \\ 111\ 0xx \end{cases}.$$

This calculation should be verified by the reader.

To get $(Z)^m$ the cubes $111\,x0x$ and $111\,0xx$ are deleted from Z because a cube with all 1's in the first m coordinates cannot be associated with any output, as will be seen upon subsequent decoding of the tag coordinates. The set of multiple output prime implicants $(Z)^m$ for this problem is

$$(Z)^m = \begin{cases} 11x\,xx1 \\ xx1\ 10x \\ xx1\ x00 \\ x1x\ 1x1 \\ 1xx\ 01x \\ xxx\ 101 \\ 1x1\ 0x0 \end{cases}.$$

Similar to the single output minimization problem discussed in Chapter 3, we wish to pick a subset of cubes of $(Z)^m$ which will cover each complex $L_1, L_2, \ldots, L_m$ and will be of minimum cost by some cost criterion. The cost criteria for multiple output problems, however, are slightly more complex than either C^a or C^b defined in Chapter 3. Note that in the first method for treating multiple output circuits discussed in Section 4.2, we did not have to consider new cost criteria in detail since we transformed the problem into a single output problem. With the tag method, however, it is necessary to introduce two new cost criteria: (1) one that gives a count of the total number of appearances of input letters (either complemented or not) that arise from different cubes; call it C^α since it is similar to C^a of Chapter 3, and (2) one that counts the letters plus the number of different terms; call this C^β since it is similar to C^b of Chapter 3.

Let $c = (c_1, c_2, \ldots, c_m, c_{m+1}, \ldots, c_{m+n})$ be a cube in $(Z)^m$. We call $(c_1, c_2, \ldots, c_m)$ the *output cube* of c and $(c_{m+1}, \ldots, c_{m+n})$ the *input cube* of c. A subset C_i of $(Z)^m$ is called a *K-cover of L_i* if for each 0-cube ω of L_i there exists a cube c of C_i such that the ith coordinate in the output cube of c is an x and such that ω of L_i is covered by the input cube of c. A subset C of $(Z)^m$ is called a *K-cover of* $L_1, L_2, \ldots, L_m$ if it is a K-cover of L_i for each i, $1 \leq i \leq m$.

If the cost of a cube $c^i \in (Z)^m$, where $c^i = (c_1, c_2, \ldots, c_m, c_{m+1}, \ldots, c_{m+n})$ is the number of non-x coordinates in the input cube $(c_{m+1}, \ldots, c_{m+n})$ of c^i, and we denote this cost by $|c^i|$, then the cost C^α of C, a subset of cubes of $(Z)^m$, is defined as

$$C^\alpha = \sum_{i=1}^{p} |c^i|, \qquad \text{where } C = \{c^1, c^2, \ldots, c^p\}.$$

The cost C^β is defined as

$$C^\beta = C^\alpha + p, \qquad \text{where } C = \{c^1, c^2, \ldots, c^p\},$$

or

$$C^\beta = \sum_{i=1}^{p} (|c^i| + 1).$$

We now discuss a method of finding a *minimum K-cover of* $L_1, L_2, \ldots, L_m$, that is, a K-cover of $L_1, L_2, \ldots, L_m$ of minimum cost when either C^α or C^β is used as a cost criterion. This method results from some simple modifications of the extraction-algorithm for obtaining a minimum K-cover of L.

Note that we should verify first that a minimum cost cover exists which is a subset of cubes of $(Z)^m$. This follows from the following theorem.

Theorem 4.3.1 If $C = \{c^1, c^2, \ldots, c^p\}$ is a minimum K-cover of $L_1, L_2, \ldots, L_m$, then there exists a $C' = \{c^{1'}, c^{2'}, \ldots, c^{p'}\}$ such that $C' \subseteq (Z)^m$ and $c^i \subseteq c^{i'}$, $1 \leq i \leq p$, where C' is also a minimum K-cover of $L_1, L_2, \ldots, L_m$.

This theorem can be seen as follows. Suppose some cube $c^i \in C$ were not an element of $(Z)^m$ where $c^i = (c_1, c_2, \ldots, c_m, c_{m+1}, \ldots, c_{m+n})$. By the tag method $(c_1, \ldots, c_m)$ has coordinate entries of only 1's and x's, and at least one x must appear in one of these coordinates. From the $*$-algorithm each prime implicant of complex K_i must appear in $(Z)^m$ with an x in the ith coordinate; similarly, for prime implicants of the intersection complexes. Thus $(c_{m+1}, \ldots, c_{m+n})$ is included in some input cube $(c'_{m+1}, \ldots, c'_{m+n})$ of $(Z)^m$, where $c^{i'} = (c'_1, \ldots, c'_m, c'_{m+1}, \ldots, c'_{m+n})$ and $c'_j = x$ when $c_j = x$ for $1 \leq j \leq m$. Now since C is a minimum cover, it follows that $(c_{m+1}, \ldots, c_{m+n}) = (c'_{m+1}, \ldots, c'_{m+n})$; otherwise replacing c^i with $c^{i'}$ in C would give a cover having less cost. Thus $c^{i'}$ differs from c^i only in that $c^{i'}$ may have x's in some of the first m coordinates where c has 1's. Thus $c^i \subseteq c^{i'}$, and c^i and $c^{i'}$ have equal cost.

Replacing each such c^i in C with the corresponding $c^{i'}$ of $(Z)^m$ gives the minimum cover $C' \subseteq (Z)^m$ of the theorem.

Since the cost criteria C^α and C^β are calculated using only the input cubes of the cover, but not the output cubes, Theorem 4.3.1 is weaker than its counterpart, Theorem 3.5.1, for single output minimization. Note that for this multiple output theorem not all minimum cost covers are subsets of $(Z)^m$, as was true for Theorem 3.5.1, but rather we have the weaker result that minimum covers exist which are subsets of $(Z)^m$.

Given $(Z)^m$ we wish to define and determine extremals for the L_1, $L_2, \ldots, L_m$ complexes. Let c' be an input cube of c, where $c \in (Z)^m$ and c has an x in coordinate i. Then the set of all such c' is denoted by $(Z)_i^m$. The cube c is called an L_i-*extremal* if $c' \in (Z)_i^m$ is an L_i-extremal of $(Z)_i^m$. From the results of the extraction algorithm it follows directly that c' must be used in any minimum K-cover of L_i; thus c must be used in any minimum K-cover of $L_1, L_2, \ldots, L_m$ which is a subset of $(Z)^m$. The cube c also covers certain vertices in $L_j, j \neq i$ if the jth coordinate of c equals x. Let $E_1(L_i, K)$ denote the set of L_i-extremals; then $\bigcup_{i=1}^{m} E_1(L_i, K)$ is the set of all extremals. A next set of complexes $L_1^2, L_2^2, \ldots, L_m^2$ can then be formed, where L_i^2 is the subcomplex of L_i not covered by cubes of $\bigcup_{i=1}^{m} E_1(L_i, K)$. These complexes $L_1^2, L_2^2, \ldots,$ L_m^2 are those parts of each L_i which still remain to be covered by cubes of $(Z)^m$.

The set $(Z)^m$ may be reduced by eliminating certain cubes from $(Z)^m$ which are no longer needed to form a minimum cover for $L_1^2, L_2^2, \ldots,$ L_m^2. For this elimination we introduce a slightly generalized $<$-operation. If $a, b \in (Z)^m$, we say that $a < b$ if (1) b has an x in coordinate positions of the output cube whenever a has an x, (2) cost $b \leq$ cost a, and (3) b covers as much (or more) of each $L_1^2, L_2^2, \ldots, L_m^2$ as is covered by a. Then a subset $(Z_2)^m$ of $(Z)^m$ is formed as follows:

$$(Z_2)^m = (Z)^m - \bigcup_{i=1}^{m} E_1(L_i, K) - \left\{ \begin{array}{l} \text{all non-} \\ \text{maximal cubes} \\ \text{under the} \\ <\text{-operation} \end{array} \right\} - \left\{ \begin{array}{l} \text{all cubes not} \\ \text{covering any} \\ \text{vertices of} \\ L_1^2, L_2^2, \ldots, L_m^2 \end{array} \right\}.$$

With $(Z_2)^m$ and $L_1^2, L_2^2, \ldots, L_m^2$ a set of "second-order extremals" may be found as previously, and this process may be iterated. Finally, a branching operation may be required to obtain a minimum K-cover of $L_1, L_2, \ldots, L_m$. Since this is analogous to the branching operation described in Chapter 3, we shall not discuss it in detail here. Rather, let us complete our example. We have

$$(Z)^m = \begin{Bmatrix} 11x\,xx1 \\ xx1\,10x \\ xx1\,x00 \\ x1x\,1x1 \\ 1xx\,01x \\ xxx\,101 \\ 1x1\,0x0 \end{Bmatrix} ,$$

$$(Z)_1{}^m = \begin{Bmatrix} 10x \\ x00 \\ 1x1 \\ 101 \end{Bmatrix} , \qquad L_1 = \begin{Bmatrix} 1x1 \\ x00 \end{Bmatrix} .$$

Thus $xx1\,x00$ is an L_1-extremal since vertex 000 of L_1 is covered only by $x00$ of $(Z)_1{}^m$. Similarly, $x1x\,1x1$ is an L_1-extremal since vertex 111 of L_1 is covered only by $1x1$ of $(Z)_1{}^m$. Thus $E_1(L_1, K) = \begin{Bmatrix} xx1\,x00 \\ x1x\,1x1 \end{Bmatrix} .$

$$(Z)_2{}^m = \begin{Bmatrix} 10x \\ x00 \\ 01x \\ 101 \\ 0x0 \end{Bmatrix} , \qquad L_2 = \begin{Bmatrix} 01x \\ x00 \\ 10x \end{Bmatrix} .$$

Thus $1xx\,01x$ is an L_2-extremal since vertex 011 of L_2 is covered only by $01x$ of $(Z)_2{}^m$.

$$(Z)_3{}^m = \begin{Bmatrix} xx1 \\ 1x1 \\ 01x \\ 101 \end{Bmatrix} , \qquad L_3 = \begin{Bmatrix} 01x \\ xx1 \end{Bmatrix} .$$

Thus $11x\,xx1$ is an L_3-extremal since vertex 001 of L_3 is covered only by $xx1$ of $(Z)_3{}^m$, and $1xx\,01x$ is an L_3-extremal since vertex 010 of L_3 is covered only by $01x$ of $(Z)_3{}^m$.
Thus

$$\bigcup_{i=1}^{3} E_1(L_i, K) = \begin{Bmatrix} xx1\,x00 \\ x1x\,1x1 \\ 1xx\,01x \\ 11x\,xx1 \end{Bmatrix}$$

and

$$L_1{}^2 = \phi,$$
$$L_2{}^2 = 101,$$
$$L_3{}^2 = \phi.$$

Since $L_2{}^2$ is the only nonempty complex remaining, we can form $(Z_2)^m$ as

$$(Z_2)^m = \begin{Bmatrix} xx1\ 10x \\ xxx\ 101 \end{Bmatrix}.$$

Now neither of these cubes is a second-order extremal, so branching would give us the result that $xx1\ 10x$ should be used for a minimum cover. Thus a minimum K-cover of L_1, L_2, L_3 is

$$C = \begin{Bmatrix} xx1\ x00 \\ x1x\ 1x1 \\ 1xx\ 01x \\ 11x\ xx1 \\ xx1\ 10x \end{Bmatrix}.$$

Using cost C^α, the cost of this cover is 9 and $C^\beta = 9 + 5 = 14$. A circuit represented by this cover is shown in Figure 4.3.1.

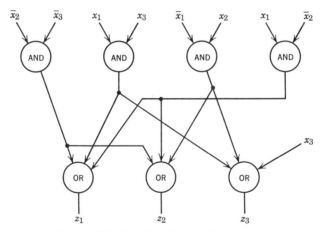

Figure 4.3.1 Circuit realization for cover C.

In this circuit we have interpreted an x in the ith coordinate of the output cube of each cube of the cover to mean that the circuit for the corresponding input cube fed the OR-element for output z_i.

In Section 4.2 we described how a minimum cost cover could be obtained under the assumption that the cost is the number of input plus output lines of the AND-elements. This cost was shown to be the sum of costs of cubes, where the cost of a cube c is the number of x's in the output cube of c plus the number of 0's and 1's in the input cube of C. This cost directly counts the number of lines in the circuit, as desired, except under the special case that an input cube has only one non-x entry. As before, we ignore this special case.

The same process as described previously can be used in the tag method. The set $(Z)^m$ can be expanded into a larger set of cubes and the minimization procedure applied to this new set of cubes, using the new cost criterion, to obtain this type of minimum cost cover. For our example we would obtain an expanded $(Z)^m$ of

$$(Z)^{m'} = \begin{cases} 11x\,xx1 \\ x11\,10x \\ 1x1\,10x \\ xx1\,10x \\ x11\,x00 \\ 1x1\,x00 \\ xx1\,x00 \\ x11\,1x1 \\ 11x\,1x1 \\ x1x\,1x1 \\ 1x1\,01x \\ 11x\,01x \\ 1xx\,01x \\ x11\,101 \\ 1x1\,101 \\ 11x\,101 \\ xx1\,101 \\ x1x\,101 \\ 1xx\,101 \\ xxx\,101 \\ 1x1\,0x0 \end{cases}.$$

Now since cubes $xx1\,x00$, $x1x\,1x1$, and $1xx\,01x$ have each been expanded into more than one cube, they are no longer extremals; therefore the only extremal is $11x\,xx1$. Thus L_3 is the only complex which is reduced in the next iteration. By the large number of cubes in $(Z)^{m'}$ and by the fact that fewer extremals occur, as shown by this example, more branching is required to obtain this type of minimum cover; we shall not pursue this further here.

An approximate minimum cover may be obtained by modifying the minimum cost C^α cover by eliminating x entries in the output cubes of C whenever possible. As was seen previously in our example, cube $xx1\,10x$ is not required for output Z_1 and cube $x1x\,1x1$ is not required for output

z_3, thus an approximate minimum cover C' for our example is

$$C' = \begin{cases} xx1\ x00 \\ x11\ 1x1 \\ 1xx\ 01x \\ 11x\ xx1 \\ 1x1\ 10x \end{cases} \begin{array}{l} = 2 + 2 = 4 \\ = 1 + 2 = 3 \\ = 2 + 2 = 4 \\ = 1 + 1 = 2 \\ = 1 + 2 = 3 \end{array}$$

$$\text{Cost of cover} \qquad 16$$

The resulting circuit is the circuit shown in Figure 4.2.7, with dotted lines removed, where the total number of input lines to elements is 15. This differs by 1 from the cost 16 of the cover since no AND-element is required for cube $11x\,xx1$.

Some comments and comparisons of the two multiple output minimization techniques and their variations, which we have introduced in this and the previous section, are now in order. Either technique will produce a minimum cost two-level AND-OR circuit under the assumption that the circuit cost is the number of inputs to AND-elements. In addition, by the described expansion of the prime implicants, either technique will provide a minimum cost result if the cost is assumed to be the number of inputs to both the AND-elements and OR-elements. The nature of the expansion technique for the prime implicants, however, forces extensive branching to obtain a minimum solution. Thus approximate minimization techniques were discussed briefly for this type of cost criterion. The method of transformation discussed in Section 4.2 creates a cubical complex for which it is relatively difficult to obtain a minimum cover because the extra don't care conditions introduced by the transformation create a set of prime implicants that require considerable branching to obtain a solution. Some of these difficulties were seen to be alleviated by removing certain prime implicants (where pairs of cubes were formed) from Z before the extraction of extremals.

The main advantage of the transformation method is that the algorithms for single output problems can be thereby applied directly to multiple output problems. On the other hand, the tag method is superior to the transformation in that no extra don't care conditions and resulting branching are introduced. The number of cubes in the complex K is increased over the sum of cubes in the complexes for each separate output, however, by the need to form all the intersection complexes. Obviously, these intersections are important, because it is through these intersections that cubes which apply to more than one output are obtained. Since the tag coordinates are treated somewhat differently from the coordinates of the true variables of the problem, this approach, unlike the transformation method, is not simply a new application for the algorithms discussed in

Chapter 3. Finally, both methods are rather cumbersome to perform by hand computation for large problems simply because of the large number of cubes. Rather, their value for anything other than small problems is in providing precise algorithms for programs on digital computers.

4.4 FACTORING A COVER OF A CUBICAL COMPLEX

A cover of a cubical complex has been shown to represent a two-level AND-OR logical circuit in which each cube corresponds to a single AND-element. If several AND-elements have a set of common inputs, that is, inputs from the same variables or inverted variables, then by first forming the subcircuit for these cubes with the common inputs deleted and then connecting the output of this subcircuit and the common inputs to a single AND-element, the output of the AND-element will also give the same output function as before, but it will use less circuitry and also require fewer inputs to single AND- or OR-elements. This technique for changing the form of the cover is called *factoring*. Note that it corresponds to the usual concept of factorization of a Boolean function, and the techniques to be described could be considered either in cubical complex notation or Boolean function notation. Some simple examples of factoring are given in Figure 4.4.1.

A special format for representing the factoring of a cover is shown in Figure 4.4.1. We have introduced rows having 1's, 0's, and μ's. These entries are called *masking cubes*, where the 1 and 0 entries indicate the common coordinates in the cubes directly following the masking cube and the uncommon coordinates appear under the μ part of the masking cube. In Figure 4.4.1a the first coordinate is common to both cubes, giving a masking cube $1\mu\mu$. In Figure 4.4.1b the first two coordinates are common to all cubes, giving $10\mu\mu\mu\mu$, and the third coordinate is common to all cubes except $100xx00$; therefore under the μ's of the masking cube $10\mu\mu\mu\mu$ we enter $0xx00$ and then another masking cube $1\mu\mu\mu$ to indicate a second level of factoring. Similarly, we obtain a third level of factoring in this example indicated by $\mu0\mu1$. In Figure 4.4.1c we find that no coordinate is common to all cubes; but $00\mu\mu\mu$ can be a masking cube for the first three cubes, and $11\mu\mu\mu$ can be a masking cube for the last three cubes. With such splitting of the cover into two parts, the terminal element in the resulting circuit is seen to be an OR-element rather than an AND-element as in Figure 4.4.1a and b.

With the introduction of the masking cubes, we can develop an algorithm for factoring. This shall be the main concern of this section; but before doing this let us consider the purposes and limitations of obtaining a factored form.

The principal purpose of factoring, which concerns us here, is the resulting reduction in the circuitry required to realize the logical circuit for the cubical complex and the reduction of the number of inputs required for a single AND- or OR-element in the logical circuit. We have many limitations in this process, however. First, we have no assurance of obtaining a minimum factored form for the complex if we start from some given cover of the complex. Some other cover may indeed allow a factoring that results in a simpler logical circuit, and in particular it may not even be a minimum cover. Thus we can say only that the factoring produces a reduction in the cost of the logical circuit as compared with that formed by the cover with which we start. We are also considering only factoring in terms of AND-elements. Factorings using different connectives would possibly lead to simpler circuits which cannot be considered in this method. These more generalized factorings can be viewed as decompositions; therefore we discuss decomposition techniques further in Section 4.6.

We now describe a factoring algorithm using the masking cubes. Assume we are given an original cover C_0. Define a *coordinate masking product* as given in Table 4.4.1.

Table 4.4.1 Coordinate Masking Product

$\mathfrak{m}$	0	1	x	μ
0	0	μ	μ	μ
1	μ	1	μ	μ
x	μ	μ	μ	μ
μ	μ	μ	μ	μ

Then the *masking product* between a pair of cubes $c^r = (c_1, c_2, \ldots, c_n)$ and $c^s = (d_1, d_2, \ldots, d_n)$ is denoted by $c^r \mathfrak{m} c^s$, and equals $c^r \mathfrak{m} c^s = (c_1 \mathfrak{m} d_1, c_2 \mathfrak{m} d_2, \ldots, c_n \mathfrak{m} d_n)$. Note that c^r and c^s may be either the cubes from the cubical complex or masking cubes, since the coordinate masking product is defined for 0, 1, x, and μ. The masking cube $c_\mathfrak{m} = c^r \mathfrak{m} c^s$ has coordinates of 0's, 1's, and μ's. We call the coordinates which are μ's the *μ-part* of $c_\mathfrak{m}$ and the other coordinates the *λ-part* of $c_\mathfrak{m}$.

For the factoring algorithm start with cover C_0. Form $C_0 \mathfrak{m} C_0$, that is, $c^r \mathfrak{m} c^s$ for all pairs of cubes (c^r, c^s) in C_0. Pick a resulting masking cube which has the maximum number of coordinates in its λ-part, calling this $c_{\mathfrak{m}1}$.

Let $\hat{M}_1$ be the set of cubes of C_0 in which $c^i \mathfrak{m} c^j = c_{\mathfrak{m}1}$; and let M_1 be the cubes of $\hat{M}_1$ with the λ-part coordinates of $c_{\mathfrak{m}1}$ deleted. Let $\hat{C}_1 = C_0 - \hat{M}_1$ and $C_1 = \hat{C}_1 \cup c_{\mathfrak{m}1}$. We can now represent C_0 in factored

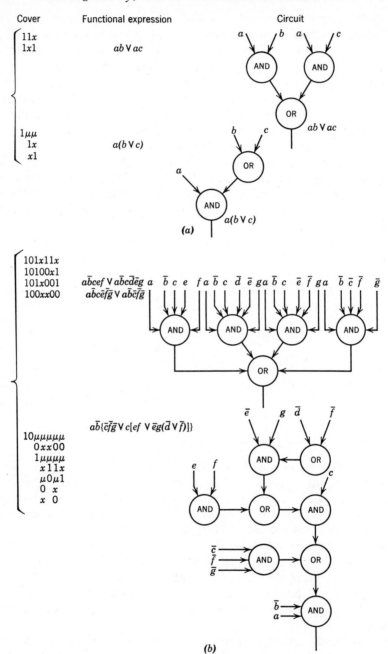

Cover   Functional expression   Circuit

$ab \lor ac$

$a(b \lor c)$

(a)

$a\bar{b}cef \lor a\bar{b}c\bar{d}\bar{e}g$
$a\bar{b}c\bar{e}fg \lor a\bar{b}\bar{c}\bar{f}\bar{g}$

$a\bar{b}\{\bar{c}\bar{f}\bar{g} \lor c[ef \lor \bar{e}g(\bar{d} \lor \bar{f})]\}$

(b)

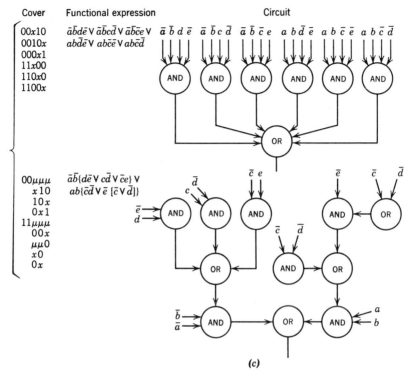

Figure 4.4.1 Factoring examples.

form as the following list:

$$\begin{pmatrix} C_1 \\ c_{m1} \\ M_1 \end{pmatrix},$$

where the coordinates of M_1 appear directly below the respective μ-part coordinates of c_{m1}. Now we take C_1, form $C_1 \text{ m } C_1$, and again pick the masking with the maximum number of λ-part coordinates. This is called c_{m2}. We keep repeating this process until all masking cubes have an empty λ-part, and the resulting representation of C_0 gives the factored form. The following two examples illustrate the factoring algorithm. Let

$$C_0 = \begin{matrix} & x_1 & x_2 & x_3 & x_4 & x_5 & x_6 & x_7 \\ & \begin{pmatrix} 1 & 1 & 0 & 0 & 0 & 1 & x \\ 1 & 1 & 0 & 0 & 1 & x & 0 \\ 1 & 1 & 0 & 0 & x & 0 & 1 \\ 0 & 0 & 0 & 0 & 1 & 1 & 1 \\ 1 & 0 & 1 & 1 & 1 & 1 & x \end{pmatrix} & \begin{matrix} a \\ b \\ c \\ d \\ e \end{matrix} \end{matrix},$$

where we denote the cubes by a through e.

Then

$$a \mathbin{m} b = 1100\mu\mu\mu,$$
$$a \mathbin{m} c = 1100\mu\mu\mu,$$
$$a \mathbin{m} d = \mu\mu00\mu1\mu,$$
$$a \mathbin{m} e = 1\mu\mu\mu\mu1\mu,$$
$$b \mathbin{m} c = 1100\mu\mu\mu,$$
$$b \mathbin{m} d = \mu\mu001\mu\mu,$$
$$b \mathbin{m} e = 1\mu\mu\mu1\mu\mu,$$
$$c \mathbin{m} d = \mu\mu00\mu\mu1,$$
$$c \mathbin{m} e = 1\mu\mu\mu\mu\mu\mu,$$
$$d \mathbin{m} e = \mu0\mu\mu11\mu,$$

We then pick $c_{m1} = 1100\mu\mu\mu$, $\hat{M}_1 = \{a, b, c\}$ and $C_1 = \{d, e, c_{m1}\}$. This gives the first factored representation of C_0 as

$$
\left\{
\begin{matrix}
\left(\begin{matrix} 0000111 \\ 101111x \\ 1100\mu\mu\mu \end{matrix}\right) & \begin{matrix} d \\ e \\ c_{m1}. \end{matrix} \\[2ex]
\left.\begin{matrix} 01x \\ 1x0 \\ x01 \end{matrix}\right\} & M_1
\end{matrix}
\right.
$$

From previous masking products we have

$$d \mathbin{m} e = \mu0\mu\mu11\mu,$$

and we form

$$c_{m1} \mathbin{m} d = \mu\mu00\mu\mu\mu,$$
$$c_{m1} \mathbin{m} e = 1\mu\mu\mu\mu\mu\mu.$$

Thus $c_{m2} = d \mathbin{m} e = \mu0\mu\mu11\mu$, giving the new factored form of C_0 as

$$
\left\{
\begin{bmatrix}
\mu0\mu\mu11\mu \\
0\ \ 00\ \ \ 1 \\
1\ \ 11\ \ \ x \\
1100\mu\mu\mu \\
01x \\
1x0 \\
x01
\end{bmatrix}
\right\}.
$$

Since $C_2 = (c_{m1}, c_{m2})$ and $c_{m1} \mathbin{m} c_{m2} = \mu\mu\mu\mu\mu\mu\mu$, no further factoring is possible. The resultant circuit is shown in Figure 4.4.2.

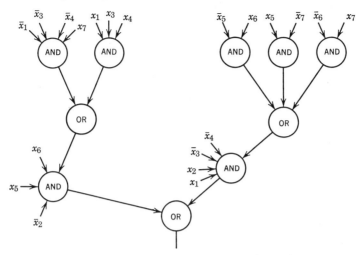

Figure 4.4.2   Logical circuit formed from a factored cover.

For the second example consider the problem of Figure 4.4.1*b*.

$$C_0 = \begin{cases} 101x11x & a \\ 10100x1 & b \\ 101x001 & c \\ 100xx00 & d \end{cases}$$

$$a \sqcap b = 101\mu\mu\mu\mu,$$
$$a \sqcap c = 101\mu\mu\mu\mu,$$
$$a \sqcap d = 10\mu\mu\mu\mu\mu,$$
$$b \sqcap c = 101\mu0\mu1,$$
$$b \sqcap d = 10\mu\mu\mu\mu\mu,$$
$$c \sqcap d = 10\mu\mu\mu0\mu,$$
$$c_{m1} = b \sqcap c = 101\mu0\mu1,$$
$$\hat{M}_1 = b, c,$$
$$C_1 = \{a, d, c_{m1}\}.$$

The factored form of C_0 at this point is

$$\begin{cases} 101x11x & a \\ 100xx00 & d \\ 101\mu0\mu1 & c_{m1} \end{cases} C_1 \\ \begin{matrix} 0\ x & b \\ x\ 0 & c \end{matrix} \Big\} M_1 \end{cases} .$$

Forming $C_1 \, \mathfrak{m} \, C_1$, we obtain

$$a \, \mathfrak{m} \, d = 10\mu\mu\mu\mu,$$
$$a \, \mathfrak{m} \, c_{m1} = 101\mu\mu\mu\mu,$$
$$d \, \mathfrak{m} \, c_{m1} = 10\mu\mu\mu\mu\mu.$$

Thus $c_{m2} = a \, \mathfrak{m} \, c_{m1} = 101\mu\mu\mu\mu$, giving the factored form

$$\left\{ \begin{pmatrix} 100xx00 \\ 101\mu\mu\mu\mu \\ x11x \\ \mu0\mu1 \\ 0 \ x \\ x \ 0 \end{pmatrix} \begin{matrix} d \\ c_{m2} \\ a \\ c_{m1} \\ b \\ c \end{matrix} \right.$$

We continue with $C_2 = (d, c_{m2})$.

$$d \, \mathfrak{m}.c_{m2} = 10\mu\mu\mu\mu\mu,$$

giving the final factored form

$$\left\{ \begin{bmatrix} 10\mu\mu\mu\mu \\ 0xx00 \\ 1\mu\mu\mu\mu \\ x11x \\ \mu0\mu1 \\ 0 \ x \\ x \ 0 \end{bmatrix} \right\}.$$

This is the factored form given in Figure 4.4.1b, where the derived logical circuit is also shown.

We would now like to define a cost for the factored cover and compare it with the cost C^b of a cover to determine when a factoring reduces the cost. Let us consider the ith step in the factoring algorithm, where $\hat{M}_i$ is the unfactored cover. Then the cost C^b of $\hat{M}_i$ is

$$C^b = \{\textstyle\sum \text{cost of cubes}\} + \text{number of cubes}.$$

Let k be the number of cubes in $\hat{M}_i$, let c_{mi} have p coordinates in the λ-part, and let $d(C^a)$ be cost C^a for M_i (that is, the sum of 0's and 1's in the μ-parts of the cubes of $\hat{M}_i$). Then

$$C^b = d(C^a) + kp + k$$

since kp equals the number of non-x entries in the λ-parts of the cubes in $\hat{M}_i$ and k equals the number of cubes in $\hat{M}_i$.

Now the cost C^f of the factored cover is defined as

$$C^f = d(C^a) + k + (p+1) + \delta,$$

where $d(C^a)$ correspond to the number of inputs to AND-elements for M_i, k represents the number of inputs to the OR-elements for the M_i cubes, $p + 1$ represents the number of inputs to the terminal AND-element for the p coordinates of the λ-part plus the one input from the μ-part OR-element, and δ equals 0 or 1, depending on the iterative form of the factorization. A $\delta = 1$ corresponds to the output of the $\begin{Bmatrix} C_{mi} \\ M_i \end{Bmatrix}$ part of the circuit being required as an input to some OR-element, such as in Figure 4.4.1c.

With this cost, when is $C^f \leq C^b$?

$$d(C^a) + k + p + 1 + \delta \leq d(C^a) + kp + k$$

if $p + 1 + \delta \leq kp$.

From the factoring algorithm, k and p are integers where $k \geq 2$ and $p \geq 1$. Thus, when $\delta = 0$, $p + 1 \leq kp$ for all possible values of k and p, showing that the factored cost is always less than or equal to the cost of the original cover. In addition, the costs are equal only when $p = 1$ and $k = 2$, that is, when the largest λ-part of $\hat{M}_i$ is exactly one coordinate and only one pair of cubes has this λ-part. This case is shown in Figure 4.4.3 where each circuit has eight arrowheads.

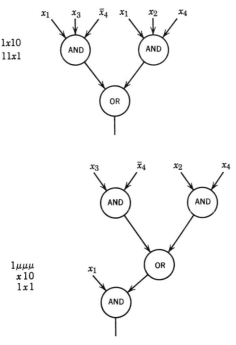

Figure 4.4.3   Example of equal factored and nonfactored costs.

For $\delta = 1$, the $C^f > C^b$ when $k = 2$ and $p = 1$; $C^f = C^b$ when $k = p = 2$ or when $k = 3, p = 1$; and $C^f < C^b$ for $k > 2, p > 2$, or $k > 3, p = 1$.

For $\delta = 1$ an example of when the factored cost C^f is greater than the unfactored cost C^b is

$$C_0 = \begin{Bmatrix} 101 \\ 110 \\ 011 \\ 000 \end{Bmatrix} \qquad \text{where } C^b = 16,$$

which gives a factored form

$$\begin{Bmatrix} 1\mu\mu \\ 01 \\ 10 \\ 0\mu\mu \\ 00 \\ 11 \end{Bmatrix},$$

where $C^f = 18$.

As seen by the inequalities, however, the factored cost C^f is usually less than the unfactored cost C^b. To illustrate that the given algorithm, where c_{mi} is chosen on the basis of the largest λ-part, does not necessarily yield a lowest cost factored form, consider the cover

$$C_0 = \begin{Bmatrix} 00011x \\ 000x01 \\ 1xxx01 \\ xx1x01 \\ x1x110 \\ 1xx11x \end{Bmatrix}.$$

A factored form obtained by the algorithm is

$$\begin{Bmatrix} \mu\mu\mu11\,1\mu \\ x1x\quad 0 \\ 1xx\quad x \\ \mu\mu\mu\mu01 \\ 1xxx \\ xx1x \\ 000\mu\mu\mu \\ 11x \\ x01 \end{Bmatrix},$$

which results in a circuit having twenty-five arrowheads.

Another factored form, not obtainable from the algorithm, is

$$
\left\{
\begin{array}{l}
\mu\mu\mu\mu 01 \\
000x \\
1xxx \\
xx1x \\
\mu\mu\mu 11\mu \\
000 \quad x \\
x1x \quad 0 \\
1xx \quad x
\end{array}
\right\},
$$

which gives a circuit with twenty-two arrowheads.

The reader may attempt to derive a criterion for picking each c_{mi} which gives a best-cost factored-form for any starting cover C_0. The advantage of the method described is that it provides an extremely simple and straight-forward method of forming multilevel AND-OR circuits from a given cover and the conditions for cost reduction at each step are known.

4.5 ANALYSIS OF LOGICAL DIAGRAMS HAVING NO FEEDBACK

In Section 3.2 we found that logical diagrams having no feedback were a special type of combinational circuit. In this section we give a systematic method for obtaining expressions for the outputs of such logical diagrams in terms of the inputs to the logical diagram. In Section 3.2 we showed that a Boolean function could be obtained for an output by writing a set of equations for the decision elements and then substituting back into the output equation until only inputs remained. Here we formalize this process; in particular, we express each output as a cover of a cubical complex, where the coordinates of the complex correspond to the inputs of the logical diagram.

Because the analysis of switching circuits is usually much simpler than synthesis, not much attention is given to analysis. Nevertheless, analysis helps in the understanding of switching circuits. In particular, this section helps in the understanding of switching circuit structures represented by decompositions which are discussed in the next section. In addition, techniques for the location and diagnosis of faults in switching circuit operation are often based on suitable and efficient analysis techniques.

We consider first a special type of logical diagram called a Boolean tree. A *Boolean tree* is a logical diagram satisfying the following additional properties.

1. No feedback,
2. Exactly one output,
3. An output of a decision element can be attached to *only one* input of a decision element.
4. Each input branch is connected to only a single input of a decision element.

Thus a Boolean tree has exactly one output branch, and each internal branch connects the output of some decision element to exactly one input of some other decision element. An example of a Boolean tree is shown in Figure 4.5.1.

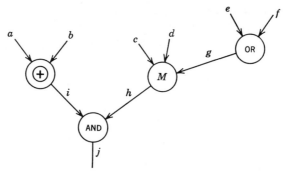

Figure 4.5.1   A Boolean tree.

The input branches for this Boolean tree are labeled *a, b, c, d, e,* and *f.* The internal branches are labeled *g, h,* and *i,* and the output branch is labeled *j.*

To obtain a cover of the cubical complex represented by a Boolean tree, we may start with the output branch, having a value of 1, and progress backward through the internal branches to express the conditions which cause the output to equal 1. At each step we must express the output of some decision element being equal to 1 (or 0) in terms of its inputs. Each decision element is defined by some logical connective (such as AND, $\oplus$, OR, Majority) and can be easily expressed as a cover with its inputs as coordinates for the case when the output equals 1 (called the "on-array") or when the output equals 0 (called the "off-array"). In our example $j = 1$ for $h = 1$ and $i = 1$, giving an on array of $\{11\}$, and $j = 0$ for all other conditions, giving an off array $\left\{\begin{matrix} 0x \\ x0 \end{matrix}\right\}$. Thus, for each decision element, the switching operation performed by the element may be described by an on-array or an off-array. The iterative operation for obtaining a cover for the cubical complex defined by the Boolean tree of Figure 4.5.1 is illustrated in Figure 4.5.2.

	a	b	c	d	e	f	g	h	i	j	
α										1	$\Pi_j^{\&hi}$
β								1	1		Π_h^{Mcdg}
γ			1	1			x		1		
			1	x			1		1		
			x	1			1		1		
δ	1	0	1	1			x				$\Pi_i^{\oplus ab}$
	0	1	1	1			x				
	1	0	1	x			1				
	0	1	1	x			1				
	1	0	x	1			1				
	0	1	x	1			1				
ε	1	0	1	1	x	x					Π_g^{Vef}
	0	1	1	1	x	x					
	1	0	1	x	1	x					
	1	0	1	x	x	1					
	0	1	1	x	1	x					
	0	1	1	x	x	1					
	1	0	x	1	1	x					
	1	0	x	1	x	1					
	0	1	x	1	1	x					
	0	1	x	1	x	1					

Figure 4.5.2   Table of injection operators for Boolean tree of Figure 4.5.1.

We start with the condition that the output branch *j* equals 1. This is depicted as row α of Figure 4.5.2. We consider the change from row α to row β as a transformation $\Pi_j^{\&hi}$ from branch *j* to conditions on branches *h* and *i* of the AND-element, which will make branch *j* equal 1. This type of transformation is called an *injection operator*. In going from row β to the set of rows γ, we replace the *h* branch entry with the inputs *c*, *d*, and *g* to the majority element, that is, we perform the injection operator Π_h^{Mcdg}. Since the *h* entry equals 1, we must substitute the on array of the majority

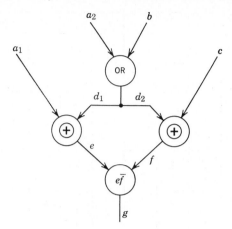

Figure 4.5.3   A Boolean graph.

	a_1	a_2	b	c	d_1	d_2	e	f	g	
α									1	Π_g^{ef}
β							1	0		
γ				1		1	1			$\Pi_f^{\oplus d_2 c}$
				0		0	1			
δ	1			1	0	1				$\Pi_e^{\oplus d_1 a_1}$
	0			1	1	1				
	1			0	0	0				
	0			0	1	0				
	0			1	1					Consistency $d_1 = d_2$
	1			0	0					
ε	0	1	x	1						$\Pi_d^{\vee a_2 b}$
	0	x	1	1						
	1	0	0	0						
		0	1	1						Consistency $a_1 = a_2$

Figure 4.5.4   Table showing the injection and consistency operations for the Boolean graph of Figure 4.5.3.

element, which is

$$\begin{Bmatrix} 11x \\ 1x1 \\ x11 \end{Bmatrix},$$

for the h entry of 1. As yet the i entry, for internal branch i, has not been eliminated by an injection operator; thus the 1 in entry i of row β must be brought down to γ, repeating this 1 in each row of γ. Proceeding from γ to δ rows is done as before, but now because γ has more than one row, each row (or cube) of γ must be treated by the injection operator $\Pi_i^{\oplus ab}$ to eliminate entry i from the row. The on array for $\oplus$ is $\begin{Bmatrix} 01 \\ 10 \end{Bmatrix}$, so each row of γ is transformed into a pair of rows in δ as indicated. Finally $\Pi_g^{\vee ef}$ eliminates the last internal branch from the representation, and the rows of ϵ, when interpreted as cubes, form a cover of the complex, where a, b, c, d, e, and f represent the inputs.

Since a Boolean tree has no feedback, an iterative sequence of injection operations, first eliminating the output entry and then progressively eliminating internal branch entries, will eventually yield a cover in terms of the input variables. Because each internal branch connects to exactly one decision element input, the number of injection operator steps required is one plus the number of internal branches. In our example we needed four injection operations, one each for output branch j, and internal branches h, i, and g. Furthermore, since each input branch connects to only one decision element input, the cover will contain only one coordinate for each input.

A logical diagram which has no feedback, but is not restricted by properties (2), (3), and (4) of the Boolean tree, is called a *Boolean graph*. We now consider Boolean graphs with exactly one output. The analysis of Boolean graphs is similar to that of Boolean trees, except that certain internal branches or input branches may appear as more than one column at certain steps when applying the injection operator. To have a complete analysis we must have each input appearing as only one column. Furthermore, during the analysis an internal branch that feeds more than one decision element will first appear as more than one column, but it can be reduced to one column for simplification. This process of reducing multiple columns to a single column is called *reduction by consistency*. We describe this process in the next example.

Consider the Boolean graph in Figure 4.5.3. In this example input a is used twice, labeled a_1 and a_2, and the output of the OR-element is used twice, d_1 and d_2, as inputs to both $\oplus$-elements. Each use of a branch is given a different label, this being convenient for the injection operations as shown in Figure 4.5.4.

The consistency operation is performed on internal branch d (labeled d_1 and d_2) in set δ. The consistency operation eliminates any cubes in which $d_1 \neq d_2$. Note that since d_1 and d_2 are the same branch, their values must be equal. In the injection operation, however, the cubes 1101 and 0010 occur in which $d_1 \neq d_2$. Since this condition is not possible, we eliminate it by the consistency operation. The same process is followed for a_1 and

	a_1	a_2	b	c	d_1	d_2	e	f	g	
α									1	$\Pi_g^{\overline{ef}}$
β								1	0	
γ				1	1	1				$\Pi_f^{\oplus d_2 c}$
				0	0	1				
δ		1	x	1			1			$\Pi_{d_2}^{\vee a_2 b}$
		x	1	1			1			
		0	0	0			1			
ϵ	0	1	x	1	1					$\Pi_e^{\oplus d_1 a_1}$
	1	1	x	1	0					
	0	x	1	1	1					
	1	x	1	1	0					
	0	0	0	0	1					
	1	0	0	0	0					Consistency $a_2 = a_1$
	1		x	1	0					
	0		1	1	1					
	1		1	1	0					
	0		0	0	1					
η	1	0	0	1						$\Pi_{d_1}^{\vee a_2 b}$
	0	x	1	1						
	0	1	1	1						
	0	1	0	0						Consistency $a_2 = a_1$
	0		1	1						

Figure 4.5.5 Removal of coordinate d_2 before consistency operation with d_1.

a_2, for the input a, thereby eliminating any conditions where $a_1 \neq a_2$. Thus cubes $01x1$ and 1000 are eliminated, and cube $0x11$ has subcube 0111 eliminated, leaving 0011. This then gives a cover with coordinates a, b, c of $\{011\}$.

In connection with the consistency operation, it is important first to obtain a cover with the repeated internal branches (as d_1, d_2 in δ) and then perform the consistency operation before these branches are removed by succeeding injection operations. Figure 4.5.5 shows how d_2 can be

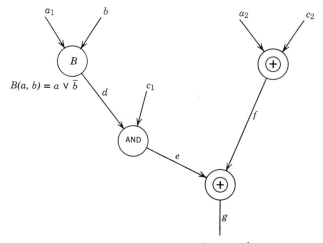

Figure 4.5.6   Another Boolean graph.

eliminated before d_1 is obtained by following the injection operation $\Pi_f^{\oplus d_2 c}$ with the injection operation $\Pi_{d_2}^{\vee a_2 b}$.

Note that if d_2 is eliminated when transforming from set γ to δ in Figure 4.5.5, no apparent difficulty arises. At a later step, however, when performing $\Pi_{d_1}^{\vee a_2 b}$ in transforming from set ϵ to η, we already have entries in column b. Additional rules on the injection operation can be specified to perform such an injection, but this can be avoided if the analysis is done in the correct order, as in Figure 4.5.4. Furthermore, if the order of Figure 4.5.5 is followed, then consistency on a_1 and a_2 is required twice, rather than once as in Figure 4.5.4.

It is easily seen that a consistency operation for any set of repetitions for an internal or input branch is only required once, if the appropriate order of injection operations is performed.

A second example of analysis of a Boolean graph is shown in Figures 4.5.6 and 4.5.7, where both inputs a and c are used twice.

If a Boolean graph has more than one output, it can be analyzed by

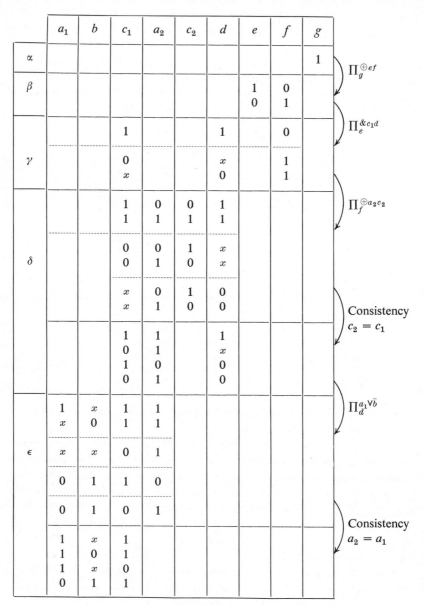

Figure 4.5.7   Analysis for Boolean graph of Figure 4.5.6.

performing a separate analysis for each output, as in the previous two examples. An example for such an analysis is shown in Figure 4.5.8.

The analyses for outputs i and j are shown in Figures 4.5.9 and 4.5.10, (pages 238 and 239) respectively.

From Figures 4.5.8, 4.5.9, and 4.5.10 note that output i is independent of input c, and output j is independent of input a; thus for the respective

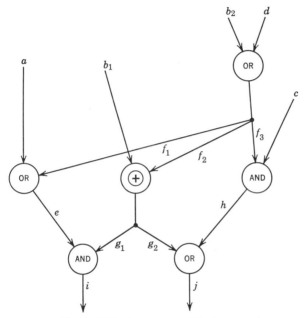

Figure 4.5.8   A two-output Boolean graph.

covers, x's are placed in these input coordinate positions. In this particular example, input a is redundant since in the cover for output i, cube $10x1$ is included in cube $x0x1$ so that $\{x0x1\}$ is also a cover for output i, therefore both outputs i and j are independent of input a.

4.6   DECOMPOSITION TECHNIQUES FOR BOOLEAN GRAPH SYNTHESIS

In Section 4.5 we considered the analysis of Boolean graphs and described a method of obtaining a cover for the cubical complex defined by a Boolean graph. A Boolean graph is the most general type of logical diagram having no feedback. The restrictions to two-level circuits or

	a	b_1	c	d	b_2	e	f_1	f_2	f_3	g_1	g_2	h	i	
α													1	$\prod_i^{\&e,g_1}$
β				1				1						$\prod_{g_1}^{\oplus b_1, f_2}$
γ		1			1	0								$\prod_e^{\vee a f_1}$
		0			1	1								
δ	1	1					x	0						
	x	1					1	0						
	1	0					x	1						Consistency
	x	0					1	1						$f_2 = f_1$
	1	1					0							
	1	0					1							
	x	0					1							
ϵ	1	1		0	0									$\prod_{f_1}^{\vee b_2, d}$
	1	0		1	x									
	1	0		x	1									
	x	0		1	x									Consistency
	x	0		x	1									$b_2 = b_1$
	1	0		1										
	x	0		1										

$$\text{Cover} \begin{pmatrix} 1 & 0 & x & 1 \\ x & 0 & x & 1 \end{pmatrix}$$

Figure 4.5.9   Analysis for output i of Figure 4.5.8.

using only AND- and OR-elements that were required in all circuit design techniques so far considered are not required for Boolean graphs. Rather, as we consider the problem of synthesis for single output Boolean graphs we shall discuss techniques for obtaining a Boolean graph under certain *design specifications*. We shall assume that the specifications for the value of the circuit output are given as covers C_0 and C_1 of cubical complexes P and L where L represents those input conditions for which the output must equal 1 (that is, the care conditions), and P represents all input conditions for which the output must equal 0. (The don't care conditions

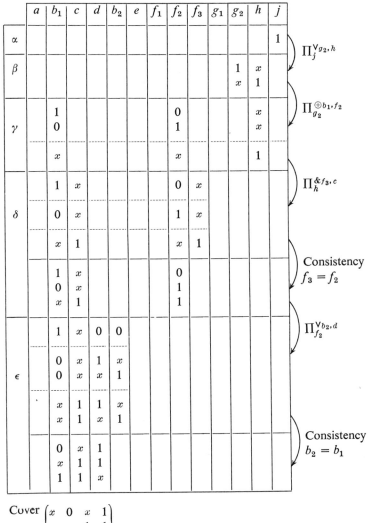

	a	b_1	c	d	b_2	e	f_1	f_2	f_3	g_1	g_2	h	j	
α													1	$\Pi_j^{\vee g_2,\,h}$
β											1	x		
											x	1		
γ		1						0			x			$\Pi_{g_2}^{\oplus b_1,\,f_2}$
		0						1			x			
		x						x				1		
δ		1	x					0	x					$\Pi_h^{\& f_3,\,c}$
		0	x					1	x					
		x	1					x	1					
		1	x					0						Consistency $f_3 = f_2$
		0	x					1						
		x	1					1						
ε		1	x	0	0									$\Pi_{f_2}^{\vee b_2,\,d}$
		0	x	1	x									
		0	x	x	1									
		x	1	1	x									
		x	1	x	1									
		0	x	1										Consistency $b_2 = b_1$
		x	1	1										
		1	1	x										

$$\text{Cover} \begin{cases} x & 0 & x & 1 \\ x & x & 1 & 1 \\ x & 1 & 1 & x \end{cases}$$

Figure 4.5.10   Analysis for output *j* of Figure 4.5.8.

are thus those that do not appear in $L \cup P$ and in our previous notation complex $K = Z_2{}^n \,\#\, P$.)

The synthesis of a Boolean graph may thus be viewed as an inverse of analysis, since we wish to start with covers and obtain a Boolean graph, whereas in analysis we start with a Boolean graph and obtain a cover of a complex. There are also other design specifications in synthesis, however, and thus synthesis is not precisely an inverse of the analysis process. In synthesis we also assume that the types of decision elements which may be used are specified by a set of decision elements D, and that associated with each decision element of D is a positive cost for the element. (We shall assume that the cost of each element is given as a positive integer.)

A Boolean graph B is said to *satisfy the design specifications* if each decision element of B is an element of the set D, and if the cubical complex R represented by B is such that

$$L \subseteq R \subseteq Z_2{}^n \mathbin{\#} P$$

for the design specifications L and P, where $Z_2{}^n$ is the complex for the complete n-dimensional unit cube.

We define the *cost* of B as the sum of the costs of the decision elements of B. Thus B is said to be of *minimum cost* for some design specifications if B satisfies the design specifications and no other Boolean graph which satisfies the design specifications has a cost less than that of B.

For a practical design problem, the set of decision elements D would be those primitive logical elements available to the logical designer in the type of technology he is using; and the cost of each element could represent the actual monetary cost for the circuit, its associated wiring, and installation.

We now discuss how functional decomposition is related to Boolean graphs. In Section 2.14 we considered two special types of functional decomposition of switching functions: simple disjoint decomposition and simple nondisjoint decomposition. Each of these types was seen to represent a logical diagram (in particular, a Boolean graph) having two decision elements. More generally, a decomposition of a switching function $f(x_1, x_2, \ldots, x_n)$ is defined as follows.

Definition 4.6.1 A *decomposition* of a switching function $f(x_1, x_2, \ldots, x_n)$ is a sequence of functions

$$\alpha_1(Y^1, Z^1), \alpha_2(Y^2, Z^2), \ldots, \alpha_m(Y^m, Z^m),$$

where

1. $Z^j \subseteq \{x_1, x_2, \ldots, x_n\}$ $1 \leq j \leq m$,
2. $Y^j \subseteq \{\alpha_1, \ldots, \alpha_{j-1}\}$ $1 \leq j \leq m$,
3. For every $(x_1', x_2', \ldots, x_n')$, $x_j' = 0$ or 1, for which $f(x_1', x_2', \ldots, x_n')$ is defined, α_m is defined and equal to f.

In this definition, the α_j functions may have a range with more than two elements, that is, the α_j in general need not be switching functions. We shall be particularly interested here, however, in the case where all

α_j are switching functions, and unless otherwise stated we shall henceforth assume the α_j to be switching functions.

For the simple disjoint decomposition

$$f(x_1, x_2, \ldots, x_n) = \phi_2[\phi_1(y_1, y_2, \ldots, y_s), z_1, z_2, \ldots, z_{n-s}],$$

we have $m = 2$, $Y^2 = \phi_1 = \alpha_1$, and

$$Z^2 = \{z_1, z_2, \ldots, z_{n-s}\}, \qquad \alpha_2 = \phi_2,$$
$$Z^1 = \{y_1, y_2, \ldots, y_s\}, \quad \text{and} \qquad Y^1 \text{ is empty.}$$

The variables $(x_1, x_2, \ldots, x_n)$ are called the *independent variables* and the α_j, $1 \leq j \leq m$ are called the *dependent variables* of the decomposition.

Note that in Definition 4.6.1 the switching functions may either be partial or complete switching functions where part 3 of the definition requires that α_m is equal to f for any combination of 0's and 1's of the variables for which f is defined. If f is a complete switching function in the independent variables, α_m is also a complete switching function in the independent variables, and by part 3, $\alpha_m = f$. If, however, $f(x_1, x_2, \ldots, x_n)$ is partial, α_m may either be partial or complete in the independent variables, but α_m must be equal to f when f is defined. In this case we call α_m an *extension* of f and denote this by $f(x_1, x_2, \ldots, x_n) \leq \alpha_m(x_1, x_2, \ldots, x_n)$.

For a switching function, f is represented by cubical complexes P and L. If $P \cup L = Z_2{}^n$, then f is complete; otherwise f is partial. If $P \cup L \neq Z_2{}^n$ and the function α_m is represented by complexes A_1 for α_m defined equal to 1 and A_0 for α_m defined equal to 0, then α_m being an extension of f means that

$$A_1 \supseteq L, \qquad A_0 \supseteq P.$$

Note that $A_0 \cap A_1 = \phi$ for α_m to be a switching function.

From the previous section, it is readily seen that any single output Boolean graph corresponds to a decomposition of the complete switching function represented by the graph. The sequence of injection operators used in the analysis corresponds to the sequence of α_j switching functions. For example, in Figure 4.5.3 we have the decomposition

$$\alpha_4(Y^4, Z^4) = \alpha_2\bar{\alpha}_3,$$

where

$$Y^4 = \{\alpha_3, \alpha_2\},$$
$$Z^4 = \phi.$$

Here α_4 corresponds to the output decision element, and thus α_4 corresponds to the $\Pi_g^{e\bar{f}}$ injection operator. Continuing with this example, we obtain

$$\alpha_3(Y^3, Z^3) = c \oplus \alpha_1,$$

where

$$Y^3 = \{\alpha_1\},$$

$$Y^3 = \{c_3\},$$

$$\alpha_2(Y^2, Z^2) = a \oplus \alpha_1,$$

where

$$Y^2 = \{\alpha_1\},$$

$$Z^2 = \{a\},$$

and

$$\alpha_1(Y^1, Z^1) = a \vee b,$$

where

$$Y^1 = \phi,$$

$$Z^1 = \{a, b\}.$$

Similarly, any decomposition of a switching function, in which each α_j is a complete switching function, corresponds directly to a Boolean graph, which is readily constructed through the decomposition, where each α_j corresponds to a decision element of the Boolean graph.

If a decomposition of a switching function has some α_j which are partial, then completing these α_j by arbitrary extensions of α_j yields an associated Boolean graph for the decomposition.

Thus for synthesis of Boolean graphs it suffices to find a decomposition of the switching function that satisfies the design specifications and also gives a Boolean graph of minimum cost or near minimum cost.

In Section 2.14, Theorems 2.14.1 and 2.14.2 gave conditions for which nontrivial simple disjoint and nondisjoint decompositions of a switching function exist, and we discussed a method for finding them. Here we consider two additional existence questions for simple disjoint decompositions.

1. Given a function γ, does there exist a simple disjoint decomposition for the given switching function $f(x_1, x_2, \ldots, x_n) \leq \alpha_2(\alpha_1(Y), Z)$ where $\alpha_1 = \gamma$?

2. Given a function δ, does there exist a disjoint decomposition $f(x_1, \ldots, x_n) \leq \alpha_2(\alpha_1(Y), Z)$ such that $\alpha_2 = \delta$?

For synthesis we are interested in knowing the answer to these questions, for example, when γ and δ are functions realized by a single decision element of the set D of decision elements.

Note that Y and Z are subsets of the set of independent variables $\{x_1, x_2, \ldots, x_n\}$ where $Y \cap Z = \phi$, and Y and Z equal the sets $\{y_1, y_2, \ldots, y_s\}$ and $\{z_1, z_2, \ldots, z_{n-s}\}$, respectively, of the notation used in Theorem 2.14.1. There are 2^s different possible combinations of values which the variables $y_1 \times y_2 \times \cdots \times y_s$ of Y can assume, and we label these combinations $y^0, y^1, y^2, \ldots, y^{2^s-1}$, where $y^0 = (0, 0, \ldots, 0)$ etc. We denote this set of 2^s combinations by y. Similarly, we label the 2^{n-s} combinations of values for $z_1 \times z_2 \times \cdots \times z_{n-s}$ of Z by $z^0, z^1, z^2, \ldots$.

Definition 4.6.2 Two elements y^j and y^k are said to be *compatible for* $f(Y, Z)$, (denoted by $y^j \sim y^k$ for f) if for all z^i such that $f(y^j, z^i)$ and $f(y^k, z^i)$ are both defined, then $f(y^j, z^i) = f(y^k, z^i)$. Otherwise y^j and y^k are called *incompatible* for f, denoted by $y^j \nsim y^k$ for f.

With these definitions, the answer to question (1) is given in the next theorem.

Theorem 4.6.1 For given functions $f(Y, Z)$ and $\alpha_1(Y)$, there exists a function α_2 such that $f(Y, Z) \leq \alpha_2(\alpha_1(Y), Z)$ if and only if

(i) $\alpha_1(y^j) = \alpha_1(y^k)$ implies that $y^j \sim y^k$ for f, or equivalently
(ii) $y^j \nsim y^k$ for f implies that $\alpha_1(y^j) \neq \alpha_1(y^k)$.

PROOF. Suppose (i) holds. Then for each $z^i, f(y^j, z^i) = f(y^k, z^i)$ if both are defined, and since f is a switching function, $f(y^j, z^i) = f(y^k, z^i) = a$, where a equals 0 or 1. Then the function α_2 can be defined by $\alpha_2(\alpha_1(y^j), z^i) = \alpha_2(\alpha_1(y^k), z^i) = a$ for each z^i for which $f((y^j, z^i)$ and $f(y^k, z^i)$ are defined. It follows then that $f(Y, Z) \leq \alpha_2(\alpha_1(Y), Z)$. Conversely, suppose (i) does not hold. Then for some y^j and y^k, $\alpha_1(y^j) = \alpha_1(y^k)$ and there exists a z^i such that both $f(y^j, z^i)$ and $f(y^k, z^i)$ are defined, but $f(y^j, z^i) \neq f(y^k, z^i)$. Then $\alpha_2(\alpha_1(y^j), z^i)$ and $\alpha_2(\alpha_1(y^k), z^i)$ must not be equal if $f(Y, z) \leq \alpha_2(\alpha_1(Y), z)$; however, no such α_2 can be defined since $\alpha_1(y^j) = (\alpha_1(y^k)$. Thus the theorem is proved.

Note that nowhere in the proof of this theorem did we use the fact that α_1 or α_2 were required to be switching functions. Thus α_1 may indeed have a range of more than two elements. We shall be interested in this case in the next theorem as well as later in the section.

If the conditions of Theorem 4.6.1 hold, then there is a unique function α_2, which is called the *image* of the decomposition, such that if $f(Y, Z) \leq \alpha_2(\alpha_1(Y), Z)$ and if $f(Y, Z) \leq \alpha_2'(\alpha_1(Y), Z)$, then α_2' is an extension of α_2 (that is, $\alpha_2 \leq \alpha_2'$).

Corollary 1 Let $k(y; f)$ be the smallest number of sets into which the set y can be partitioned such that any two elements in the same set of the partition are compatible for f, then any decomposition of the form $f(Y, Z) \leq \alpha_2(\alpha_1(Y), Z)$ is such that α_1 has at least $k(y; f)$ elements in its range, and there exists a decomposition such that α_1 has exactly $k(y; f)$ elements in its range.

Note that this corollary is a generalization of Theorem 2.14.1. For this theorem we require α_1 to be a switching function, and thus $k = 2$. This $k = 2$ is reflected in Theorem 2.14.1 in the conditions that the non-constant columns of the Karnaugh map be either equal to some column vector A or the negation of A.

For question (2) we consider the case where $\delta = \alpha_2$ is a complete function and we want to determine if there exists an α_1 such that $f(Y, Z) \leq \alpha_2(\alpha_1(Y), Z_1)$.

Theorem 4.6.2 For given functions $f(Y, Z)$ and $\alpha_2(\xi, Z)$, $f(Y, Z) \leq \alpha_2(\alpha_1(Y), Z)$ if and only if for each y^j, $f(y^j, Z) \leq \alpha_2(\xi^i, Z)$ for some ξ^i of ξ.

PROOF. If $f(y^j, Z) \leq \alpha_2(\xi^i, Z)$, defining $\alpha_1(y^j)$ equal to ξ^i gives $f(y^j, Z) \leq \alpha_2(\alpha_1(Y), Z)$. If $f(y^j, Z)$ is undefined for all z^i, then α_1 may be undefined as well. Conversely, if $f(Y, Z) \leq \alpha_2(\alpha_1(Y), Z)$, then if $f(y^j, z^k)$ is defined, $\alpha_2(\alpha_1(y^j), z^k)$ is equal to $f(y^j, z^k)$. Thus $\alpha_1(y^j)$ must assume a value ξ^i such that $f(y^j, z^k) = \alpha_2(\xi^i, z^k)$ for each z^k; hence $f(y^j, Z) \leq \alpha_2(\xi^i, Z)$ and the theorem is proved.

Let us consider the example shown in Figure 4.6.1.

$$f(Y, Z) = f(y_1, y_2, z_1, z_2),$$

where

$$y_1 = x_1, \qquad y_2 = x_2, \qquad z_1 = x_3, \qquad z_2 = x_4.$$

y_1	y_2	z_1 z_2	0 0	0 1	1 1	1 0
0	0		0	0	d	d
0	1		d	d	1	1
1	1		0	d	1	d
1	0		0	1	1	1

$$f(Y, Z)$$

$$\alpha_2(\xi, Z) = \alpha_2(\xi, z_1, z_2)$$

ξ	z_1 z_2	0 0	0 1	1 1	1 0
0		0	0	1	0
1		0	1	1	1

$$\alpha_2(\xi, Z)$$

Figure 4.6.1

Both f and α_2 are shown in Karnaugh map form. Note that α_2 is a majority function on variables ξ, z_1, and z_2 and could be denoted by the on array

$$\begin{pmatrix} 1 & 1 & x \\ 1 & x & 1 \\ x & 1 & 1 \end{pmatrix}$$

and off array

$$\begin{pmatrix} 0 & 0 & x \\ 0 & x & 0 \\ x & 0 & 0 \end{pmatrix}.$$

The switching function f is partial, where complex L for f is defined by the cover

$$\begin{bmatrix} 0 & 1 & 1 & x \\ x & 1 & 1 & 1 \\ 1 & x & 1 & 1 \\ 1 & 0 & x & 1 \\ 1 & 0 & 1 & x \end{bmatrix}$$

and complex P is defined by the cover

$$\begin{pmatrix} 0 & 0 & 0 & x \\ 1 & x & 0 & 0 \end{pmatrix},$$

where the order of variables is (y_1, y_2, z_1, z_2). For this example, $f(Y, Z)$ can be expressed by $f(Y, Z) \leq \alpha_2(\alpha_1(Y), Z)$ by letting $\alpha_1(Y)$ be defined as follows:

$$\alpha_1(0, 0) = 0,$$

$$\alpha_1(0, 1) = 1,$$

$$\alpha_1(1, 1) = 0 \quad \text{or} \quad 1,$$

$$\alpha_1(1, 0) = 1.$$

This is easily seen as follows. The $y_1 = 0$, $y_2 = 0$ row for f must be equal to the one of the rows for α_2 for any positions where f is defined. In this case, this is true only for the $\xi = 0$ row of α_2. Thus $\alpha_1(0, 0)$ must map to 0 if $\alpha_2(\xi, z_1, z_2)$ is to be an extension of f for the set $\{y_1, y_2\}$ equal to 0 0. Similar reasoning shows that $\alpha_1(0, 1) = 1$ and $\alpha_1(1, 0) = 1$. Thus

$f(x_1, x_2, x_3, x_4)$ can be realized by the Boolean graph shown in Figure 4.6.2, where α_1 is either an $\oplus$-element or an $\vee$-element, depending on $\alpha_1(1, 1)$ being chosen equal to 0 or 1, respectively.

Theorem 4.6.1 and Corollary 1 have answered question (1) for simple disjoint decompositions, but if a switching function is represented by C_1 and C_0, we must determine first the compatibilities of pairs of elements y^j and y^k, from the covers, to use the theorem. If $C_1 = \{a^1, a^2, \ldots, a^p\}$, $C_0 = \{b^1, b^2, \ldots, b^q\}$, where a^r and b^s are n coordinate cubes, and sets Y and Z for $f(Y, Z)$ are given, let us call the coordinates for Y the λ-parts of the a^r and b^s cubes, denoting these by a_λ^r and b_λ^s respectively, and the coordinates for Z the μ-parts of the a^r and b^s cubes, denoting these by a_μ^r and b_μ^s, respectively. Separating the λ and μ parts in the covers, we write C_1 and C_0 as

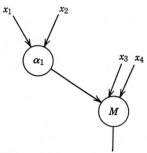

Figure 4.6.2   Boolean graph realizing $f(Y, Z)$ of Figure 4.6.1 using $\alpha_2 = M$.

$$C_1 = \{a_\lambda^i, a_\mu^i \mid i = 1, 2, \ldots, p\}$$

and

$$C_0 = \{(b_\lambda^j, b_\mu^j) \mid j = 1, 2, \ldots, q\}.$$

The following theorem follows directly from the definition of compatibility (see Exercise 11 at end of chapter).

Theorem 4.6.3   Given y^i and y^j, $y^i \sim y^j$ if and only if there are cubes $(a_\lambda^r, a_\mu^r) \in C_1$ and $(b_\lambda^s, b_\mu^s) \in C_0$ such that

(i) $a_\mu^r \cap b_\mu^s \neq \phi$, and

(ii) Either $a_\lambda^r \supseteq y^i$ and $b_\lambda^s \supseteq y^j$

or $a_\lambda^r \supseteq y^j$ and $b_\lambda^s \supseteq y^i$.

As an example of this theorem let us reconsider the example of Figure 4.6.1 in which the switching function $f(x_1, x_2, x_3, x_4)$ is defined by following

$$
\begin{array}{cc}
\lambda\text{-Part} & \mu\text{-Part}
\end{array}
$$

$$
\begin{array}{cccc}
x_1 & x_2 & x_3 & x_4
\end{array}
$$

$$
C_0 = \begin{cases}
\begin{pmatrix} 0 & 0 & 0 & x \end{pmatrix} & b^1 \\
\begin{pmatrix} 1 & x & 0 & 0 \end{pmatrix} & b^2
\end{cases}
$$

$$
C_1 = \begin{cases}
\begin{bmatrix} 0 & 1 & 1 & x \end{bmatrix} & a^1 \\
x & 1 & 1 & 1 & a^2 \\
1 & x & 1 & 1 & a^3 \\
1 & 0 & x & 1 & a^4 \\
1 & 0 & 1 & x & a^5
\end{bmatrix}
\end{cases}
$$

where
$$\lambda = \{x_1, x_2\} \qquad \mu = \{x_3, x_4\}.$$

Now we look for $a_\mu^r \cap b_\mu^s \neq \phi$ and find

$$a_\mu^4 \cap b_\mu^1 = 0\,1 \quad \text{which implies that} \quad 1\,0 \sim 0\,0.$$

Since all other intersections are empty, this is the only incompatible pair in the λ-parts.

Using Theorem 4.6.1, we can answer this question. Does there exist a decomposition $f(Y, Z) \leq \alpha_2(\alpha_1(Y), Z)$ where $Y = \{x_1, x_2\}$, $Z = \{x_3, x_4\}$ such that $\alpha_1(x_1, x_2) = x_1 \cdot x_2$? The answer is *no* since $\alpha_1(1, 0) = \alpha_1(0, 0)$, but by the above computation $1\,0 \sim 0\,0$. Now by using Corollary 1 and the preceding calculation for incompatible y^i and y^j, it is obvious that $k(y; f) = 2$ where any partitition with $1\,0$ in one set of the partition and $0\,0$ in the other set of the partition is suitable. Thus any function α_1 such that $\alpha_1(0, 0) \neq \alpha_1(1, 0)$ will satisfy Theorem 4.6.1, giving a decomposition of the form $f(X, Y) = \alpha_2(\alpha_1(Y), Z)$.

For any given α_1, it would be of interest to construct the image function α_2. For this purpose we define A_λ^i as the set of values assumed by α_1 for cube a_λ^i. Thus in our example if α_1 is defined by the on- and off-arrays,

$$\text{Off-array} \begin{pmatrix} 0 & 0 \\ 1 & 1 \end{pmatrix}.$$

$$\alpha_1$$

$$\text{On-array} \begin{pmatrix} 1 & 0 \\ 0 & 1 \end{pmatrix}$$

Then for C_1,

$$C_1 = \begin{matrix} 1 \\ 2 \\ 3 \\ 4 \\ 5 \end{matrix} \left\{ \begin{bmatrix} 0 & 1 & 1 & x \\ x & 1 & 1 & 1 \\ 1 & x & 1 & 1 \\ 1 & 0 & x & 1 \\ 1 & 0 & 1 & x \end{bmatrix} \right\}.$$

The A_λ^i are

	a_λ^i		A_λ^i	
1	0 1		1	
2	x 1	$\begin{pmatrix} 0 & 1 \\ 1 & 1 \end{pmatrix}$	$\begin{pmatrix} 1 \\ 0 \end{pmatrix} = x$	
3	1 x	$\begin{pmatrix} 1 & 0 \\ 1 & 1 \end{pmatrix}$	$\begin{pmatrix} 1 \\ 0 \end{pmatrix} = x$	.
4	1 0		1	
5	1 0		1	

The on array D_1 for α_2 is then defined by the set of cubes $\{A_\lambda{}^i \times a_\mu{}^i\}$. Thus for our example

$$D_1 = \left\{ \begin{array}{c|cc} 1 & 1 & x \\ x & 1 & 1 \\ x & 1 & 1 \\ 1 & x & 1 \\ 1 & 1 & x \end{array} \right\} = \left(\begin{array}{c|cc} 1 & 1 & x \\ x & 1 & 1 \\ 1 & x & 1 \end{array} \right).$$

Similarly, for C_0 we can calculate $B_\lambda{}^i$ and obtain the off array D_0 for α_2.

$$C_0 = \begin{array}{c} 1 \\ 2 \end{array} \left(\begin{array}{cc|cc} 0 & 0 & 0 & x \\ 1 & x & 0 & 0 \end{array} \right)$$

$$
\begin{array}{ccc}
\quad b_\lambda{}^i & & \quad B_\lambda{}^i \\
1 \quad 0 \quad 0 & & 0 \\
2 \quad 1 \quad x & \left\{ \begin{array}{cc} 1 & 0 \\ 1 & 1 \end{array} \right. & \left. \begin{array}{c} 1 \\ 0 \end{array} \right\} = x.
\end{array}
$$

Thus

$$D_0 = \left\{ \begin{array}{c|cc} 0 & 0 & x \\ x & 0 & 0 \end{array} \right\}.$$

From this calculation the image function α_2 is defined by D_1 and D_0; and the calculation verifies the decomposition shown earlier in Figure 4.6.2, since the majority function is an extension of α_2 where the condition $0 \, x \, 0$ is appended to the off array D_0.

   We have now seen how to detect disjoint decompositions and to compute their images. By iteratively applying these decomposition processes to images of a previous decomposition, we can construct a decomposition which represents a Boolean tree, if indeed such a decomposition exists for the given switching function and set D of decision elements. The cost of the Boolean tree is then simply the sum of the cost of its elements. By successively inspecting all possible sequences of disjoint decompositions using elements of D and making the appropriate cost calculations as we proceed, a minimum cost Boolean tree which satisfies the design specifications can be obtained. We illustrate such an algorithm with the following example. Let $f(x_1, x_2, x_3, x_4)$ be defined by

$$C_1 = \left\{ \begin{array}{cccc} x_1 & x_2 & x_3 & x_4 \\ 1 & 0 & x & 1 \\ 1 & 0 & 1 & x \\ 0 & 1 & x & 1 \\ 0 & 1 & 1 & x \end{array} \right. \begin{array}{c} a^1 \\ a^2 \\ a^3 \\ a^4 \end{array}$$

$$C_0 = \left\{ \begin{array}{cccc} 0 & 0 & x & x \\ x & x & 0 & 0 \\ 1 & 1 & x & x \end{array} \right. \begin{array}{c} b^1 \\ b^2 \\ b^3 \end{array}$$

and let D be the set of two input elements for OR-element, AND-element, and $\oplus$-element, where each element has a cost of 1.

We must first choose a λ-part and a μ-part. Let $\lambda = \{x_1, x_2\}$ and $\mu = \{x_3, x_4\}$. Thus we are looking for a decomposition of the form

$$f(x_1, x_2, x_3, x_4) = \alpha_2(\alpha_1(x_1, x_2), x_3, x_4),$$

where α_1 is an element of D.

From Theorem 4.6.3 we calculate the incompatible λ-parts.

$$a_\mu^1 \cap b_\mu^1 \neq \phi \Rightarrow 0\,0 \sim 1\,0,$$
$$a_\mu^1 \cap b_\mu^3 \neq \phi \Rightarrow 1\,0 \sim 1\,1,$$
$$a_\mu^2 \cap b_\mu^1 \neq \phi \Rightarrow 0\,0 \sim 1\,0,$$
$$a_\mu^2 \cap b_\mu^3 \neq \phi \Rightarrow 1\,0 \sim 1\,1,$$
$$a_\mu^3 \cap b_\mu^1 \neq \phi \Rightarrow 0\,1 \sim 0\,0,$$
$$a_\mu^3 \cap b_\mu^3 \neq \phi \Rightarrow 0\,1 \sim 1\,1,$$
$$a_\mu^4 \cap b_\mu^1 \neq \phi \Rightarrow 0\,1 \sim 0\,0,$$
$$a_\mu^4 \cap b_\mu^3 \neq \phi \Rightarrow 0\,1 \sim 1\,1.$$

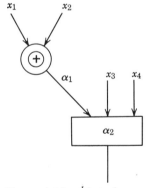

Figure 4.6.3 First decomposition for Boolean tree synthesis problem.

Thus $0\,0 \sim 1\,1$ and $0\,1 \sim 1\,0$. Thus if any α_1 which is an element of D is to be used for decomposition, it must be $\alpha_1 = x_1 \oplus x_2$ because for the OR-operation we require that $1\,0 \sim 1\,1$, and for the AND-operation we require that $0\,0 \sim 1\,0$. We thus obtain a decomposition of the form shown in Figure 4.6.3.

The image α_2 can be computed as follows.

For C_1

$$
\begin{array}{ccc}
 & a_\lambda^i & A_\lambda^i \\
1 & 10 & 1 \\
2 & 10 & 1 \\
3 & 01 & 1 \\
4 & 01 & 1
\end{array}
$$

Therefore

$$
D_1 = \{A_\lambda^i \times a_\mu^i\} = \begin{matrix} \alpha_1 & x_3 & x_4 \\ \begin{pmatrix} 1 & x & 1 \\ 1 & 1 & x \end{pmatrix} & \begin{matrix} a^1 \\ a^2 \end{matrix} \end{matrix}
$$

For C_0

$$
\begin{array}{ccc}
 & b_\lambda^i & B_\lambda^i \\
1 & 00 & 0 \\
2 & xx & x \\
3 & 11 & 0
\end{array}
$$

Thus

$$
D_0 = \{B_\lambda^i \times b_\mu^i\} = \begin{matrix} \alpha_1 & x_3 & x_4 \\ \begin{pmatrix} 0 & x & x \\ x & 0 & 0 \end{pmatrix} & \begin{matrix} b^1 \\ b^2 \end{matrix} \end{matrix}.
$$

Given D_1 and D_0 we attempt a second decomposition. Here we try $\lambda = \{\alpha_1, x_3\}$, $\mu = \{x_4\}$. (Note we again use labels a^1, a^2 and b^1, b^2, but now to denote cubes of D_1 and D_0 respectively.)

$$
\begin{array}{lll}
a_\mu^1 \cap b_\mu^1 = 1 \cap x \neq \phi & \text{therefore} & 1\,x \sim 0\,x, \\
a_\mu^2 \cap b_\mu^1 = x \cap x \neq \phi & \text{therefore} & 1\,1 \sim 0\,x, \\
a_\mu^2 \cap b_\mu^2 = x \cap 0 \neq \phi & \text{therefore} & 1\,1 \sim x\,0.
\end{array}
$$

Thus the maximum compatible sets are $\{0\,0, 0\,1\}$, $\{1\,0\}$, $\{1\,1\}$, and $k = 3$, so that no decomposition with $\lambda = \{\alpha_1, x_3\}$ and $\mu = \{x_4\}$ is possible using an element of D. Now we try a second decomposition with $\lambda = \{x_3, x_4\}$ and $\mu = \{\alpha_1\}$. The reader may verify that in this case $x\,1 \sim 0\,0$ and $1\,x \sim 0\,0$ so that a decomposition using an OR-element of D is possible. Denoting this decomposition by $\alpha_2(\alpha_1, x_3, x_4) = \alpha_2'(\alpha_1'(x_3, x_4), \alpha_1)$ and computing the image for α_2' using E_1 and E_0 for covers, we obtain

$$
E_1 = \{1\ 1\},
$$

$$
E_0 = \begin{pmatrix} 0 & x \\ x & 0 \end{pmatrix}.
$$

Since E_1 and E_0 can be represented by an AND-element, we have completed the sequence of decompositions required to get a Boolean tree which satisfies the design specifications. This circuit has cost 3 and is shown in Figure 4.6.4.

Because no less than three two-input elements could possibly be used to realize a four variable function and because the cost of each element of D is equal to 1, this circuit is a *minimum cost* Boolean tree for our problem.

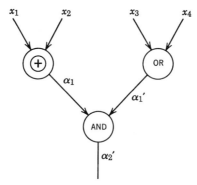

Figure 4.6.4 A minimum cost Boolean tree satisfying the design specifications.

In general, however, the other possible decompositions would have to be tried in order to find a minimum cost realization. Furthermore, note that sometimes this algorithm could become lengthy if many possible Boolean trees existed for the given problem.

This synthesis algorithm may, indeed, fail to give a Boolean tree for some problems since not all switching functions can be realized by Boolean trees using elements from some specified set D. For example, let us use the same set D as in the previous example, but have as a design specification the majority function $f(x_1, x_2, x_3)$,

$$C_0 = \begin{cases} \begin{pmatrix} x & 0 & 0 \\ 0 & x & 0 \\ 0 & 0 & x \end{pmatrix} & \begin{matrix} b^1 \\ b^2, \\ b^3 \end{matrix} \end{cases}$$

$$C_1 = \begin{cases} \begin{pmatrix} x & 1 & 1 \\ 1 & x & 1 \\ 1 & 1 & x \end{pmatrix} & \begin{matrix} a^1 \\ a^2. \\ a^3 \end{matrix} \end{cases}$$

With $\lambda = (x_1, x_2), \mu = \{x_3\}$ we have

$$a_\mu^3 \cap b_\mu^1 = x \cap 0 \neq \phi \qquad \text{therefore} \quad 1\,1 \sim x\,0,$$
$$a_\mu^3 \cap b_\mu^2 \neq \phi \qquad \text{therefore} \quad 1\,1 \sim 0\,x,$$
$$a_\mu^3 \cap b_\mu^3 \neq \phi \qquad \text{therefore} \quad 0\,0 \sim 1\,1,$$
$$a_\mu^1 \cap b_\mu^3 \neq \phi \qquad \text{therefore} \quad 0\,0 \sim 1\,x,$$
$$a_\mu^2 \cap b_\mu^3 \neq \phi \qquad \text{therefore} \quad 0\,0 \sim x\,1.$$

In this case for an α_1 to exist if $\alpha_2(\alpha_1(x_1, x_2), x_3)$ we would require α_1 to range over three elements since $k(y; f) = 3$, where the minimum partition is $\{0\,0\}$, $\{1\,1\}$, and $\{0\,1, 1\,0\}$. Thus no disjoint decomposition using an α_1 from D is possible. By symmetry on the variables this is true for any λ-part with two coordinates. Hence, a Boolean tree using elements of the set D does not exist for this problem. To obtain a realization for this problem, using only elements of D, we must go to a more general structure, namely, that of a Boolean graph. For this type of synthesis we study other types of decomposition: nondisjoint decompositions and decompositions in which α_1 may have a range greater than two.

Let us now consider a decomposition of the form

$$(4.6.1) \quad f(x_1, x_2, \ldots, x_n)$$
$$\leq \beta(\alpha_1(y_1, \ldots, y_s), \ldots, \alpha_r(y_1, \ldots, y_s), z_1, \ldots, z_{n-s}),$$

where

$$Y = \{y_1, \ldots, y_s\} \subseteq \{x_1, \ldots, x_n\} = X,$$
$$Z = \{z_1, \ldots, z_{n-s}\} \subseteq \{x_1, \ldots, x_n\},$$
$$Y \cap Z = \phi, \; Y \cup Z = X,$$

and f, β, and $\alpha_1, \ldots, \alpha_r$ are switching functions. The following corollary for this type of decomposition can be obtained from Corollary 1.

Corollary 2 If f, β, and $\alpha_1, \ldots, \alpha_r$ are switching functions satisfying Equation (4.6.1), then $k(y; f) \leq 2^r$. There also exists a decomposition for f of the form of Equation (4.6.1) such that $2^{r-1} < k(y; f) \leq 2^r$.

This follows directly from Corollary 1 when (4.6.1) is viewed as a decomposition $f(Y, Z) \leq \alpha_2'(\alpha_1'(Y), Z)$, where α_1' has a range p such that $2^{r-1} < p \leq 2^r$. The elements of the range of α_1' may then be encoded with r switching functions $\alpha_1, \ldots, \alpha_r$, with a resulting correspondence between α_2' and β of (4.6.1).

The Boolean graph which corresponds to a decomposition of the form of Equation (4.6.1) is shown in Figure 4.6.5.

In our previous examples of Boolean tree synthesis the numerical value of $k(y; f)$ was easily determined from the incompatibilities of the y^i, y^j using Theorem 4.6.3. In general, $k(y; f)$ may not be readily apparent

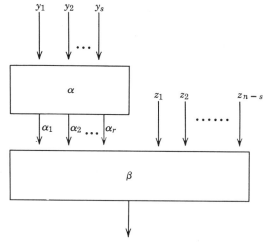

Figure 4.6.5   The Boolean graph represented by Equation (4.6.1).

for more complex examples. Since $k(y; f)$ is essential to Corollary 2, and thus to obtaining decompositions of type (4.6.1), we now describe a method for its calculation. As before we use Theorem 4.6.3 to calculate incompatibilities in the λ-parts of the covers [that is, the y^i, y^j of $f(Y, Z)$ given sets Y and Z].

The first step in the calculation of $k(y; f)$ is to calculate all subsets of $y = \{y^1, y^2, \ldots, y^{2^s-1}\}$ in which (1) any pair of elements in a subset are compatible and (2) no other subset with property (1) contains the subset. The procedure to calculate these *maximum compatible sets* is based on computing the incompatibilities and successively forming subsets of y. The steps of the computation are the following.

1. Starting with set y, if $y^i \nsim y^j$, then form two subsets of y, $S_1^1 = \{y - y^i\}$ and $S_2^1 = \{y - y^j\}$.

2. In general, if we have obtained a class of subsets $S_1^k, S_2^k, \ldots, S_p^k$ at the kth step and some new incompatible pair $y^r \nsim y^s$ is found, form S_1^{k+1}, $S_2^{k+1}, \ldots, S_q^{k+1}$ by first reducing each S_i^k which contains both y^r and y^s into two subsets as in Step 1 and then deleting any subset contained in some other subset.

3. After one step for each pair of incompatible elements in y, the class of subsets is the set of all maximum compatible sets. A minimum "cover" of the elements in y by maximum compatible sets can then be obtained by an extraction algorithm, where the maximum compatible sets act as prime implicants. The number of sets in this cover is $k(y; f)$, noting that a partition of the elements of y can be obtained simply by arbitrarily deleting duplicate appearances of any y^i in the sets of the minimum cover.

By our previous calculation of incompatibilities for the example of Figure 4.6.1, with $\lambda = \{x_1, x_2\}$ and $\mu = \{x_3, x_4\}$ we have only one pair $10 \sim 00$. Thus the maximum compatible sets for this example are $\{00, 01, 11\}$ and $\{01, 10, 11\}$, so that $k(y; f) = 2$. For the majority function discussed earlier.

$$C_0 = \begin{Bmatrix} x & 0 & 0 \\ 0 & x & 0 \\ 0 & 0 & x \end{Bmatrix},$$

$$C_1 = \begin{Bmatrix} x & 1 & 1 \\ 1 & x & 1 \\ 1 & 1 & x \end{Bmatrix}.$$

With $\lambda = \{x_1, x_2\}$ and $\mu = \{x_3\}$ we found that

$$11 \sim x0$$
$$11 \sim 0x$$
$$00 \sim 1x$$
$$00 \sim x1.$$

Since the majority function is complete, the compatibility relation is an equivalence relation and the class of maximum compatible sets is the partition formed by the equivalence relation. The process of obtaining these maximum compatible sets is shown below.

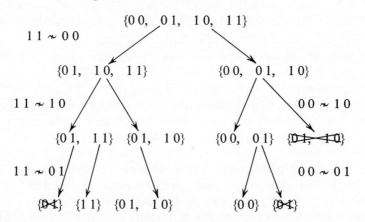

Thus, the class of maximum compatible sets is

$$\{00\}, \{01, 10\}, \{11\}, \quad \text{and} \quad k(y; f) = 3.$$

As another example of finding $k(y; f)$ we let $f(x_1, x_2, x_3, x_4)$ be defined by

$$C_1 = \begin{pmatrix} 0 & 0 & 1 & x \\ 1 & 0 & 0 & 1 \end{pmatrix} \begin{matrix} a^1 \\ a^2 \end{matrix} \qquad C_0 = \begin{pmatrix} 0 & 1 & 1 & 1 \\ 1 & 1 & 0 & x \end{pmatrix} \begin{matrix} b^1 \\ b^2 \end{matrix}$$

and consider $\lambda = \{x_1, x_2\}$, $\mu = \{x_3, x_4\}$.
Then

$$a_\mu{}^1 \cap b_\mu{}^1 \neq \phi \qquad \text{therefore} \quad 0\,0 \sim 0\,1$$

and

$$a_\mu{}^2 \cap b_\mu{}^2 \neq \phi \qquad \text{therefore} \quad 1\,0 \sim 1\,1.$$

The class of maximum compatible sets computation is

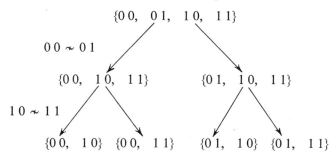

Of these four sets either the pair $\{0\,0, \quad 1\,0\}$, $\{0\,1, \quad 1\,1\}$ or the pair $\{0\,0, \quad 1\,1\}$, $\{0\,1, \quad 1\,0\}$ give a minimum cover, and thus $k(y; f) = 2$ for this example.

Having determined $k(y; f)$, from Corollary 2 it follows that a decomposition of type (4.6.1) and a corresponding Boolean graph, as depicted by Figure 4.6.5, exist, where r is determined by the inequalities $2^{r-1} < k(y; f) \leq 2^r$. For synthesis, after selecting functions $\alpha_1, \ldots, \alpha_r$ we may then consider the subproblems depicted by β and $\alpha_1, \ldots, \alpha_r$ in Figure 4.6.5 and attempt to find additional decompositions for these functions. Such an iterative process could then be continued until each subfunction was either a single decision element of the set D or could be represented by an already known minimum Boolean graph. (We could envision that minimum Boolean graphs for functions of only a few variables are precomputed and the synthesis uses these by looking them up in a table.)

The selection of the $\alpha_1, \ldots, \alpha_r$ functions clearly must be such that they give the same r-tuple of values on the $\alpha_1, \ldots, \alpha_r$ lines for elements of y which are compatible and appear in the same set of the partition, and similarly different r-tuples of values must be assigned to these lines for incompatible input conditions. Although this mutually restricts the $\alpha_1, \ldots, \alpha_r$ functions, certain flexibility in choosing these functions may still be available. Various heuristics or properties may be used to try to make an assignment of $\alpha_1, \ldots, \alpha_r$ which will yield a minimum or near minimum cost Boolean graph in the subsequent decompositions. We shall simply consider two examples to demonstrate this selection and the use of this type of decomposition to obtain Boolean graphs that satisfy the design specification.

As a first example let us reconsider the majority function synthesis problem we treated earlier which could not be realized by a Boolean tree. For this example we have $k(y; f) = 3$, where $Y = \{x_1, x_2\}$ and $Z = \{x_3\}$.

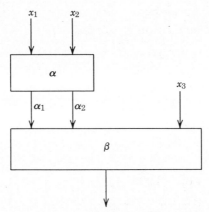

Figure 4.6.6   First decomposition for majority function example.

Thus $r = 2$ and we can realize this function by the Boolean graph shown in Figure 4.6.6.

Naturally, one possible assignment of α_1 and α_2 is $\alpha_1 = x_1$ and $\alpha_2 = x_2$, but this obviously accomplishes nothing because then the synthesis problem on β is identical to the previous step.

Retaining the set D used earlier and noting that the minimum partition for y is $\{0\,0\}, \{1\,1\}, \{0\,1, \quad 1\,0\}$, we see that α_1 and α_2 can simply be $\oplus$ and AND respectively. Then for set $\{0\,1, \quad 1\,0\}$, $\alpha_1 = 1$ and $\alpha_2 = 0$; for set $\{1\,1\}$, $\alpha_1 = 0$, $\alpha_2 = 1$; and for set $\{0\,0\}$, $\alpha_1 = 0$, $\alpha_2 = 0$. This decomposition is shown in Figure 4.6.7.

The image of this decomposition can be computed as before, except now r

Figure 4.6.7   A suitable assignment for α_1 and α_2.

coordinates, rather than one, are used to replace the λ-parts. (In this example $r = 2$.) For our example,

$$C_1 = \begin{Bmatrix} x & 1 & 1 \\ 1 & x & 1 \\ 1 & 1 & x \end{Bmatrix} \begin{matrix} a^1 \\ a^2 \\ a^3 \end{matrix}.$$

with λ μ column labels.

$$C_0 = \begin{Bmatrix} x & 0 & 0 \\ 0 & x & 0 \\ 0 & 0 & x \end{Bmatrix} \begin{matrix} b^1 \\ b^2 \\ b^3 \end{matrix}.$$

with λ μ column labels.

i	a_λ^i	A_λ^i

$$\begin{matrix} & & \alpha_1 & \alpha_2 \\ 1 & x\,1 & \begin{pmatrix} 0\,1 & 1 & 0 \\ 1\,1 & 0 & 1 \end{pmatrix} \\ 2 & 1\,x & \begin{pmatrix} 1\,0 & 1 & 0 \\ 1\,1 & 0 & 1 \end{pmatrix} \\ 3 & 1\,1 & \;\;\;0 \;\; 1 \end{matrix}.$$

Thus

$$D_1 = \begin{Bmatrix} \alpha_1 & \alpha_2 & x_3 \\ 1 & 0 & 1 \\ 0 & 1 & 1 \\ 1 & 0 & 1 \\ 0 & 1 & 1 \\ 0 & 1 & x \end{Bmatrix} \quad \text{or} \quad \begin{Bmatrix} 1 & 0 & 1 \\ 0 & 1 & x \end{Bmatrix}.$$

Similarly,

i	b_λ^i	B_λ^i

$$\begin{matrix} & & \alpha_1 & \alpha_2 \\ 1 & x0 & \begin{Bmatrix} 0\,0 & 0 & 0 \\ 1\,0 & 1 & 0 \end{Bmatrix} = x\,0 \\ 2 & 0x & \begin{Bmatrix} 0\,0 & 0 & 0 \\ 0\,1 & 1 & 0 \end{Bmatrix} = x\,0 \\ 3 & 00 & \;\;\;0 \;\; 0 \end{matrix}.$$

Thus

$$D_0 = \begin{Bmatrix} \overset{\alpha_1}{x} & \overset{\alpha_2}{0} & \overset{x_3}{0} \\ x & 0 & 0 \\ 0 & 0 & x \end{Bmatrix} \quad \text{or} \quad \begin{pmatrix} x & 0 & 0 \\ 0 & 0 & x \end{pmatrix}.$$

Now if D_0 and D_1 are used for a second decomposition and we pick $\lambda = \{\alpha_1, x_3\}$, $\mu = \{\alpha_2\}$, we obtain

$$D_1 = \begin{Bmatrix} \overset{\lambda}{\overbrace{\overset{\alpha_1}{1} \quad \overset{x_3}{1}}} & \Big| & \overset{\mu}{\overset{\alpha_2}{0}} \\ 0 & x & \Big| & 1 \end{Bmatrix} \begin{matrix} a^1 \\ a^2 \end{matrix}$$

$$D_0 = \begin{Bmatrix} \overset{\lambda}{\overbrace{\overset{\alpha_1}{x} \quad \overset{x_3}{0}}} & \Big| & \overset{\mu}{\overset{\alpha_2}{0}} \\ 0 & x & \Big| & 0 \end{Bmatrix} \begin{matrix} b^1 \\ b^2 \end{matrix},$$

$$a_\mu^{\,1} \cap b_\mu^{\,1} \neq \phi \qquad \text{therefore} \quad 1\,1 \sim x\,0,$$
$$a_\mu^{\,1} \cap b_\mu^{\,2} \neq \phi \qquad \text{therefore} \quad 1\,1 \sim 0\,x.$$

We have $k(y; \beta) = 2$ with a partition $\{1\,1\}$, $\{0\,0,\ \ 0\,1,\ \ 1\,0\}$, and this partition corresponds directly to an AND-element. Calculating the images again, we obtain

i	$a_\lambda^{\,i}$		$A_\lambda^{\,i}$
	α_2	x_3	α_3
1	1	1	1
2	0	x	0

Therefore
$$E_1 = \begin{Bmatrix} \overset{\alpha_3}{1} & \overset{\alpha_2}{0} \\ 0 & 1 \end{Bmatrix}$$

i	$b_\lambda^{\,i}$		$B_\lambda^{\,i}$
1	x	0	0
2	0	x	0

Therefore
$$E_0 = \{\overset{\alpha_3}{0} \quad \overset{\alpha_2}{0}\}.$$

Since this image can be realized by an OR-element, we arrive at a Boolean graph for $f(x_1, x_2, x_3)$ as shown in Figure 4.6.8.

The cost of this Boolean graph is four. Is this a minimum cost Boolean graph satisfying the design specification?

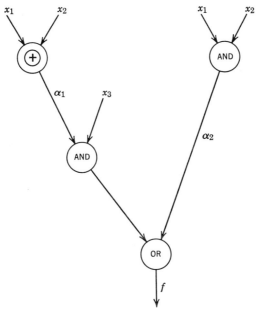

Figure 4.6.8   A Boolean graph for the majority function which satisfies the design requirements.

As a second example consider the synthesis, from our same set D, of a Boolean graph for $f(x_1, x_2, x_3, x_4)$ where

$$
C_1 = \begin{cases}
\begin{array}{cc|cc}
& \lambda & & \mu \\
x_1 & x_2 & x_3 & x_4 \\
\end{array} \\
\left(\begin{array}{cc|cc}
1 & 1 & 1 & x \\
0 & 0 & 1 & x \\
0 & 1 & 1 & 0 \\
1 & 0 & 1 & 0 \\
\end{array}\right)
\begin{array}{c}
a^1 \\
a^2 \\
a^3 \\
a^4 \\
\end{array}
\end{cases}
$$

and

$$
C_0 = \begin{cases}
\begin{array}{cc|cc}
& \lambda & & \mu \\
\end{array} \\
\left(\begin{array}{cc|cc}
1 & 0 & x & 1 \\
0 & 1 & x & 1 \\
x & x & 0 & 1 \\
0 & 0 & 0 & x \\
\end{array}\right)
\begin{array}{c}
b^1 \\
b^2 \\
b^3 \\
b^4 \\
\end{array}
\end{cases} .
$$

Considering a decomposition for $\lambda = \{x_1, x_2\}$, $\mu = \{x_3, x_4\}$, we obtain

$$a_\mu^1 \cap b_\mu^1 \neq \phi \qquad \text{therefore} \quad 1\,1 \sim 1\,0$$
$$a_\mu^1 \cap b_\mu^2 \neq \phi \qquad \text{therefore} \quad 1\,1 \sim 0\,1$$
$$a_\mu^2 \cap b_\mu^1 \neq \phi \qquad \text{therefore} \quad 0\,0 \sim 1\,0$$
$$a_\mu^2 \cap b_\mu^2 \neq \phi \qquad \text{therefore} \quad 0\,0 \sim 0\,1 .$$

The class of maximum compatibles is thus $\{0\,0, \ 1\,1\}$, $\{0\,1, \ 1\,0\}$; $k(y; f) = 2$, and the $\oplus$-element of D will satisfy the required compatibilities (by Theorem 4.6.1). Thus let $\alpha_1 = x_1 \oplus x_2$ and obtain the image for this decomposition (shown in Figure 4.6.9).

i	a_λ^i		A_λ^i
	x_1	x_2	α_1
1	1	1	0
2	0	0	0
3	0	1	1
4	1	0	1

therefore $D_1 = \begin{pmatrix} \alpha_1 & x_3 & x_4 \\ 0 & 1 & x \\ 1 & 1 & 0 \end{pmatrix}$

i	b_λ^i		B_λ^i
	x_1	x_2	α_1
1	1	0	1
2	0	1	1
3	x	x	x
4	0	0	0

therefore $D_0 = \begin{pmatrix} \alpha_1 & x_3 & x_4 \\ 1 & x & 1 \\ x & 0 & 1 \\ 0 & 0 & x \end{pmatrix}$

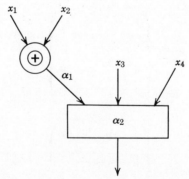

Figure 4.6.9   First decomposition in synthesis procedure example.

Picking a second λ as $\lambda = \{\alpha_1 x_3\}$, $\mu = \{x_4\}$,

$$
D_1 = \begin{matrix} & \lambda & \mu \\ & \overset{\alpha_1\ \ x_3}{} \; \overset{x_4}{} & \\ \begin{pmatrix} 0 & 1 & x \\ 1 & 1 & 0 \end{pmatrix} & \begin{matrix} a^1 \\ a^2 \end{matrix} \end{matrix},
$$

$$
D_0 = \begin{matrix} & \lambda & \mu \\ & \overset{\alpha_1\ \ x_3}{}\; \overset{x_4}{} & \\ \begin{pmatrix} 1 & x & 1 \\ x & 0 & 1 \\ 0 & 0 & x \end{pmatrix} & \begin{matrix} b^1 \\ b^2 \\ b^3 \end{matrix} \end{matrix},
$$

$a_\mu^{\,1} \cap b_\mu^{\,1} \neq \phi$ therefore $0\,1 \sim 1\,x$

$a_\mu^{\,1} \cap b_\mu^{\,2} \neq \phi$ therefore $0\,1 \sim x\,0$.

$a_\mu^{\,2} \cap b_\mu^{\,3} \neq \phi$ therefore $0\,0 \sim 1\,1$

The set of maximum compatible sets is thus $\{0\,1\}$, $\{0\,0, \ 1\,0\}$, and $\{1\,0, \ \ 1\,1\}$. Since $k(y; f) = 3$ for this case, this decomposition cannot be accomplished by any single element of D, but by Corollary 2 a decomposition of the form $\alpha_2(\alpha_1, x_3, x_4) \leq \beta(\alpha_1'(\alpha_1, x_3), \alpha_2'(\alpha_1, x_3), x_4)$ exists where α_2' and α_1' are switching functions. If we look at possible ways of forming α_1' and α_2' from elements of D, we require that the partition on the λ-part α_1, x_3 be a partition in which each of its sets is a subset of the maximum compatible sets $\{0\,1\}$, $\{0\,0, \ \ 1\,0\}$, and $\{1\,0, \ \ 1\,1\}$, and that the pair of values of α_1', α_2' are equal for elements in the same set of the partition and unequal otherwise.

From the following table we see that if we define

$$\alpha_1' = \alpha_1,$$
$$\alpha_2' = \alpha_1 \lor x_3,$$

then the values of α_1' and α_2' are suitable for the partition $\{0\,0\}$, $\{0\,1\}$, and $\{1\,0, \ \ 1\,1\}$.

α_1	x_3	$\alpha_1' = \alpha_1$	$\alpha_2' = \alpha_1 \lor x_3$
$\{0$	0	0	0
$\{0$	1	0	1
$\{1$	0	1	1
$\{1$	1	1	1

Although other possibilities may exist for α_1' and α_2', we shall assume this one for the moment, giving us the Boolean graph of Figure 4.6.10. The image β is calculated from D_0 and D_1 as follows:

i	a_λ^i				A_λ^i		
	α_1	x_3	α_1'	α_2'			
1	0	1	0	1			
2	1	1	1	1			

therefore $E_1 = \begin{Bmatrix} \alpha_1' & \alpha_2' & x_4 \\ 0 & 1 & x \\ 1 & 1 & 0 \end{Bmatrix}$.

i	b_λ^i		B_λ^i	
	α_1	x_3	α_1'	α_2'
1	1	x	1	1
2	x	$0 \begin{Bmatrix} 0 & 0 \\ 1 & 0 \end{Bmatrix}$	$\begin{matrix} 0 & 0 \\ 1 & 1 \end{matrix}$	
3	0	0	0	0

$$E_0 = \begin{Bmatrix} \alpha_1' & \alpha_2' & x_4 \\ 1 & 1 & 1 \\ 0 & 0 & 1 \\ 1 & 1 & 1 \\ 0 & 0 & x \end{Bmatrix}.$$

Thus covers for β are

$$E_1 = \begin{Bmatrix} \alpha_1' & \alpha_2' & x_4 \\ 0 & 1 & x \\ 1 & 1 & 0 \end{Bmatrix} \qquad E_0 = \begin{Bmatrix} \alpha_1' & \alpha_2' & x_4 \\ 1 & 1 & 1 \\ 0 & 0 & x \end{Bmatrix}.$$

For a third decomposition some λ and μ must again be picked. If we pick $\lambda = \{\alpha_1', x_4\}$, $\mu = \{\alpha_2'\}$, we obtain the following:

$$E_1 = \begin{Bmatrix} \overset{\lambda}{\overbrace{\alpha_1' \quad x_4}} & \overset{\mu}{\overbrace{\alpha_2'}} \\ 0 \quad x & 1 \\ 1 \quad 0 & 1 \end{Bmatrix} \begin{matrix} a^1 \\ a^2 \end{matrix},$$

$$E_0 = \begin{Bmatrix} \overset{\lambda}{\overbrace{\alpha_1' \quad x_4}} & \overset{\mu}{\overbrace{\alpha_2'}} \\ 1 \quad 1 & 1 \\ 0 \quad x & 0 \end{Bmatrix} \begin{matrix} b^1 \\ b^2 \end{matrix},$$

$$a_\mu^1 \cap b_\mu^1 \neq \phi \qquad \text{therefore} \quad 0\,x \sim 1\,1$$

$$a_\mu^2 \cap b_\mu^1 \neq \phi \qquad \text{therefore} \quad 1\,0 \sim 1\,1.$$

The maximum compatible sets are then calculated as

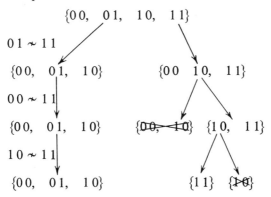

Thus an AND-element can be used for α_1'' of the decomposition $\beta \leq \alpha_2''(\alpha_1''(\alpha_1', x_4), \alpha_2')$, giving the image for α_2'':

i	a_λ^i	A_λ^i	$\alpha_1''\ \alpha_2'$	
1	0 x	0		$F_1 = \{0\ \ 1\}$
2	1 0	0		

i	b_λ^i	B_λ^i	$\alpha_1''\ \alpha_2'$	
1	1 1	1		$F_0 = \begin{pmatrix} 1 & 1 \\ 0 & 0 \end{pmatrix}$
2	0 x	0		

Since the $\oplus$-element is an extension for α_2'', we obtain a final realization for this example, using elements of the set D, as shown in Figure 4.6.11.

For a complete synthesis to obtain a minimum cost Boolean graph for this example we would have to inspect all other possible decompositions that might lead to a Boolean graph of cost three. We know that cost three is a lower bound on the cost for this example because at least three two-input elements are required to realize a function of four variables.

To summarize, we have discussed one method for Boolean tree synthesis and one method for Boolean graph synthesis. These methods can be used to obtain minimum or near minimum cost

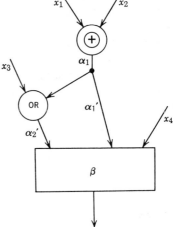

Figure 4.6.10 Second decomposition in synthesis procedure example.

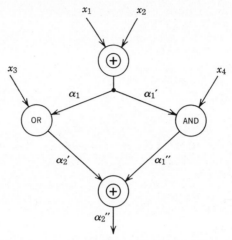

Figure 4.6.11   Boolean graph satisfying design specifications.

Boolean trees or graphs by examining all possible decompositions of the forms considered and by using cost bounds to eliminate any sequences of decompositions that cannot give a minimum cost circuit. Obviously, numerous choices are usually available even in examples having only three or four independent variables. If a computer is used to carry out the processes, however, it is feasible to try many possible sequences of decompositions. By selecting the best circuit realization obtained, reasonably good circuit designs may often be acquired. Various heuristics for selecting a "best" decomposition at each stage in the sequence of decompositions have been proposed in the literature, such that it is likely to obtain a near minimum cost realization as one of the first sequences of decompositions leading to a realization. It is hoped that further study of different types of decompositions and their properties will eventually lead to synthesis algorithms for Boolean graphs that require considerably less searching for possible solutions and will also treat more adequately multiple output problems such as

$$\alpha_1(y_1, \ldots, y_s), \alpha_2(y_1, \ldots, y_s), \ldots, \alpha_r(y_1, \ldots, y_s),$$

which is a natural outgrowth of a decomposition of the form of Equation (4.6.1).

Exercises

1. Prove that no prime implicant for $L(F) \cup N(G)$ in the multiple output method has both 1 and 0 entries in the first m coordinates.

2. (a) Find a minimum cost cover for the following three output problem where the cost is assumed to be C^α.

(b) Modify this cover to give an approximate minimum cost circuit when the cost is assumed to be the number of inputs both to AND-elements and OR-elements.

$$Z_1 = \begin{Bmatrix} 1 & x & 1 \\ x & 0 & 0 \end{Bmatrix},$$

$$Z_2 = \begin{Bmatrix} 0 & 1 & x \\ x & 0 & 0 \\ 1 & 0 & x \end{Bmatrix},$$

$$Z_3 = \begin{Bmatrix} 0 & 1 & x \\ x & x & 1 \end{Bmatrix},$$

$$g = \{1 \quad 1 \quad 0\}.$$

(Note that this problem is exactly the same as an example of Sections 4.2 and 4.3 except that the don't care condition $g = \{1 \quad 1 \quad 0\}$ has been added.)

3. Find a minimum cost multiple output AND-OR circuit for

$$z_1 = \begin{pmatrix} x & 1 & 1 & 0 & x & 0 & 0 \\ 0 & 0 & 1 & 1 & 1 & 1 & x \\ 0 & 1 & x & x & 0 & 0 & 1 \end{pmatrix} \qquad z_2 = \begin{Bmatrix} x & 1 & x & 0 & 0 & x & 0 \\ 0 & x & 1 & 1 & 1 & x & x \end{Bmatrix}$$

$$z_3 = \begin{pmatrix} x & 0 & 1 & 1 & 1 & x & 0 \\ 0 & 1 & x & 0 & 0 & 0 & x \\ 1 & 1 & 1 & 1 & 1 & 1 & 1 \end{pmatrix} \qquad g = \begin{Bmatrix} 0 & 0 & 0 & 0 & 0 & 0 & 0 \\ 1 & 1 & 1 & 1 & 0 & 0 & 0 \\ 0 & 0 & 0 & 1 & 1 & 1 & 1 \end{Bmatrix}$$

(a) where the cost of the circuit is the number of input lines to the AND-elements,

(b) where the cost of the circuit is the number of input and output lines of the AND-elements.

4. Find a minimum cost multiple output AND-OR circuit, where outputs z_1, z_2, and z_3 are defined by covers of complexes as given in the following:

$$z_1 = \begin{Bmatrix} x & 0 & 0 & x \\ x & x & 0 & 1 \end{Bmatrix},$$

$$z_2 = \begin{Bmatrix} x & 0 & x & 1 \\ 1 & 0 & 1 & x \\ 1 & x & 1 & 0 \end{Bmatrix},$$

$$z_3 = \begin{pmatrix} 0 & 0 & x & 1 \\ x & 1 & 0 & 1 \\ 1 & x & 1 & 1 \\ 0 & 1 & 1 & 0 \end{pmatrix},$$

and don't care conditions for all three outputs are defined by a set of cubes g

$$g = \{0 \quad 1 \quad 0 \quad 0\}.$$

Let the cost of the circuit be equal to the total number of input lines to the AND-elements.

5. Find factored forms for the following covers:

(a)

$$\left\{\begin{bmatrix} 1 & x & x & 0 & x \\ 0 & x & x & 1 & x \\ x & 1 & 1 & x & x \\ x & 1 & x & 1 & x \\ x & 0 & x & 0 & 0 \\ x & x & x & 1 & 1 \\ x & 1 & x & x & 1 \end{bmatrix}\right\},$$

(b)

$$\left\{\begin{bmatrix} 1 & x & x & 0 & x \\ 0 & x & x & 1 & x \\ x & 1 & 1 & x & x \\ x & 1 & x & 1 & 0 \\ x & 1 & x & 0 & 1 \\ x & 0 & x & 1 & 1 \\ x & 0 & x & 0 & 0 \end{bmatrix}\right\},$$

(c)

$$\left\{\begin{bmatrix} 1 & x & 0 & x & x \\ 0 & x & 1 & x & x \\ x & 1 & 1 & 0 & x \\ 0 & 0 & x & 0 & x \\ 1 & 1 & x & 0 & x \\ x & 0 & 0 & 0 & x \end{bmatrix}\right\}.$$

6. Find a factored form for

$$f = \left\{\begin{pmatrix} x & 1 & 0 & 1 \\ 1 & 0 & 1 & x \\ 0 & 1 & x & 1 \\ 1 & x & 1 & 0 \end{pmatrix}\right\}.$$

Also find another factored form by finding $\bar{f} = (x \quad x \quad x \quad x) \,\#\, f$, eliminating any cubes of $\bar{f}$ included in another cube of $\bar{f}$, factoring $\bar{f}$, and then inverting the factored form.

7. Find factored forms for the following covers:

(a)

$$\left\{\begin{bmatrix} x & 1 & 0 & x & 0 & 0 \\ 1 & 1 & 0 & 1 & 0 & 1 \\ 0 & 1 & 0 & 0 & x & x \\ x & 0 & 1 & 1 & 0 & 0 \\ x & 1 & 1 & 1 & x & x \\ 0 & x & 1 & 1 & x & 1 \end{bmatrix}\right\},$$

(b)

$$\left\{\begin{pmatrix} 0 & 0 & 0 & x & 1 & x \\ 1 & 1 & 0 & 1 & x & 1 \\ x & 0 & 0 & 0 & 1 & 1 \\ 1 & x & 0 & 1 & x & 0 \\ 1 & 0 & 0 & 1 & 0 & x \end{pmatrix}\right\}.$$

8. Using injection operators, find covers for the following Boolean trees.
   (*a*)

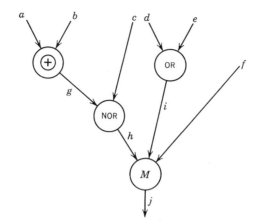

where   NOR $(c, g) = \overline{c \vee g}$,

$$M(f, h, i) = fh \vee fi \vee hi.$$

   (*b*)

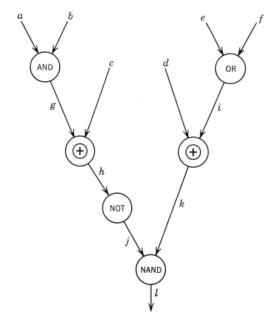

where   NAND $(j, k) = \overline{j \cdot k}$.

9. Using the injection and consistency operations, find covers for the following Boolean graphs.

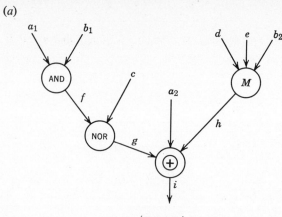

(a)

where $\begin{Bmatrix} a_1 = a_2 \\ b_1 = b_2 \end{Bmatrix}$

(b)

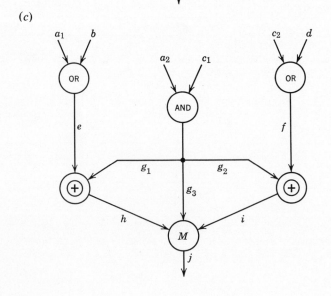

(c)

(*d*)

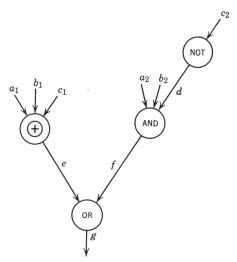

10. In Section 4.4 a cost comparison was made between the cost of the unfactored cover C^b versus the cost of the factored cover C^f. Each of these costs was shown to relate to the resulting logical diagram. Give similar cost comparison equations for the unfactored cover versus the factored cover for relay contact networks, where each relay contact has a unit cost.

11. Prove Theorem 4.6.3.

12. Assume that a switching function $f(x_1, \ldots, x_n)$ can be expressed in the composite form

$$f(x_1, \ldots, x_n) \leq \beta(\phi_1(x_1, \ldots, x_s), \phi_2(x_1, \ldots, x_s), x_{s+1}, \ldots, x_n).$$

Is this composite form a decomposition of f? (Definition 4.6.1.) If so, give m, all Z^j, Y^j, and α_j for the composite form.

13. Give the decompositions which represent the Boolean trees and Boolean graphs for Exercises 8 and 9.

14. Let the set D for Boolean tree synthesis be defined by the following two elements, with their associated on- and off-arrays:

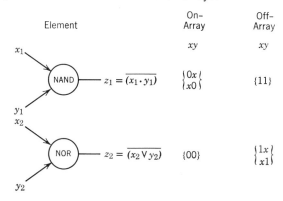

Element	On-Array xy	Off-Array xy
NAND $z_1 = \overline{(x_1 \cdot y_1)}$	$\left\{ \begin{array}{l} 0x \\ x0 \end{array} \right\}$	$\{11\}$
NOR $z_2 = \overline{(x_2 \vee y_2)}$	$\{00\}$	$\left\{ \begin{array}{l} 1x \\ x1 \end{array} \right\}$

and let the cost of each element equal one. If realizable as Boolean trees, find minimum cost Boolean trees that satisfy the design specifications for the following covers. In each case prove your result to be of minimum cost. Also if (*a*), (*b*), and (*c*) are not realizable, show why.

(*a*)

$$C_1 = \begin{cases} \begin{matrix} x_1 & x_2 & x_3 \end{matrix} \\ \begin{pmatrix} 1 & x & 0 \\ x & 1 & 0 \\ 1 & 0 & x \\ 0 & 1 & x \end{pmatrix} \end{cases}, \qquad \begin{matrix} x_1 & x_2 & x_3 \end{matrix} \\ C_0 = \{0 \quad 0 \quad 1\}$$

(*b*)

$$C_1 = \begin{cases} \begin{matrix} x_1 & x_2 & x_3 \end{matrix} \\ \begin{pmatrix} 1 & 1 & 0 \\ 0 & 1 & 1 \\ 1 & 0 & 1 \end{pmatrix} \end{cases}, \qquad \begin{matrix} x_1 & x_2 & x_3 \end{matrix} \\ C_0 = \begin{cases} \begin{pmatrix} 0 & 0 & 0 \\ 1 & 1 & 1 \end{pmatrix} \end{cases}$$

(*c*)

$$C_1 = \begin{cases} \begin{matrix} x_1 & x_2 & x_3 & x_4 \end{matrix} \\ \begin{pmatrix} x & x & x & 0 \\ x & 1 & x & x \\ 0 & x & 0 & x \end{pmatrix} \end{cases}, \qquad \begin{matrix} x_1 & x_2 & x_3 & x_4 \end{matrix} \\ C_0 = \begin{cases} \begin{pmatrix} 1 & 0 & x & 1 \\ x & 0 & 1 & 1 \end{pmatrix} \end{cases}.$$

15. In Section 4.6 each Boolean graph was shown to correspond to a decomposition of a complete function and each decomposition with $\alpha_1, \dots, \alpha_m$ being switching functions was shown to correspond to a particular Boolean graph.
    (*a*) Describe the analogous correspondences between relay switching networks and functional decomposition. (*Hint:* Extra relay coils may be introduced by a decomposition.)
    (*b*) Discuss the possible advantages and disadvantages of using decomposition for relay network synthesis.
16. Using the set D as the set of two input elements for OR-, AND-, and ⊕-elements, each of cost one, carry out the Boolean graph synthesis procedure to find Boolean graphs which satisfy each of the following design specifications and cost requirements as indicated.

(*a*) $$C_1 = \begin{cases} \begin{matrix} x_1 & x_2 & x_3 \end{matrix} \\ \begin{pmatrix} 0 & x & 1 \\ 1 & 0 & 0 \\ 1 & 1 & 1 \end{pmatrix} \end{cases} \qquad C_0 = \begin{cases} \begin{pmatrix} 1 & 0 & 1 \\ 0 & 0 & 0 \end{pmatrix} \end{cases},$$

where cost of graph ≤ 2.

$$x_1 \ x_2 \ x_3$$

(b) $\quad C_1 = \begin{pmatrix} 1 & 1 & x \\ 0 & 0 & 1 \\ 1 & x & 0 \end{pmatrix} \qquad C_0 = \begin{pmatrix} 0 & x & 0 \\ 0 & 1 & x \\ 1 & 0 & 1 \end{pmatrix},$$

where cost of graph ≤ 3.

$$x_1 \ x_2 \ x_3$$

(c) $\quad C_1 = \begin{pmatrix} 0 & 1 & 1 \\ x & 0 & 1 \end{pmatrix} \qquad C_0 = \begin{pmatrix} x & 0 & 0 \\ 1 & x & 0 \\ 1 & 1 & 1 \end{pmatrix},$$

where cost of graph ≤ 3.

17. Assume that we wish to convert from the 8-4-2-1 representation of decimal digits to the excess-3 representation as shown in the following:

$x_1 \ x_2 \ x_3 \ x_4$	Decimal Digit	$y_1 \ y_2 \ y_3 \ y_4$
8 4 2 1		
0 0 0 0	0	0 0 1 1
0 0 0 1	1	0 1 0 0
0 0 1 0	2	0 1 0 1
0 0 1 1	3	0 1 1 0
0 1 0 0	4	0 1 1 1
0 1 0 1	5	1 0 0 0
0 1 1 0	6	1 0 0 1
0 1 1 1	7	1 0 1 0
1 0 0 0	8	1 0 1 1
1 0 0 1	9	1 1 0 0

8-4-2-1 Representation   Excess-3 Representation

(a) Find covers C_{y_1}, C_{y_2}, C_{y_3}, and C_{y_4} for the cubical complex for the "on" conditions of y_1, y_2, y_3, and y_4 in terms of the input variables x_1, x_2, x_3, and x_4. Also find covers for the "off" conditions of the four outputs y_1, y_2, y_3, and y_4.

(b) Can you find a two coordinate λ-part which can be used to form disjoint decompositions for all the excess-3 digit conditions y_1, y_2, y_3, and y_4?

(c) Obtain Boolean trees for y_1, y_2, y_3, and y_4, where the set of building blocks consists of all possible two variable functions.

18. The compatibility relation given in Definition 4.6.2 is a binary relation between elements of the set y for a switching function $f(Y, Z)$.

(a) Prove that this binary relation $(\sim)$ is reflexive and symmetric but is not, in general, transitive.

(b) Under what conditions is the binary relation also transitive so as to form an equivalence relation?

REFERENCE NOTATIONS

The multiple output minimization method, which transforms the problem to a single output problem, as discussed in Section 4.2, was originated by D. E. Muller [9]. More recently, tag methods, somewhat similar to that given in Section 4.3, have been suggested by Bartee [2] and Polansky [10]. One of the most interesting recent developments in combinational switching circuit synthesis techniques has arisen from the exploitation of decompositions of Boolean functions. The basic early work in decomposition is due to Ashenhurst [1]. Many extensions of decomposition appear in a number of articles and a book by Curtis [3, 4, 5]. Section 4.6 describes some simple approaches to decomposition, based to a large extent on a paper by Karp [6]; other forms of decompositions and approaches to synthesis appear in [7, 11–13] as well as in the previously mentioned works [3–6].

REFERENCES

1. Ashenhurst, R. L., "The Decomposition of Switching Functions," *Proceedings of an International Symposium on the Theory of Switching*, April 2–5, 1957, Vol. 29 of *Annals of Computation Laboratory of Harvard University*, pp. 74–116, 1959.
2. Bartee, T. C., "Computer Design of Multiple Output Logical Networks," *IRE Transactions on Electronic Computers*, Vol. EC-10, No. 1, pp. 21–30, March 1961.
3. Curtis, H. A., "A Generalized Tree Circuit," *A.C.M. Journal*, Vol. 8, No. 4, pp. 484–496, October 1961.
4. Curtis, H. A., *A New Approach to the Design of Switching Circuits*, Van Nostrand, Princeton, New Jersey, 1962.
5. Curtis, H. A., "Generalized Tree Circuit—The Basic Building Block of an Extended Decomposition Theory," *A.C.M. Journal*, Vol. 10, No. 4, pp. 562–581, October 1963.
6. Karp, R. M., "Functional Decomposition and Switching Circuit Design," *IBM Research Report* RC-662, March, 1962, and *SIAM Journal*, pp. 291–335, June 1963.
7. Karp, R. M., F. E. McFarlin, J. P. Roth, and J. R. Wilts, "A Computer Program for the Synthesis of Combinational Switching Circuits," *Proceedings of the Second Annual A.I.E.E. Symposium on Switching Circuit Theory and Logical Design*, October 1961, pp. 182–194.
8. Miller, R. E., "Switching Theory and Logical Design of Automatic Digital Computer Circuits," *IBM Research Report* RC-473, pp. 79–115, June 1961.
9. Muller, D. E., "Application of Boolean Algebra to Switching Circuit Design and to Error Detection," *IRE Transactions on Electronic Computers*, pp. 6–12, September 1954.
10. Polansky, R. B., "Minimization of Multiple-Output Switching Circuits," *A.I.E.E. Conference Paper* CP 60-1223, Fall General Meeting, October 9–14, 1960.
11. Roth, J. P. and E. G. Wagner, "Algebraic Topological Methods for the Synthesis of Switching Systems, Part III. Minimization of Nonsingular Boolean Trees," *IBM Journal of Research and Development*, Vol. 4, No. 4, pp. 326–344, October 1959.
12. Roth, J. P., "Minimization over Boolean Trees," *IBM Journal of Research and Development*, Vol. 4, No. 5, pp. 543–558, November 1960.
13. Roth, J. P. and R. M. Karp, "Minimization over Boolean Graphs," *IBM Journal of Research and Development*, Vol. 6, No. 2, pp. 227–238, April 1962.

5

Bilateral Switching Networks

5.1 INTRODUCTION

In this chapter we discuss methods for describing and synthesizing combinational switching networks having bilateral elements. A bilateral switching element has the same switching characteristics in both directions. A relay contact is the most common example.

Since many modern digital systems may be most appropriately modeled by decision elements and their interconnection rather than bilateral elements, much of the recent work in switching theory has been associated with decision element models, rather than the models for the bilateral networks to be discussed in this chapter. Nevertheless, as we shall exemplify by the cryotron circuits in Section 5.8, the bilateral element model and associated design techniques also apply to switching elements other than relay contacts. Since the extensive results and techniques obtained for relay contact networks may also apply to switching elements to be developed in the future, some familiarity with this work is advisable.

Early works in the design of switching circuits were primarily concerned with relay contact circuit design, and much material on this subject has appeared in previous books. In this chapter we discuss only a few common types of combinational bilateral switching networks plus the "Boolean matrix" model for general bilateral switching networks described in Sections 5.6 and 5.7. In the Reference Notations references to more extended treatments of this subject are given.

In Section 2.5 we saw how Boolean algebra could be used to describe two-terminal series-parallel relay contact networks. In general, a two-terminal series-parallel network can be defined inductively as either a series or a parallel connection of two series-parallel networks, where a single element (relay contact) is an elementary series-parallel network. In Section 3.2, however, the analogy between Boolean algebra and another type of network, called a "bridge" network, was seen to be fairly indirect. In Sections 5.6 and 5.7 a Boolean matrix formulation for bilateral switching networks is discussed, which provides a more adequate model for the structure and switching properties of bilateral switching networks—bridge networks as well as series-parallel networks. Various operations on Boolean matrices are given which give further insight into the analysis and synthesis of bilateral switching networks.

As discussed in Chapter 3, a cover $C = \{c_1, c_2, \ldots, c_p\}$ of a cubical complex has been seen to represent a very special type of relay contact network, that is, a parallel connection of p series networks, where each series network corresponds to one cube of C. Thus, from a minimum cover we obtain a relay contact network of this special type which contains a minimum number of contacts. In Exercise 10, of Chapter 4, for example, it is seen how the factoring of a cover can reduce the number of contacts in a circuit, and in Exercise 15, of Chapter 4, we consider how functional decomposition affects the circuit structure of relay circuits. In Section 5.7 still other techniques, that is, operations on Boolean matrices, are discussed. These operations can be interpreted as changes in network structure and can be used to synthesize economical networks.

In Section 5.2 another important type of bilateral switching network is discussed, relay tree networks. This is a special type of multiple output network often used for selection or decoding operations. Methods of simplification for partial relay tree networks and for two terminal networks derived from relay tree networks are also briefly discussed in this section.

In Section 5.3 a special class of networks, called planar networks, are discussed. Dual and complementary networks can be defined for a planar network, and these concepts are useful in bilateral network synthesis.

A special type of function called a symmetric switching function (see Section 2.11) can be realized by a bilateral switching network having many fewer elements than the best series-parallel network to realize the function. These "symmetric networks" are discussed in Section 5.4, and a method for determining symmetries of a function is given in Section 5.5.

Finally, in Section 5.8 another type of bilateral switching element, the cryotron, is discussed, and several types of cryotron network structures are considered. Here we see that techniques developed for relay contact networks are readily extended to this newer type of switching element (the cryotron). It seems likely that other bilateral switching elements will be developed in the future, and that the techniques discussed here will also apply to these elements as well as relay contacts and cryotrons.

5.2 RELAY TREE NETWORKS

A relay tree network is a special type of combinational multiple terminal relay contact network having a single input terminal and many output terminals. As discussed in Section 3.2, each output can be expressed as a

Boolean function of the input variables (for a relay circuit the input variables $x_1, x_2, \ldots, x_n$ are represented by relays $X_1, X_2, \ldots, X_n$). For an m-output relay tree we thus have functions

$$
\left\{
\begin{aligned}
z_1 &= z_1(x_1, x_2, \ldots, x_n) \\
z_2 &= z_2(x_1, x_2, \ldots, x_n) \\
&\;\;\vdots \\
z_m &= z_m(x_1, x_2, \ldots, x_n)
\end{aligned}
\right.
$$

and the input terminal and output terminal conditions are shown in Figure 5.2.1. For a relay tree the configuration of the two terminal network from the input terminal to any particular output terminal is

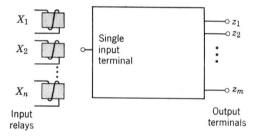

Figure 5.2.1   Terminals for relay tree.

simply a series connection of n relay contacts, one contact from each of the relays $X_1, X_2, \ldots, X_n$. This implies that each function

$$
z_i = z_i(x_1, \ldots, x_n)
$$

can be expressed as a single conjunction, where each of the variables $x_1, \ldots, x_n$ appears exactly once, either uncomplemented or complemented in the conjunction; that is, each output function corresponds to a single conjunction $x_1^{e_1} x_2^{e_2} \cdots x_n^{e_n}$ like those which appear in the disjunctive canonical form (see Equation 2.7.1). Also for a relay tree, we require that at most one output is connected to the input terminal for any possible input condition (that is, the outputs are disjoint; $z_i \cap z_j = \phi$ for $i \neq j$, $1 \leq i \leq m$, and $1 \leq j \leq m$).

For a *complete relay tree network* $m = 2^n$; thus each canonical conjunction $x_1^{e_1} x_2^{e_2} \cdots x_n^{e_n}$ is represented by one of the output terminals. If a relay tree is not complete, it is called a *partial relay tree*. A complete relay tree for four variables x_1, x_2, x_3, x_4 is shown in Figure 5.2.2. The conjunctions corresponding to each of the $2^4 = 16$ output terminals are shown to the right of the network. The structure for *n*-variables is readily seen as a simple extension of the network shown in Figure 5.2.2, and is a "tree" in the graph theoretic sense. Such a network requires 2 contacts on relay X_1, $2^2 = 4$ contacts on relay X_2, etc. Thus the total number of

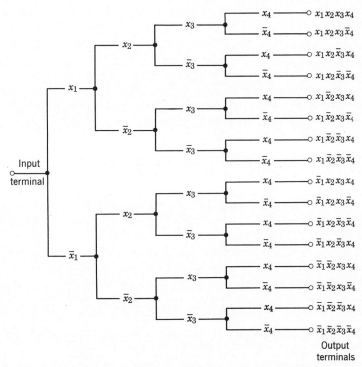

Figure 5.2.2   A complete relay tree for four variables.

contacts in the network is $2 + 2^2 + \cdots + 2^n = 2(2^n - 1)$. These contacts appear in pairs $(x_i, \bar{x}_i)$ in the complete relay tree, where the left end of the pair is connected together. Relays are often built with a special type of contact pair, called a *transfer contact*, which are used for constructing a relay tree. For this reason this type of network is also called a *transfer tree*. A transfer contact is a three-terminal device (a relay-operated single pole double throw switch) as depicted in Figure 5.2.3, in which the top contact (also called a "make" or "normally open" contact) corresponds to the x_i contact, and the bottom contact (also called a "break" or "normally closed" contact) corresponds to the

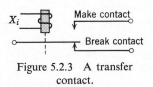

Figure 5.2.3   A transfer contact.

$\bar{x}_i$ contact. Each of the three elements making up the transfer contact is called a "spring" because of its physical structure as a springlike moving element.

The purpose of a complete relay tree network is to provide a closed path from the input terminal to exactly one particular output terminal for each possible combination of values for the variables $x_1, \ldots, x_n$. This function of such a network is called *complete decoding* or *complete selection*. It has many applications and is thus an important type of network. If we also do not allow any closed path between two output terminals for any combination of values of the variables (that is, no "sneak paths" between terminals), then, as has recently been shown by Moore [20], the complete relay tree network has the minimum possible number of contacts for complete decoding. Furthermore, he has shown that any relay contact network which provides (1) complete decoding, (2) has no "sneak paths" between output terminals for any combination of variables, and (3) has a minimum number of contacts, is a complete relay tree network.

In some applications condition 2 may not be required of a circuit for complete decoding. For example, if the input terminal were a power source and the output terminals were connected to relay coils so that the power source would energize one relay for each possible combination of inputs, we might allow a sneak path to exist between two output terminals, neither of which was connected to the input terminal, because this sneak path would not cause any erroneous relay coils to be energized. Without condition 2 being required, Lupanov [15] has obtained a network for $n = 5$ which has 60 contacts rather than the 62 contacts required by the complete relay tree. He also shows how such networks can be generalized to larger n, where for increasing n the number of contacts required for this generalized network asymptotically approaches one-half the number required by a complete relay tree. Lupanov's network for $n = 5$ is shown in Figure 5.2.4. Sneak paths exist between output terminals for various combinations of inputs in this network. For example, a sneak path between output terminals labeled i and j is seen to exist when $x_1 = x_2 = 1$; but here the input terminal is connected by a closed path to one of the output terminals near the bottom of the network (depending on the values of $x_3, x_4,$ and x_5) and the input terminal is not connected to more than one output terminal by any of the sneak paths between output terminals.

For the complete relay tree shown in Figure 5.2.2, the relay X_4 requires very many (2^4) contacts or eight transfer contacts, whereas relay X_3 requires only four transfer contacts, relay X_2 two transfer contacts, and relay X_1 only one transfer contact. By rearranging some of the subtrees of the tree, the contact distribution can be somewhat more evenly spread

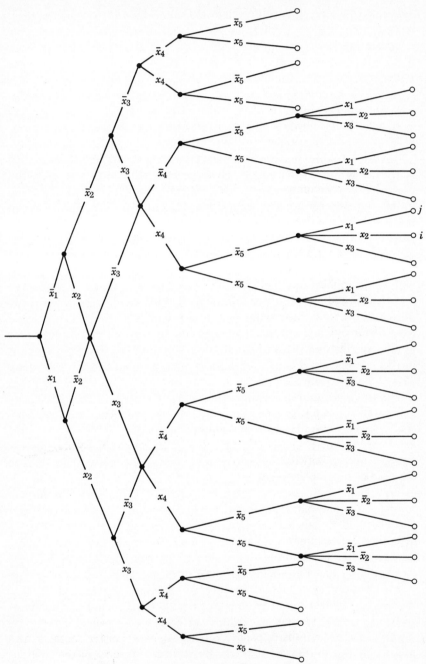

Figure 5.2.4   Lupanov's complete decoding network.

over the different relays, this being quite desirable for practical reasons. An example of such a redistribution is shown in Figure 5.2.5. In this complete relay tree the numbers of transfer contacts for relays X_1, X_2, X_3, and X_4 are respectively 1, 4, 5, and 5. A complete relay tree which has a redistribution of contacts as in Figure 5.2.5 is called a *folded tree*, and a sequence of n numbers, such as 1, 4, 5, 5, which is the number of transfer contacts required on each relay, is called an *admissible sequence* if there exists a folded complete relay tree requiring that number of contacts, respectively, for each relay.

Because variables may be interchanged in any way without altering the operation of the tree, we simply consider admissible sequences such that the numbers do not decrease as we proceed through the sequence. Given n, determining the possible admissible sequences is of interest for two reasons: (1) in order to find an admissible sequence that provides the most even contact distribution over the relays, and (2) given several types of relays, with specified number of transfer contacts on each relay, to find an admissible sequence which enables us to form a complete relay tree with a minimum number of relays. Consider the second problem for $n = 4$, where relays with two, four, and six transfer contacts per relay are available. In this case the tree shown in Figure 5.2.2 requires five relays (two relays for X_4), whereas the folded tree of Figure 5.2.5 requires only four relays. On the other hand, if only relays with two and four transfers were available, the tree of Figure 5.2.2 would require one less relay than that of Figure 5.2.5.

The first number in an admissible sequence must be a 1. This corresponds to the left-most transfer contact of the tree. Then the remaining $n - 1$ numbers of an admissible sequence must sum to $2^n - 2$, since the total number of transfer contacts in a complete relay tree is $2^n - 1$. Without any redistribution of contacts, the admissible sequence for an n-variable tree is

$$1, 2, 4, 8, \ldots, 2^{n-1}.$$

We now describe a simple procedure by which we can obtain other admissible sequences from this sequence; it has been shown that any admissible sequence can be obtained in this way.

An admissible sequence can be obtained from $1, 2, 4, 8, \ldots, 2^{n-1}$ by moving one or more units from a larger number to a smaller number, or by a succession of such operations, without moving any units to the number 1. The admissible sequences for $n = 4$ are as follows, with associated distribution of contacts on the two three-variable x_2, x_3, x_4 trees shown at the right.

$n = 4$ Admissible Sequence	Three Variable Contact Distribution	
	Upper Tree	Lower Tree
1, 2, 4, 8	1, 2, 4	1, 2, 4
1, 2, 5, 7	1, 2, 4	1, 3, 3
1, 2, 6, 6	1, 2, 4	1, 4, 2
1, 3, 3, 8	1, 2, 4	2, 1, 4
1, 3, 4, 7	1, 3, 3	2, 1, 4
1, 3, 5, 6	1, 4, 2	2, 1, 4
1, 4, 4, 6	1, 3, 3	3, 1, 3
1, 4, 5, 5	1, 4, 2	3, 1, 3

A method of obtaining a suitable contact distribution from any admissible sequence has been developed in [4], but it will not be discussed here. It should be noted, however, that sometimes essentially different

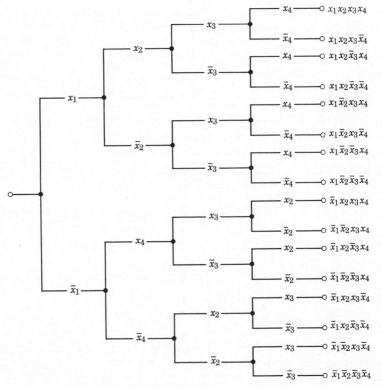

Figure 5.2.5   A folded complete relay tree for $n = 4$.

trees may correspond to the same admissible sequence. For example, Figure 5.2.5 gave one tree for sequence 1, 4, 5, 5, whereas Figure 5.2.6 gives another tree for this same admissible sequence. These two trees are readily seen to be essentially different, since Figure 5.2.5 requires contacts from

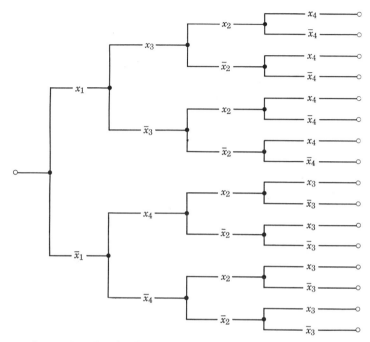

Figure 5.2.6   Another folded tree for admissible sequence 1, 4, 5, 5.

three different relays in the right-most column of contacts, but Figure 5.2.6 requires contacts only from two different relays in the right-most column.

The complete relay tree is indeed a very general type of network because it realizes all the canonical conjunctions. It can be used as the basis for the design of other types of networks. For example, a two-terminal network to realize any Boolean function of n-variables can be made by simply tying together the appropriate output terminals of an n-variable complete relay tree. Certain simplifications of this resulting network then may also become apparent. Also, by using Shannon's expansion theorem, the Boolean function may be expressed as

$$f(x_1, \ldots, x_n) = x_n g(x_1, \ldots, x_{n-1}) \vee \bar{x}_n h(x_1, \ldots, x_{n-1}) \vee k(x_1, \ldots, x_{n-1}),$$

where g, h, and k are disjoint. Then a two-terminal network for $f(x_1, \ldots, x_n)$ may be formed from a complete relay tree on variables $x_1, \ldots, x_{n-1}$ by tying the output terminals of the tree directly to a terminal for terms of $k(x_1, \ldots, x_{n-1})$, tying through a contact x_n for terms of g, and through a contact $\bar{x}_n$ for terms of h. Finally, multiple output relay networks, having disjoint outputs, may be realized by similar construction from a complete relay tree. Such a two output network, and its reduced form, for

$$\begin{cases} f_1 = x_1 x_2 \vee \bar{x}_1 \bar{x}_2 x_3 \\ f_2 = \bar{x}_1 \bar{x}_3 \vee \bar{x}_1 x_2 \vee x_1 \bar{x}_2 \end{cases}$$

is shown in Figure 5.2.7a and b, respectively. Notice that it would have

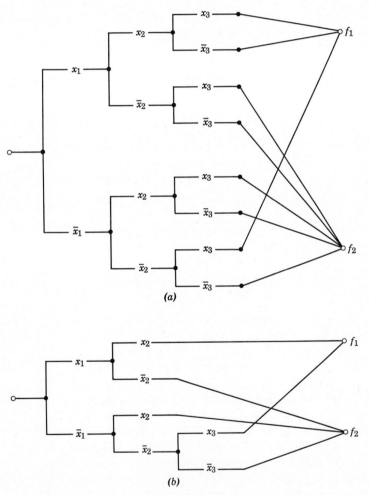

Figure 5.2.7   A two output network designed from a complete relay tree.

required ten contacts, even with factored forms, to represent f_1 and f_2 as two separate series-parallel networks, whereas the network in 5.2.7b requires eight contacts: one transfer on X_1, two transfers on X_2, and one transfer on X_3.

Frequently, rather than "complete decoding," we require only a partial relay tree where less than 2^n outputs are needed. This tree can easily be obtained by starting with a complete relay tree and eliminating the contacts

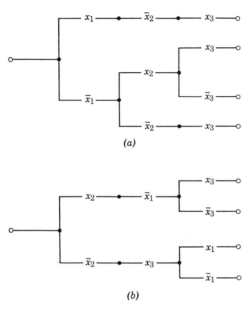

(a)

(b)

Figure 5.2.8   Two partial relay trees.

that are not connected to a required output terminal. Starting with different folded complete relay trees and deleting contacts will give networks requiring a different number of transfer contacts. Assuming that the relays have only transfer-type contacts, we may wish to minimize the total number of transfer contacts required in the partial relay tree; that is, roughly speaking, we attempt to distribute the contacts so that both the front and the back contacts of a transfer contact are used as often as possible. For example, let us assume that we require a partial relay tree, $n = 3$, where outputs are required for conjunctions $\bar{x}_1 x_2 x_3$, $\bar{x}_1 x_2 \bar{x}_3$, $x_1 \bar{x}_2 x_3$, and $\bar{x}_1 \bar{x}_2 x_3$. Two partial trees for this requirement are shown in Figure 5.2.8. For this example tree (a) requires a total of six transfer contacts or nine contacts, whereas (b) requires only five transfer contacts or eight contacts.

If the $n - 1, n - 2, \ldots,$ one variable subtrees of a complete relay tree are called *minor trees*, the number of transfer contacts removed from a complete tree to form a partial tree is the number of output terminals removed minus the number of minor trees removed. This can be seen as follows. For an n-variable complete relay tree there are 2^n output terminals and a total of $2^n - 1$ transfer contacts. Assuming a partial tree with m output terminals, then $2^n - m$ output terminals are removed from the complete tree. Assume that k minor trees are removed in this process, where $2^{j_1}, 2^{j_2}, \ldots, 2^{j_k}$ are the number of output terminals on each of these minor trees. Then $2^n - m = 2^{j_1} + 2^{j_2} + \cdots + 2^{j_k}$. If a minor tree has 2^{j_i} output terminals, it contains $2^{j_i} - 1$ transfer contacts. Thus the total number of transfer contacts removed by the k minor trees is

$$(2^{j_1} - 1) + (2^{j_2} - 1) + \ldots + (2^{j_k} - 1) = \left[\sum_{i=1}^{k} 2^{j_i} \right] - k = (2^n - m) - k.$$

This is the desired result.

The number of transfer contacts is thus

$$(2^n - 1) - [(2^n - m) - k] = m - 1 + k,$$

where m is the number of output terminals of the partial relay tree and k is the number of minor trees removed. Thus, since m is constant for a given requirement, to minimize the number of transfer contacts we must minimize the number of minor trees removed from the complete tree. That is, we look for a folded complete relay tree in which the output terminals not required are represented by as few minor trees as possible. For example, from Figure 5.2.8a and b the minor trees removed from the complete relay trees are shown within the dotted lines in Figure 5.2.9a and b respectively.

As seen by this example, the different order of the variables in the folded trees is a crucial point in reducing the number of minor trees which are removed to form a partial tree.

Note that each minor tree removed corresponds to a single cube of the complex defined by the canonical conjunctions not required in the partial tree. Thus for part a minor tree 1 corresponds to cube $11x$, minor tree 2 corresponds to cube 100, and minor tree 3 corresponds to cube 000. Similarly, for part b, minor tree 1 corresponds to cube $11x$ and minor tree 2 corresponds to cube $x00$, where in both cases the cubes form a cover of the complex defined by vertices:

$$\begin{Bmatrix} 110 \\ 111 \\ 100 \\ 000 \end{Bmatrix}.$$

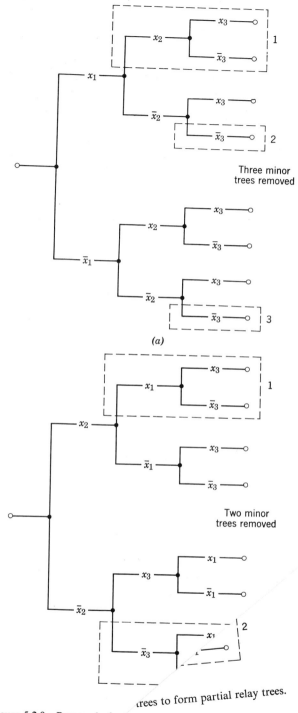

Three minor
trees removed

(a)

Two minor
trees removed

Figure 5.2.9   Removal of m‎‎... ‎rees to form partial relay trees.

285

It appears, then, that to find a partial relay tree with a minimum number of contacts, we simply need to find a cover of the unrequired vertices which covers each vertex exactly once and which uses a minimum number of cubes. Unfortunately, this is not quite the case because sometimes the cubes of such a "minimum" cover cannot be realized by a set of minor trees from any complete relay tree. This condition is illustrated in the following example, where $n = 4$ and the unrequired vertices are

$$\begin{matrix} x_1 & x_2 & x_3 & x_4 \end{matrix}$$

$$\left\{\begin{bmatrix} 0 & 1 & 0 & 0 \\ 1 & 1 & 0 & 0 \\ 0 & 0 & 0 & 1 \\ 0 & 0 & 1 & 1 \\ 1 & 1 & 1 & 0 \\ 1 & 1 & 1 & 1 \\ 1 & 0 & 1 & 0 \\ 1 & 0 & 1 & 1 \end{bmatrix}\right\}.$$

Here the unique cover using a minimum number of cubes is $\{x100, 00x1, 1x1x\}$, and this is not attainable from any complete relay tree. This is easily seen as follows. The left-most pair of contacts of any complete relay tree is a transfer contact for some variable. Now if the unrequired vertices do not include the $(n-1)$-cube with a 0 or 1 entry in the coordinate for that variable (x's elsewhere), then both contacts of this first transfer contact are required in the partial tree. [In our example no $(n-1)$-cube is in the complex of unrequired vertices.] If both contacts of this variable are used, then each cube of the cover of unrequired vertices must either have a 0 or a 1 in the coordinate of that variable. In our case, in the cover

$$\left\{\begin{matrix} x100 \\ 00x1 \\ 1x1x \end{matrix}\right\}$$

no $(n$

cover can

cubes with a is present and also no column is free of x's, and thus the ed to form a partial tree. By replacing one of these bes such as

$$\left\{\begin{matrix} 0 & 1 & 0 & 0 \\ & 1 & 0 & 0 \\ & & x & 1 \\ 1 & x & 1 & \end{matrix}\right\},$$

variable x_1 satisfies the condition, that is, the cover can be partitioned on x_1, giving

$$
\begin{array}{cccc}
x_1 & x_2 & x_3 & x_4
\end{array}
$$

$$
\left\{
\begin{array}{c|c}
\begin{matrix} 0 \\ 0 \end{matrix} & \left. \begin{matrix} 1 & 0 & 0 \\ 0 & x & 1 \end{matrix} \right\} \; A \\
\hline
\begin{matrix} 1 \\ 1 \end{matrix} & \left. \begin{matrix} 1 & 0 & 0 \\ x & 1 & x \end{matrix} \right\} \; B
\end{array}
\right\},
$$

so that x_1 is the left-most contact.

Now iteratively A and B must each satisfy the same criteria as before for some coordinate. For B this is true since variable x_3 has cube $x1x$; and for A it is true since A can be partitioned on either variable x_2 or x_4. This iterative partitioning of the cover must then be satisfied for the cover to produce a partial relay tree. Furthermore, the iterative partitioning gives the order in which the transfer contacts appear in the partial tree. Carrying out a partitioning in our example, we obtain

$$
\begin{array}{cccc}
x_1 & x_2 & x_3 & x_4
\end{array}
$$

$$
\left\{
\begin{array}{c|c|c|c}
0 & 1 & 0 & 0 \\
\hline
0 & 0 & x & 1 \\
\hline
1 & x & 1 & x \\
1 & 1 & 0 & 0
\end{array}
\right\}
$$

and the partial tree so resulting is shown in Figure 5.2.10. This tree has a minimum number of transfer contacts. In general, however, it is quite difficult to insure that a cover, having the iterative partitioning property as described, also contains a minimum number of cubes—as required to obtain a partial relay tree with a minimum number of transfer contacts. Karnaugh maps are useful for small n. For large n, we can use the extraction algorithm, with subsequent trials of iterative partitions to obtain a good, if not exactly minimum, partial tree realization.

Note that in a relay tree we require each variable to have a contact in each input-terminal to output-terminal series of contacts. If this were not required, further network simplification could, of course, be obtained by removing certain contacts from the partial relay tree. Depending on the particular application, contact removal may or may not be desirable.

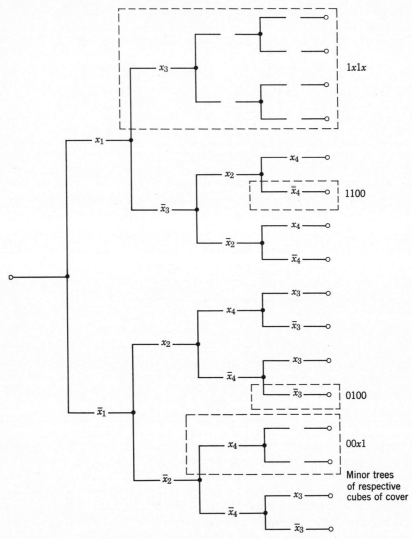

Figure 5.2.10   Partial tree for *n* = 4 example.

For Figure 5.2.10 contact removal would give the network shown in Figure 5.2.11.

The network of Figure 5.2.11 will have the required input-terminal to output-terminal closed paths, but the paths will also be closed for some other variable combination, namely, some which are unrequired conditions. Note that the network of Figure 5.2.10 requires eleven transfer contacts,

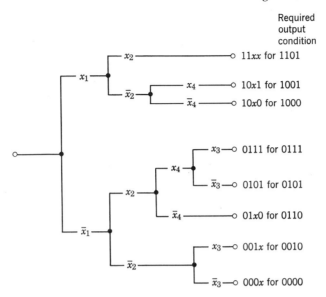

Figure 5.2.11 Contact removal from partial relay tree of Figure 5.2.10.

whereas that of Figure 5.2.11 requires only seven transfer contacts. If the unrequired conditions never actually occur as input variable combinations, no trouble could arise from the contact removal. If, however, these variable combinations do arise in the given application and we desire no output terminal to be connected for such variable combinations, then we cannot use a network in which contacts have been removed.

5.3 PLANAR AND DUAL NETWORKS

An interesting class of bilateral switching networks is called "planar" networks. The concept of a network being planar is based on an analogous graph theory concept. If the interconnection points for contacts of a network are called *nodes*, and the lines between nodes containing contacts are called *branches*, then the resulting structure of nodes and branches is called a *linear graph*. A linear graph is called *planar* if it can be drawn so that each node is a different point and no two branches intersect at any point which is not a node. (More precisely, the graph is planar if it can be imbedded in a plane.) For a two-terminal network the two output terminals correspond to two distinguished nodes of the linear graph. Let the *augmented graph* for a two-terminal network consist of the linear graph for the two-terminal network plus one added node and two added branches which connect the added node to each of the two distinguished nodes. The two-terminal network is called *planar* if the corresponding augmented graph is planar. A similar definition is possible for multiterminal planar networks. Any series-parallel network can be shown to be planar, and also some, but not all, bridge networks are planar. Several examples of planar and nonplanar networks are depicted in Figure 5.3.1.

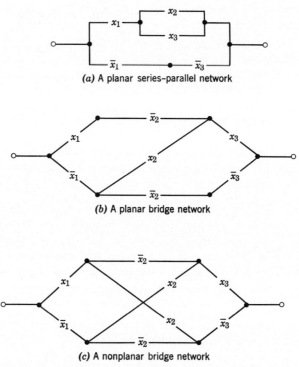

(a) A planar series–parallel network

(b) A planar bridge network

(c) A nonplanar bridge network

Figure 5.3.1   Planar and nonplanar two-terminal networks.

Obviously, the networks of Figure 5.3.1*a* and *b* are planar since their graphs contain no crossing branches and a branch can be drawn between the output terminals without crossing any branches. For *c* we must show that the augmented graph cannot be drawn so as to contain no intersecting branches. The augmented graph is shown in the following diagram. It is well known that this graph is not planar. This is indicated, for example, by noting that the branch labeled α cannot be redrawn in any way, to connect its two nodes, without intersecting at least one other branch of the graph.

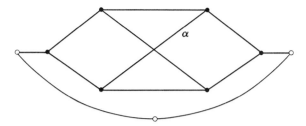

Planar networks are of interest since for any of these a dual network can be obtained, where this dual network realizes the dual of the Boolean function that is realized by the original planar network. The dual network is obtained through the dual graph for the network since a dual graph exists for any planar graph.* We give a geometric description for dual graphs and dual networks, for this provides a simple method for constructing the dual of a two-terminal network. For a planar graph, the *regions* of the graph are those areas of the plane which are bounded by branches of the graph and contain no branches or nodes in the interior of the area. The *dual* of a planar graph *G* is formed by placing a node in each region of *G* and also a branch between two nodes in the dual graph for each branch of the original graph *G* that forms a boundary between its corresponding two regions. In an example of a planar graph and its dual in Figure 5.3.2, the branches of the dual graph are indicated by dots. Note that the dual graph has a branch corresponding to each branch of the original planar graph.

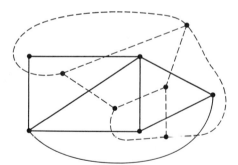

Figure 5.3.2   A planar graph and its dual.

The dual of a planar two-terminal network has the graphical configuration of the dual of its augmented graph. For convenience we consider the augmented graph to be drawn so that the two output terminals occur on a

* Since a graph has a dual graph if and only if the graph is planar, the concept of a dual network is also restricted to planar networks.

horizontal axis, the added node of the augmented graph appears at infinity on this axis, and the added branches extend horizontally to the left from the left-most distinguished node and to the right from the right-most distinguished node. The dual network is then formed from the dual

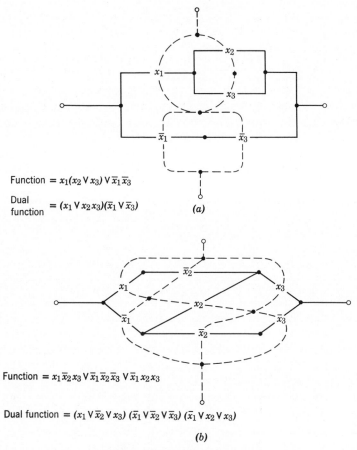

Function $= x_1(x_2 \lor x_3) \lor \bar{x}_1 \bar{x}_3$

Dual
function $= (x_1 \lor x_2 x_3)(\bar{x}_1 \lor \bar{x}_3)$

(a)

Function $= x_1 \bar{x}_2 x_3 \lor \bar{x}_1 \bar{x}_2 \bar{x}_3 \lor \bar{x}_1 x_2 x_3$

Dual function $= (x_1 \lor \bar{x}_2 \lor x_3) \, (\bar{x}_1 \lor \bar{x}_2 \lor \bar{x}_3) \, (\bar{x}_1 \lor x_2 \lor x_3)$

(b)

Figure 5.3.3   Dual networks.

of the augmented graph by (1) eliminating the two branches corresponding to the added branches, (2) letting the two output terminals of the dual network correspond to the nodes for the upper infinite region and lower infinite region respectively, and (3) placing the same contact in each branch as appeared in the corresponding branch of the original two-terminal network. Several two-terminal networks and their dual networks are shown in Figure 5.3.3, where the dual networks are shown by dotted lines. The Boolean functions and resulting dual functions are also given, where the dual networks realize the dual functions.

In Figure 5.3.3a the dual network is easily seen to represent the dual function since duality of the function is a replacement of OR with AND and AND with OR. This is depicted in the dual network for the series-parallel network of part *a* by replacing parallel paths with a series path and replacing each series path by parallel paths. For part *b* (a bridge network) it is not quite so clear that the dual network actually realizes the dual function. By tracing paths in the dual networks, however, we see that the dual network represents the function

$$f = x_1 x_2 \bar{x}_3 \vee \bar{x}_1 \bar{x}_2 \vee \bar{x}_1 x_2 x_3 \vee \bar{x}_2 x_3$$

$$= x_1 x_2 \bar{x}_3 \vee \bar{x}_1 \bar{x}_2 \bar{x}_3 \vee \bar{x}_1 \bar{x}_2 x_3 \vee \bar{x}_1 x_2 x_3 \vee x_1 \bar{x}_2 x_3.$$

By expanding the dual function of the figure, we obtain

$$\text{dual function} = x_1 \bar{x}_2 x_3 \vee x_1 x_2 \bar{x}_3 \vee \bar{x}_1 \bar{x}_2 \vee \bar{x}_1 x_3 \vee \bar{x}_2 \, x_3$$

$$= x_1 \bar{x}_2 x_3 \vee x_1 x_2 \bar{x}_3 \vee \bar{x}_1 \bar{x}_2 \bar{x}_3 \vee \bar{x}_1 \bar{x}_2 x_3 \vee \bar{x}_1 x_2 x_3,$$

showing that, indeed, the dual network does represent the dual function. Unfortunately, dual graphs do not exist for nonplanar graphs; thus, for example, a network which represents the dual of the function represented by Figure 5.3.1c cannot be obtained through this dual graph process.

In Section 2.7, we discussed how duality in Boolean functions enables us to change from a disjunctive normal form of a function to a conjunctive normal form, and also to obtain a complement of a function *f* by obtaining the dual of *f*, and then changing the sense of complementation on each variable appearance. Thus the process for obtaining a dual network for a planar network can also be used to obtain a network for the complement of the function realized by the planar network. The "complementary networks" for the networks of Figure 5.3.3a and *b* are shown in Figure 5.3.4a and *b*, respectively. These are obtained directly from the dual networks by simply replacing each x_i appearance with an $\bar{x}_i$, and each $\bar{x}_i$ appearance with an x_i.

This technique of obtaining dual networks and complementary networks is very useful in designing bilateral switching networks. In the next section we include an application of this technique to symmetric networks.

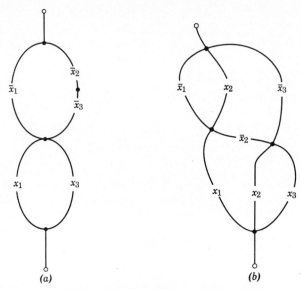

(a)   (b)

Figure 5.3.4   Complementary networks.

5.4 SYMMETRIC NETWORKS

Quite often in switching network synthesis, the given switching function to be realized is a totally symmetric function (see Definition 2.11.2), or some extension of the given switching function is a totally symmetric function. For example, both the binary sum and binary carry functions discussed earlier are totally symmetric functions. Totally symmetric functions can be realized by a special form of relay contact networks called *symmetric networks*. A symmetric network realization, in all but some trivial cases, has significantly fewer contacts than the best possible series-parallel network realization of the totally symmetric function. As an example of this, consider the totally symmetric function

$$S_{0,2}(x_1, x_2, x_3) = \bar{x}_1\bar{x}_2\bar{x}_3 \lor x_1x_2\bar{x}_3 \lor x_1\bar{x}_2x_3 \lor \bar{x}_1x_2x_3$$
$$= x_1(x_2\bar{x}_3 \lor \bar{x}_2x_3) \lor \bar{x}_1(x_2x_3 \lor \bar{x}_2\bar{x}_3).$$

A series-parallel representation for this function is shown in Figure 5.4.1. This network requires a total of ten contacts or five transfer contacts. A symmetric network for $S_{0,2}(x_1, x_2, x_3)$ is shown in Figure 5.4.2. This symmetric network requires eight contacts or four transfer contacts—one less transfer contact than the series-parallel realization. Although there is only a difference of one transfer contact between the two networks for

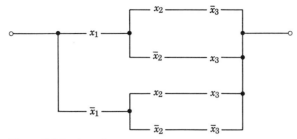

Figure 5.4.1   A series-parallel network for $S_{0,2}(x_1, x_2, x_3)$.

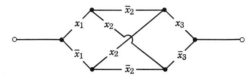

Figure 5.4.2   A symmetric network for $S_{0,2}(x_1, x_2, x_3)$.

this example, greater savings can be obtained for symmetric functions having more variables. A basic symmetric network can be constructed in a general way for any given number n of variables, and any symmetric function of n-variables can be realized from the basic symmetric network. The basic symmetric network for $n = 3$ is shown in Figure 5.4.3.

Like a relay tree, this network has one input terminal and many output terminals (in this case, $n + 1$ output terminals), and the network can be constructed from transfer contacts. The basic symmetric network, however, is not graphically a tree. As drawn in Figure 5.4.3 each variable has contacts only in one column, and also various horizontal levels are formed and attached to output terminals. These levels correspond to all the

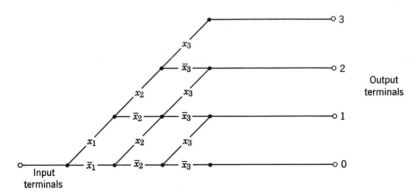

Figure 5.4.3   Basic symmetric network for $n = 3$.

possible a-numbers of a totally symmetric function of n-variables; in this case, 0, 1, 2, and 3. Thus, for example, a closed path will be formed between the input terminal and the output terminal labeled 2 if and only if exactly two out of the three relays X_1, X_2, X_3 are energized. By iteration—adding columns and rows of contacts—it should be clear how the basic symmetric network is formed for general n.

Since a function $f(x_1, x_2, \ldots, x_n)$ is totally symmetric in the variables $x_1, x_2, \ldots, x_n$ if and only if it can be specified by a set of a-numbers $a_1, a_2, \ldots, a_k$, where $0 \leq a_i \leq n$, and written as

$$f(x_1, x_2, \ldots, x_n) = S_{a_1, a_2, \ldots, a_k}(x_1, x_2, \ldots, x_n)$$

(see Theorem 2.11.1), it is a simple matter to realize any totally symmetric function of the variables $x_1, x_2, \ldots, x_n$ from the n-variable basic symmetric network by simply connecting together the output terminals corresponding to the a-numbers $a_1, a_2, \ldots, a_k$ to form the output terminal of the two-terminal network for

$$S_{a_1, a_2, \ldots, a_k}(x_1, x_2, \ldots, x_n).$$

When the output terminals are interconnected, certain contacts can also be eliminated or combined to further reduce the network. In our example for $S_{0,2}(x_1, x_2, x_3)$ the steps for obtaining the network of Figure 5.4.2 are shown in Figure 5.4.4.

From Figure 5.4.4a to b the superfluous contacts to levels 3 and 1 which cannot form any closed paths to levels 0 or 2 are eliminated. From b to c we note that contact $\bar{x}_3$ labeled β and contact $\bar{x}_3$ labeled α can be combined into one contact with no erroneous "sneak paths" being introduced. When this is done, Figure 5.4.4c is the same network as in Figure 5.4.2.

If the variables of symmetry of a function are not $x_1, x_2, \ldots, x_n$ but have some complemented variables, a slight modification of the basic symmetric network is necessary. If x_i is not complemented as a variable of symmetry, in column i of the basic symmetric network the diagonal contacts are x_i contacts and the horizontal contacts are $\bar{x}_i$ contacts. If x_i is complemented as a variable of symmetry, however, reversing the types of contacts on horizontal and diagonal entries to x_i and $\bar{x}_i$ respectively produces a basic symmetric network where any subset of the variables of symmetry may be complemented. As an example of this, Figure 5.4.5 shows the steps in obtaining a simplified symmetric network for the function $S_{0,1,4}(x_1, \bar{x}_2, \bar{x}_3, x_4)$.

For certain symmetric functions (particularly those where the set of a-numbers forms an arithmetic progression in which the number following the largest a-number in the progression is greater than n), an important type of simplification of the basic symmetric network can be accomplished.

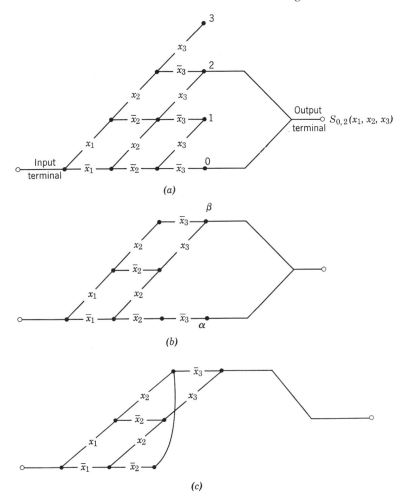

Figure 5.4.4   Obtaining a simplified symmetric network for $S_{0,2}(x_1, x_2, x_3)$ from the basic symmetric network.

This is called a "shifting down" or "folding," in which the interconnections of certain diagonal contacts are changed to go down one or more levels, rather than up, thus combining a higher level with a lower level. An example of this technique is given for the function $S_{3,5}(x_1, x_2, x_3, x_4, x_5)$. By "folding" down the 4-level to the 2-level, the 3-level of the basic symmetric network also becomes the 5-level; that is, the output on level-3 is connected to the input terminal when both exactly three variables equal 1 and five variables equal 1. The application of this

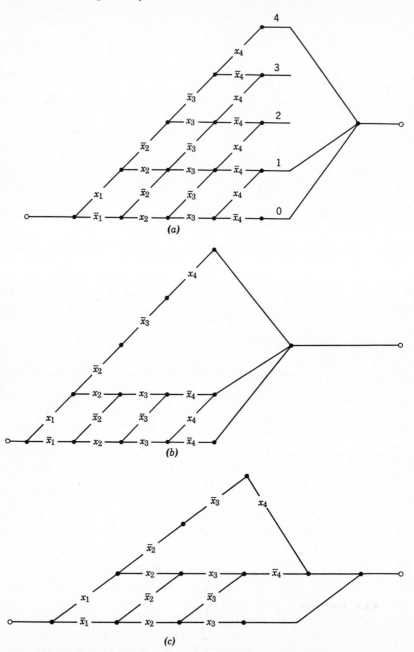

Figure 5.4.5   Symmetric network for $S_{0,1,4}(x_1, \bar{x}_2, \bar{x}_3, x_4)$.   (*a*) Basic symmetric network with output terminals connected.   (*b*) Superfluous contacts removed.   (*c*) Redundant contacts removed.

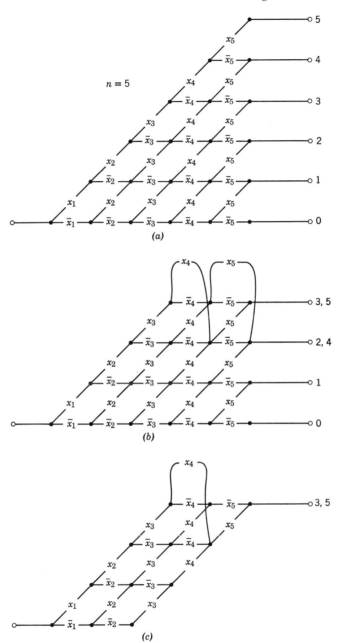

Figure 5.4.6 Folding for $S_{3,5}(x_1, x_2, x_3, x_4, x_5)$. (*a*) Basic symmetric network. (*b*) Folding 4-level to 2-level. (*c*) Superfluous contacts removed.

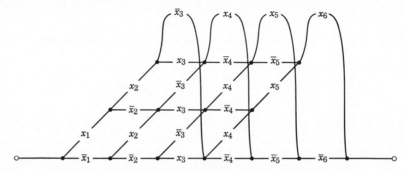

Figure 5.4.7   Symmetric network for $S_{0,3,6}(x_1, x_2, \bar{x}_3, x_4, x_5, x_6)$.

technique and the resulting network are shown in Figure 5.4.6. The folding technique folds a level down k levels for an arithmetic progression of difference k, thus in the preceding example, $k = 2$, and we folded level 4 down two levels to level 2. Two other symmetric networks obtained by folding are shown in Figures 5.4.7 and 5.4.8. Note that $S_{1,3,5}(x_1, x_2, x_3, x_4, x_5)$ has value 1 if and only if an odd number of variables equal 1. This type of circuit is also called an "odd parity check" circuit.

Care must be taken in the folding process to make sure that no sneak paths are introduced. The network for $S_{1,3}(x_1, x_2, x_3, x_4, x_5)$ cannot be simplified by folding, as can be checked by the reader, but here Theorem 2.11.5 supplies an equivalent form $S_{2,4}(\bar{x}_1, \bar{x}_2, \bar{x}_3, \bar{x}_4, \bar{x}_5)$ to which the folding technique may be applied.

By using the basic symmetric network on n-variables, a network having outputs for more than one symmetric function can be formed if the symmetric functions have mutually disjoint sets of a-numbers and also the same variables of symmetry. Thus, for example, the single network in Figure 5.4.9 realizes both symmetric functions $S_{0,2,4}(x_1, x_2, x_3, x_4, x_5)$ and $S_{1,3,5}(x_1, x_2, x_3, x_4, x_5)$.

The technique of folding may also be used for this two output network

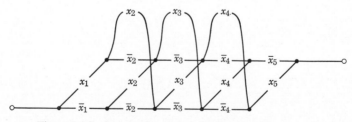

Figure 5.4.8   Symmetric network for $S_{1,3,5}(x_1, x_2, x_3, x_4, x_5)$.

$$S_{1,3,5}\,(x_1, x_2, x_3, x_4, x_5)$$

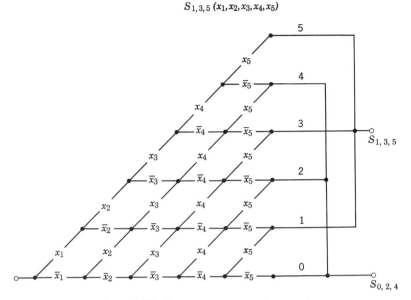

Figure 5.4.9   Two-output symmetric network.

since the *a*-numbers are arithmetic sequences for both functions. This simplified circuit is shown in Figure 5.4.10.

We now show how the techniques of complementary networks discussed in Section 5.3 can be applied to symmetric network design. From Theorem 2.11.4 we know that the complement of a symmetric function is also a symmetric function and

$$\overline{S_{a_1, a_2, \ldots, a_k}(x_1, \ldots, x_n)} = S_{a_1', a_2', \ldots, a_j'}(x_1, x_2, \ldots, x_n),$$

where

$$\{a_1', a_2', \ldots, a_j'\} = \{0, 1, \ldots, n\} - \{a_1, a_2, \ldots, a_k\}.$$

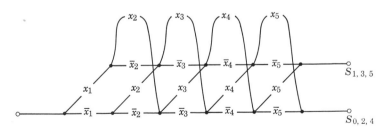

Figure 5.4.10   Simplification by folding for $S_{1,3,5}(x_1, x_2, x_3, x_4, x_5)$ and $S_{0,2,4}(x_1, x_2, x_3, x_4, x_5)$.

Thus if a symmetric network can be obtained for $S_{a_1', \ldots, a_j'}(x_1, \ldots, x_n)$ and this network is planar, then the complementary network realizes the function $S_{a_1, a_2, \ldots, a_k}(x_1, \ldots, x_n)$. This complementary symmetric network may give a simpler realization for $S_{a_1, \ldots, a_k}(x_1, \ldots, x_n)$ than obtainable

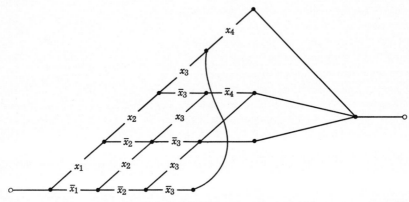

Figure 5.4.11   Network for $S_{1,2,4}(x_1, x_2, x_3, x_4)$.

from a direct realization. As an example of this consider designing a symmetric network for $S_{1,2,4}(x_1, x_2, x_3, x_4)$. By using the basic symmetric network and folding to eliminate one x_4 contact and by removing redundant contacts, we obtain the network shown in Figure 5.4.11. This

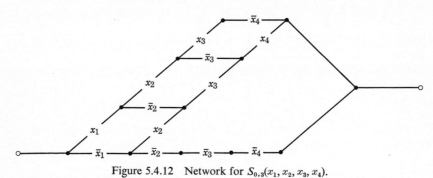

Figure 5.4.12   Network for $S_{0,3}(x_1, x_2, x_3, x_4)$.

network requires exactly seven transfer contacts. If, however, we use the relation that

$$\overline{S_{1,2,4}(x_1, x_2, x_3, x_4)} = S_{0,3}(x_1, x_2, x_3, x_4)$$

to design a network for $S_{0,3}$, we obtain the network shown in Figure 5.4.12. This network could be folded to eliminate an $\bar{x}_4$ contact, but a nonplanar network from which we could not form a graphical dual would be formed. Taking the graphical dual of the unfolded network and complementing contacts gives another realization for $S_{1,2,4}(x_1, x_2, x_3, x_4)$, as shown in Figure 5.4.13. This network requires six transfer contacts plus one contact for x_4, which is one less contact than required in Figure 5.4.11.

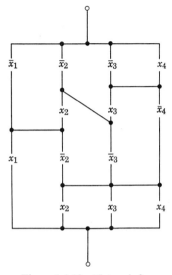

Certain Boolean functions which are not totally symmetric functions, may be symmetric in some subset of the variables, that is, the functions are "partially symmetric." The techniques for symmetric networks and relay tree networks may then be combined to obtain rather economical network realizations. As an example consider the function

$$f = \bar{x}_1\bar{x}_2\bar{x}_3 \lor x_4\bar{x}_5(\bar{x}_1\bar{x}_2x_3 \lor \bar{x}_1x_2\bar{x}_3 \lor x_1\bar{x}_2\bar{x}_3)$$

$$\lor x_1x_2x_3x_5 \lor (x_4x_5 \lor \bar{x}_4\bar{x}_5)(\bar{x}_1x_2x_3 \lor x_1\bar{x}_2x_3$$

$$\lor x_1x_2\bar{x}_3).$$

Figure 5.4.13   Network for
$S_{1,2,4}(x_1, x_2, x_3, x_4)$
by complementary network of
$S_{0,3}(x_1, x_2, x_3, x_4)$.

This function is symmetric in $\{x_1, x_2, x_3\}$, but not also in $\{x_4, x_5\}$. Since it is symmetric in $\{x_1, x_2, x_3\}$ it can be realized by using the basic symmetric network for x_1, x_2, x_3 and then completing it through suitable circuits for x_4 and x_5. This network, after obvious simplifications, is shown in Figure 5.4.14.

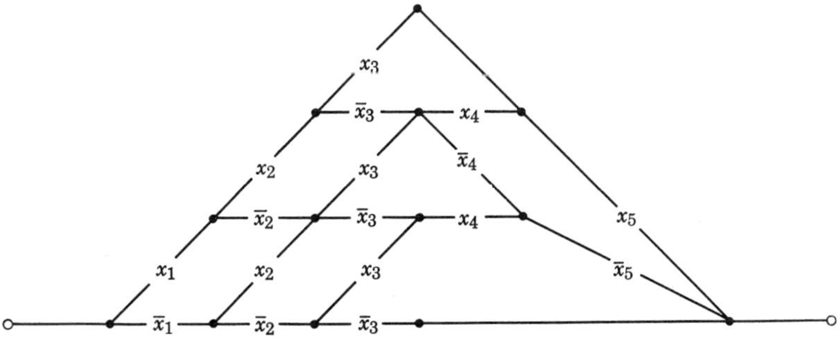

Figure 5.4.14   Realization of a partially symmetric function.

5.5 DETECTION OF TOTALLY SYMMETRIC FUNCTIONS

From Section 5.4 we saw that knowing the symmetries of a given Boolean function may be very useful, particularly if we wish to design a relay contact network for the function. In this section we describe a method for the detection of totally symmetric functions. We shall not consider the problem of detection for partial symmetries, although it should be apparent to the reader that with some added complications the method can be extended to determine this.

Given a Boolean function $f(x_1, \ldots, x_n)$ we represent f by the set of vertices for $f^{-1}(1)$. Let $V = \{v_1, v_2, \ldots, v_m\}$ be this set of vertices or 0-cubes. Remember that the jth coordinate of some 0-cube v_i corresponds to the value of the jth variable x_j. Properties of V determine whether f is totally symmetric, and if so, they determine the variables of symmetry. Let us now consider V as a rectangular array where each row corresponds to a 0-cube and each column cooresponds to a variable. We define p_j as the number of 0's in the jth column of V, and q_j the number of 1's in the jth column of V, $1 \leq j \leq n$. Now f being totally symmetric implies that either

$$\text{or} \qquad \left. \begin{aligned} \frac{p_j}{p_j} &= \frac{p_1}{q_1} \\[2mm] \frac{q_j}{p_j} &= \frac{p_1}{q_1} \end{aligned} \quad \text{for } 1 \leq j \leq n \right\} \quad \text{Condition I.}$$

This can be seen as follows. Interchanging columns 1 and j in V gives another set of vertices V'; if f is symmetric in $\{x_1, x_j\}$, V' must equal V, because for symmetry we require that $f(x_1, x_2, \ldots, x_n) = f(x_j, x_2, \ldots, x_{j-1}, x_1, x_{j+1}, \ldots, x_n)$. Since $V = V'$, however, this implies that $p_j/q_j = p_1/q_1$. Similarly, if f is symmetric in $\{x_1, \bar{x}_j\}$, we have $q_j/p_j = p_1/q_1$. For total symmetry, however, we require symmetry between all pairs of variables, proving condition I to be necessary. Given V, we can then calculate p_j and q_j for each j, $1 \leq j \leq n$. If condition I is not satisfied, then f is not totally symmetric. If condition I is satisfied, then f is totally symmetric if it also satisfies certain other conditions. Let us first assume that condition I is satisfied and $p_1 \neq q_1$, that is, that the number of 1's is not equal to the number of 0's in the first column. We then form a V' by inverting those variables with columns where $q_j > p_j$, that is, we change 0's to 1's and 1's to 0's in columns having more 1's than 0's, giving a V' with the inverted columns corresponding to inverted variables and where each column of V' has fewer 1's than 0's. Since V is assumed to satisfy condition I, V' satisfies

$$\frac{p_j'}{q_j'} = \frac{p_1'}{q_1'}, \qquad 1 \le j \le n.$$

An example is shown in Figure 5.5.1.

Obtaining V' gives the set of variables of symmetry if f is totally symmetric. In our example, if f is totally symmetric, then it is totally symmetric

$$
\begin{array}{cc}
V & V' \\
\begin{array}{cccc}
x_1 & x_2 & x_3 & x_4
\end{array} &
\begin{array}{cccc}
x_1 & x_2 & \bar{x}_3 & x_4
\end{array} \\
\left[\begin{array}{cccc}
0 & 0 & 1 & 0 \\
0 & 0 & 1 & 1 \\
0 & 0 & 0 & 0 \\
0 & 1 & 1 & 0 \\
1 & 0 & 1 & 0 \\
0 & 1 & 0 & 1 \\
1 & 0 & 0 & 1 \\
1 & 1 & 1 & 1 \\
1 & 1 & 0 & 0
\end{array}\right] &
\left[\begin{array}{cccc}
0 & 0 & 0 & 0 \\
0 & 0 & 0 & 1 \\
0 & 0 & 1 & 0 \\
0 & 1 & 0 & 0 \\
1 & 0 & 0 & 0 \\
0 & 1 & 1 & 1 \\
1 & 0 & 1 & 1 \\
1 & 1 & 0 & 1 \\
1 & 1 & 1 & 0
\end{array}\right]
\end{array}
$$

$$
\begin{array}{llcccc}
p_j & \quad & 5 & 5 & 4 & 5 \\
q_j & \quad & 4 & 4 & 5 & 4
\end{array}
\qquad
\begin{array}{llcccc}
p_j' & \quad & 5 & 5 & 5 & 5 \\
q_j' & \quad & 4 & 4 & 4 & 4
\end{array}
$$

Figure 5.5.1 Test for Condition I and conversion to V'.

in variables x_1, x_2, $\bar{x}_3$, x_4. At this point Theorem 2.11.6 could be used to test for total symmetry by the two permutations of variables of V'. Rather than doing this, however, we test for total symmetry using Theorem 2.11.1. Since f is totally symmetric if and only if it can be specified by a set of a-numbers, we can inspect V' for possible a-numbers. Let r_i be the number of 1's in row i of V', $1 \le i \le m$. We call r_i the weight of row i. Then each r_i must be an a-number if f is totally symmetric since row i of V' gives a set of values of the variables for which f equals 1. In addition, if r_i is an a-number, there are

$$\binom{n}{r_i} = \frac{n!}{(n - r_i)!\, r_i!}$$

possible 0-cubes in which each contains r_i 1's and $n - r_i$ 0's; and all such 0-cubes must correspond to conditions for $f^{-1}(1)$ if f is totally symmetric. Thus we require V' to satisfy Condition II.

If r_i is a row weight of V', then $\binom{n}{r_i}$ $\Big\}$ Condition II.
rows of V' have weight r_i.

We conclude that if $p_1 \neq q_1$ and Conditions I and II are satisfied, then f is totally symmetric, having variables of symmetry indicated by variables of V' and a-numbers indicated by the set of row weights of V'. We can test for Condition II by partitioning V' into sets of equal row weights. This is shown in Figure 5.5 2 for our example. Thus we conclude that the function is the totally symmetric function $S_{0,1,3}(x_1, x_2, \bar{x}_3, x_4)$.

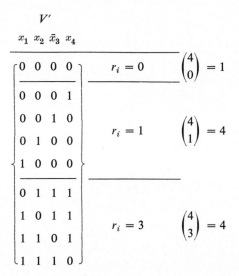

Figure 5.5.2   Partitioning V' into equal row weights.

Finally, we consider the case that $p_j = q_j$ for all j of V. Here it is not immediately evident which variables should be inverted to obtain a set of variables of symmetry if Condition II is not satisfied for V. Rather than trying all possible combinations, f can be expanded about some variable (say x_1) as

$$f(x_1, \ldots, x_n) = \bar{x}_1 f(0, x_2, \ldots, x_n) \vee x_1 f(1, x_2, \ldots, x_n).$$

Then by Theorem 2.11.7 we know that f is totally symmetric if and only if f can be expressed as

$$S_{a_1, a_2, \ldots, a_k}(x_1, x_2, \ldots, x_n) =$$
$$\bar{x}_1 \cdot S_{a_1, a_2, \ldots, a_k}(x_2, \ldots, x_n) \vee x_1 \cdot S_{a_1 - 1, a_2 - 1, \ldots, a_k - 1}(x_2, \ldots, x_n),$$

where $a_i - 1$ and a_j are eliminated in the expansion if $a_i = 0$ and $a_j = n$, respectively. This expansion will modify V to two sets of vertices, each having $n - 1$ coordinates, which may not have equal numbers of 0's and 1's in all columns. If each of these two sets does not have equal numbers of

V of $f(x_1, x_2, x_3, x_4)$

$$
\begin{array}{cccc}
x_1 & x_2 & x_3 & x_4 \\
\end{array}\quad r_j
$$

$$
\left.\begin{array}{c}
\begin{bmatrix}
0 & 0 & 1 & 0 \\
0 & 0 & 0 & 1 \\
1 & 0 & 0 & 0 \\
\hline
0 & 1 & 1 & 1 \\
1 & 1 & 1 & 0 \\
1 & 1 & 0 & 1 \\
\end{bmatrix}
\end{array}\right.
\begin{array}{c}
1 \\
1 \\
1 \\
\\
3 \\
3 \\
3 \\
\end{array}
\quad
\begin{array}{l}
\binom{4}{1} = 4 \\[10pt]
\\
\binom{4}{3} = 4 \\
\end{array}
$$

$$
\begin{array}{ccccc}
p_j & 3 & 3 & 3 & 3 \\
q_j & 3 & 3 & 3 & 3 \\
\end{array}
$$

Expanding around x_1 gives

V of $f(0, x_2, x_3, x_4)$

$$
\begin{array}{ccc}
x_2 & x_3 & x_4 \\
\end{array}
$$

$$
\left\{\begin{matrix}
0 & 1 & 0 \\
0 & 0 & 1 \\
1 & 1 & 1 \\
\end{matrix}\right\}
$$

$$
\begin{array}{cccc}
p_j & 2 & 1 & 1 \\
q_j & 1 & 2 & 2 \\
\end{array}
$$

V' of $f(0, x_2, x_3, x_4)$

$$
\begin{array}{ccc}
x_2 & \bar{x}_3 & \bar{x}_4 \\
\end{array}\quad r_j
$$

$$
\left\{\begin{matrix}
0 & 0 & 1 \\
0 & 1 & 0 \\
1 & 0 & 0 \\
\end{matrix}\right\}
\begin{array}{c}
1 \\ 1 \\ 1 \\
\end{array}
\quad \binom{3}{1} = 3
$$

$$
\begin{array}{cccc}
p'_j & 2 & 2 & 2 \\
q'_j & 1 & 1 & 1 \\
\end{array}
$$

Therefore $f(0, x_2, \bar{x}_3, \bar{x}_4) = S_1(x_2, \bar{x}_3, \bar{x}_4)$

V of $f(1, x_2, x_3, x_4)$

$$
\begin{array}{ccc}
x_2 & x_3 & x_4 \\
\end{array}
$$

$$
\left\{\begin{matrix}
0 & 0 & 0 \\
1 & 1 & 0 \\
1 & 0 & 1 \\
\end{matrix}\right\}
$$

$$
\begin{array}{cccc}
p_j & 2 & 1 & 1 \\
q_j & 1 & 2 & 2 \\
\end{array}
$$

V' of $f(1, x_2, x_3, x_4)$

$$
\begin{array}{ccc}
x_2 & \bar{x}_3 & \bar{x}_4 \\
\end{array}\quad r_j
$$

$$
\left\{\begin{matrix}
0 & 1 & 1 \\
1 & 0 & 1 \\
1 & 1 & 0 \\
\end{matrix}\right\}
\begin{array}{c}
2 \\ 2 \\ 2 \\
\end{array}
\quad \binom{3}{2} = 3
$$

$$
\begin{array}{cccc}
p'_j & 1 & 1 & 1 \\
q'_j & 2 & 2 & 2 \\
\end{array}
$$

Therefore $f(1, x_2, \bar{x}_3, \bar{x}_4) = S_2(x_2, \bar{x}_3, \bar{x}_4)$

Figure 5.5.3   Example of totally symmetric function having $p_j = q_j$.

0's and 1's in all $n - 1$ columns, then both may be tested for symmetry, finally using Theorem 2.11.7 to test f for symmetry. If the number of 1's and 0's are still equal for each new set, further expansion may be required. Such tests are depicted for two examples in Figures 5.5.3 and 5.5.4.

From the calculation in Figure 5.5.3 we have that

$$f(x_1, x_2, x_3, x_4) = \bar{x}_1 \cdot S_1(x_2, \bar{x}_3, \bar{x}_4) \vee x_1 \cdot S_2(x_2, \bar{x}_3, \bar{x}_4)$$

so that by Theorem 2.11.7 and Theorem 2.11.5,

$$f(x_1, x_2, x_3, x_4) = S_2(\bar{x}_1, x_2, \bar{x}_3, \bar{x}_4)$$
$$= S_2(x_1, \bar{x}_2, x_3, x_4).$$

Note that the V' for $f(1, x_2, x_3, x_4)$ was made to have more 1's than 0's in each column so that the variables of symmetry would be identical as $\{x_2, \bar{x}_3, \bar{x}_4\}$ for both $f(0, x_2, x_3, x_4)$ and $f(1, x_2, x_3, x_4)$ as required by Theorem 2.11.7.

$$V \text{ for } f(x_1, x_2, x_3, x_4)$$

x_1	x_2	x_3	x_4	r_j
1	0	1	0	2
1	1	0	0	2
0	0	1	1	2
0	1	0	1	2

$$\binom{4}{2} = 6$$

p_j	2	2	2	2
q_j	2	2	2	2

Expanding on x_1

$$V \text{ for } f(0, x_2, x_3, x_4)$$

0	1	1
1	0	1

p_j	1	1	0
q_j	1	1	1

$$\frac{p_1}{q_1} \neq \begin{cases} \frac{p_3}{q_3} \\ \text{or } \frac{p_3}{q_3} \end{cases}$$

Thus f is not totally symmetric.

Figure 5.5.4.   Example with $p_j = q_j$ but f not totally symmetric.

5.6 BOOLEAN MATRICES

Boolean matrices are rectangular arrays of elements in which each element of the array is a Boolean function of a Boolean algebra. In this section we describe certain properties and operations on Boolean matrices that have applications to bilateral switching networks; thus the elements of the Boolean matrices that we consider are the Boolean elements 0 and 1 and the set of complete switching functions of n-variables $x_1, x_2, \ldots, x_n$.

In previous sections we discussed the correspondence between a Boolean expression and a series-parallel two-terminal bilateral network;

we have also shown that there is no such direct correspondence between Boolean expressions and bridge network configurations. For the special case of symmetric functions, we described a special form of bridge network in Section 5.4. As we shall see in this section, Boolean matrices provide a convenient model for describing any type of bilateral network structure and are particularly useful in the analysis and synthesis of bridge and multiterminal networks. In both Section 5.2 on relay tree networks and Section 5.4 on symmetric networks we considered network behavior between some designated input terminal and one, or each of several, output terminals (that is, between pairs of terminals where one terminal of the pair was the input terminal). Such a designation may also be used in interpreting Boolean matrices, but we may also consider the behavior between any pair of terminals. Thus in this section we shall make no particular note of a particular node being the input terminal.

With any given bilateral switching network we may associate several different types of Boolean matrices, each giving a description of the network. Let the bilateral network have p nodes or terminals (usually some subset of these nodes are designated as input or output terminals). Between any pair of nodes i and j we can describe all possible closed paths between node i and node j with a Boolean function of variables x_1, $x_2, \ldots, x_n$,

$$f_{ij} = f_{ij}(x_1, x_2, \ldots, x_n).$$

By arranging the functions f_{ij} in a $p \times p$ array

$$F = [f_{ij}],$$

we obtain a Boolean matrix, called a *complete connection matrix*, for the network. An example is shown in Figure 5.6.1, where each node is numbered.

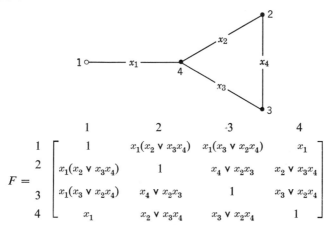

Figure 5.6.1. Bilateral switching network and associated complete connection matrix.

In this example if we interpret node 1 to be the input terminal and nodes 2 and 3 to be output terminals, then the 1, 2-entry of F describes the behavior between input terminal 1 and output terminal 2. Note, however, that the behavior between the two output terminals is also given by the 2, 3-entry of F.

If all the nodes in a p-node network are labeled, as in Figure 5.6.1, the matrix is a $p \times p$ matrix. If some nodes are not desired in the matrix representation, a connection matrix with fewer rows and columns may be used to describe the network. For example, if node 4 were not required in a matrix representation for the network of Figure 5.6.1, the following matrix would describe the network.

$$
\begin{array}{c}
 \\
1 \\
2 \\
3
\end{array}
\begin{array}{ccc}
\quad 1 & \quad 2 & \quad 3 \\
\left[\begin{array}{ccc}
1 & x_1(x_2 \vee x_3 x_4) & x_1(x_3 \vee x_2 x_4) \\
x_1(x_2 \vee x_3 x_4) & 1 & x_4 \vee x_2 x_3 \\
x_1(x_3 \vee x_2 x_4') & x_4 \vee x_2 x_3 & 1
\end{array}\right] .
\end{array}
$$

For a two-terminal network realizing a function f, the associated Boolean matrix for this network (with only the input and output terminals required and labeled 1 and 2) is simply

$$
\begin{array}{c}
 \\
1 \\
2
\end{array}
\begin{array}{cc}
1 & 2 \\
\left[\begin{array}{cc}
1 & f \\
f & 1
\end{array}\right] .
\end{array}
$$

This matrix is called the *output matrix* for the two-terminal network. In general, for a multiterminal network, if only the input and output terminals of the network are used in the matrix, the resulting Boolean matrix $F = [f_{ij}]$ is called the *output matrix* of the network.

Another type of Boolean matrix for a p-node network, called a *primitive connection matrix*, requires each node of the network to have an associated row and column in the matrix representation (that is, between any two nodes we have only a single bilateral element or group of single bilateral elements in parallel). A primitive connection matrix $P = [p_{ij}]$ has entry p_{ij}, which is the Boolean function of the "direct connection" from node i to node j. Thus each p_{ij} is a 0, a 1, a single variable, or a disjunction of single variables. The primitive connection matrix which represents the network of Figure 5.6.1 is then

$$
P =
\begin{array}{c}
 \\
1 \\
2 \\
3 \\
4
\end{array}
\begin{array}{cccc}
1 & 2 & 3 & 4 \\
\left[\begin{array}{cccc}
1 & 0 & 0 & x_1 \\
0 & 1 & x_4 & x_2 \\
0 & x_4 & 1 & x_3 \\
x_1 & x_2 & x_3 & 1
\end{array}\right] .
\end{array}
$$

In general, there are many *connection matrices* that can be used to describe a given network, which, roughly speaking, lie between the primitive connection matrix and the complete connection matrix for the network. An example of a connection matrix C is given in Figure 5.6.2, where only nodes 1, 2, and 3 are used in C.

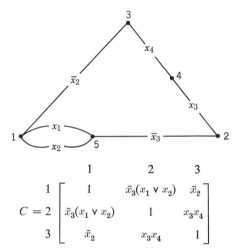

$$C = 2 \begin{array}{c@{\qquad}ccc} & 1 & 2 & 3 \\ 1 & \begin{bmatrix} 1 & \bar{x}_3(x_1 \vee x_2) & \bar{x}_2 \\ 2 & \bar{x}_3(x_1 \vee x_2) & 1 & x_3 x_4 \\ 3 & \bar{x}_2 & x_3 x_4 & 1 \end{bmatrix} \end{array}$$

Figure 5.6.2. A bilateral switching network with an associated connection matrix.

The primitive connection matrix for this network is

$$P = 3 \begin{array}{c@{\quad}ccccc} & 1 & 2 & 3 & 4 & 5 \\ 1 & \begin{bmatrix} 1 & 0 & \bar{x}_2 & 0 & x_1 \vee x_2 \\ 2 & 0 & 1 & 0 & x_3 & \bar{x}_3 \\ \bar{x}_2 & 0 & 1 & x_4 & 0 \\ 4 & 0 & x_3 & x_4 & 1 & 0 \\ 5 & x_1 \vee x_2 & \bar{x}_3 & 0 & 0 & 1 \end{bmatrix} \end{array}$$

The complete connection matrix, using all five nodes, is

$$F = 3 \begin{array}{c@{\quad}ccccc} & 1 & 2 & 3 & 4 & 5 \\ 1 & \begin{bmatrix} 1 & \bar{x}_3(x_1 \vee x_2) \vee \bar{x}_2 x_3 x_4 & \bar{x}_2 & \bar{x}_2 x_4 & x_1 \vee x_2 \\ 2 & \bar{x}_3(x_1 \vee x_2) \vee \bar{x}_2 x_3 x_4 & 1 & x_3 x_4 \vee x_1 \bar{x}_2 \bar{x}_3 & x_3 \vee x_1 \bar{x}_2 \bar{x}_3 x_4 & \bar{x}_3 \vee x_1 \bar{x}_2 x_3 x_4 \\ \bar{x}_2 & x_3 x_4 \vee x_1 \bar{x}_2 \bar{x}_3 & 1 & x_4 & x_1 \bar{x}_2 \\ 4 & \bar{x}_2 x_4 & x_3 \vee x_1 \bar{x}_2 \bar{x}_3 x_4 & x_4 & 1 & x_1 \bar{x}_2 x_4 \\ 5 & x_1 \vee x_2 & \bar{x}_3 \vee x_1 \bar{x}_2 x_3 x_4 & x_1 \bar{x}_2 & x_1 \bar{x}_2 x_4 & 1 \end{bmatrix} \end{array}$$

Note that in each type of Boolean matrix which we have associated with

a bilateral switching network the diagonal entries are all equal to 1, and
the matrices are symmetric (that is, $f_{ij} = f_{ji}$). A *switching matrix* is any
symmetric Boolean matrix having all diagonal entries equal to 1, where
each matrix element is a Boolean element 0 or 1 or a Boolean function of
n-variables.

Let $A = [a_{ij}]$ and $B = [b_{ij}]$ be $p \times p$ switching matrices. We make
the following definitions.

Definition 5.6.1 $A = B$ if and only if $a_{ij} = b_{ij}$ for $1 \leq i \leq p$ and
$1 \leq j \leq p$.

Definition 5.6.2 $A \vee B = [a_{ij} \vee b_{ij}]$, that is, the *ij* entry in matrix $A \vee B$
is the element $a_{ij} \vee b_{ij}$.

Definition 5.6.3   The logical product $A \cdot B = [a_{ij} \cdot b_{ij}]$.

Definition 5.6.4 $\bar{A} = [\alpha_{ij}]$, where

$$\alpha_{ij} = \begin{cases} \bar{a}_{ij} & \text{if} \quad i \neq j \\ 1 & \text{if} \quad i = j \end{cases}.$$

Note that the matrices $A \vee B$, $A \cdot B$, and $\bar{A}$ are also switching matrices.

Definition 5.6.5 $A \subseteq B$ (A is included in B) if and only if $a_{ij} \subseteq b_{ij}$ for
all *i* and *j*.

Theorem 5.6.1   The set of all $p \times p$ switching matrices, under the
definitions of equals, OR, AND, and NOT form a Boolean algebra.

This theorem due to Lunts [14] can be proved easily by verifying the
postulates of Boolean algebra using Definitions 5.6.1 through 5.6.4.

Definition 5.6.6   The determinant $\|A\|$ of a Boolean matrix A is the
disjunction of the $p!$ conjunctions of the elements of A in which each row
subscript and each column subscript appears once and only once in each
conjunction.

The following interesting theorem due to Aranovich [1] and Semon [23],
uses the concept of a determinant.

Theorem 5.6.2   If A is a switching matrix for some bilateral switching
network, the function (transmission) between nodes *i* and *j* is equal to the
determinant of the cofactor of A formed by eliminating row *i* and column
j of A.

This theorem is illustrated by the network of Figure 5.6.1 and the
primitive connection matrix P as follows. The function represented

between the two nodes 1 and 2 is the determinant:

$$
\begin{array}{c}
\\
2\\
3\\
4
\end{array}
\left\|
\begin{array}{c}
\begin{array}{ccc}
1 & 3 & 4
\end{array}\\
\left[
\begin{array}{ccc}
0 & x_4 & x_2\\
0 & 1 & x_3\\
x_1 & x_3 & 1
\end{array}
\right]
\end{array}
\right\|
$$

which equals

$$
0 \cdot 1 \cdot x_4 \vee x_1 \cdot x_3 \cdot 1 \vee 0 \cdot x_3 \cdot x_2 \vee x_1 \cdot 1 \cdot x_2 \vee x_4 \cdot 0 \cdot 1 \vee 0 \cdot x_3 \cdot x_3
$$

so that

$$
f_{12} = x_1 x_3 x_4 \vee x_1 x_2.
$$

This equals the 1, 2-entry in F of Figure 5.6.1, thereby verifying this computation. The reader can check other two-terminal transmissions in a similar manner, using either P or some other connection matrix which represents the network.

Definition 5.6.7 The matrix product

$$
A \times B = \left[\bigvee_{k=1}^{P} a_{ik} \cdot b_{kj} \right].
$$

Note that the definition $A \times B$ is the same rule as for ordinary matrices, except that $\vee$ replaces summation and the AND-operation replaces multiplication. We designate $A \times A$ by A^2, etc.

Theorem 5.6.3 If A is a $p \times p$ switching matrix, then there exists some positive integer $q \leq p - 1$ such that

$$
A \subseteq A^2 \subseteq \cdots \subseteq A^q = A^{q+1} = \cdots.
$$

PROOF. If $A^f - [\alpha_{ik}]$, then

$$
A^{f+1} = \left[\bigvee_k \alpha_{ik} \cdot a_{kj} \right] = \left[\alpha_{ij} \vee \bigvee_{k \neq j} \alpha_{ik} \cdot a_{kj} \right]
$$

since $a_{ij} = 1$.

Now $\alpha_{ij} \subseteq \alpha_{ij} \vee \bigvee_{k \neq j} \alpha_{ik} \cdot a_{kj}$, so that by Definition 5.6.5, $A^f \subseteq A^{f+1}$ for any positive integer f. The chain of inclusion relations of the theorem has thus been proved, and we now must show that there is a $q \leq p - 1$ such that $A^q = A^{q+1}$. We shall show, in particular, that $A^{p-1} = A^p$, which suffices to prove the theorem. The diagonal entries of A all equal 1. Thus the diagonal entries of A^{p-1} are equal to the diagonal entries of A^p (namely all 1's). The i, j off-diagonal entry of A^p may be written as the multiple $\bigvee$:

$$\bigvee_{k_1,\ldots,k_{p-1}} a_{ik_1} \cdot a_{k_1k_2} \cdots a_{k_{p-2}k_{p-1}} a_{k_{p-1}j}$$

There are $p - 1$ internal subscripts, plus i and j, making $p + 1$ subscripts; thus at least one must be repeated. If $j = k_s$, one term of the $\bigvee$ is

$$a_{ik_1} \cdots a_{k_{s-1}j} \cdot a_{jk_{s+1}} \cdots a_{k_{p-i}j}$$

and this is included in $a_{ik}, \ldots, a_{k_{s-1}j}$, a term of the ij entry of A^s. Thus this term of the ij entry of A^p is also included in a term of the ij entry of A^{p-1}. If $i = k_s$, we have a similar result, and if neither i nor j is equal to any k, then some $k_r = k_s$ and we have the conclusion that

$$a_{ik_1} \cdot \cdots \cdot a_{k_{s-1}k_r} \cdot a_{k_rk_{s+1}} \cdot \cdots \cdot a_{k_{r-1}k_r} \cdot a_{k_rk_{r+1}} \cdot \cdots \cdot a_{k_{p-1}j}$$

is included in the term

$$a_{ik_1} \cdot \cdots \cdot a_{k_{s-1}k_r} \cdot a_{k_rk_{r+1}} \cdot \cdots \cdot a_{k_{p-1}j}$$

which is included in the ij entry of A^{p-1}. Since every such term of the ij-entry of A^p is included in the ij-entry of A^{p-1} we conclude that $A^p \subseteq A^{p-1}$. Now since $A^{p-1} \subseteq A^p$ we have $A^{p-1} = A^p$, proving the theorem.

It should be noted that if we have the primitive connection matrix P, the ij entries of P give the direct connections from node i to node j (that is, terms for each path of length 1). If we form P^2, the ij entries of P^2 correspond to all the paths from node i to j of length 2 or less. This is easily verified by noting that the ij entry of P^2 is $\bigvee_{k=1}^{p} a_{ik}b_{kj}$, so that node k is an intermediate node on a path from node i to node j. Similarly, we obtain all paths of length r or less, from node i to node j, by forming P^r. Now from Theorem 5.6.3 it follows that there exists a q such that $P^q = P^{p-1}$. Since all nonredundant paths from a node i to a node j are of length $p - 1$ or less in a p node network, and since the function from node i to node j can be obtained by tracing all nonredundant paths from node i to node j, we have that $P^q = F$, where F is the $p \times p$ complete connection matrix for the network. Furthermore, if C is an $r \times r$ connection matrix for the network of r input and output nodes, it follows that the $r \times r$ output matrix is obtained by raising C to some power k, where $k \leq r - 1$. We illustrate these results for the network of Figure 5.6.1.

$$
P = \begin{array}{c} \\ 1 \\ 2 \\ 3 \\ 4 \end{array} \begin{array}{cccc} 1 & 2 & 3 & 4 \\ \begin{bmatrix} 1 & 0 & 0 & x_1 \\ 0 & 1 & x_4 & x_2 \\ 0 & x_4 & 1 & x_3 \\ x_1 & x_2 & x_3 & 1 \end{bmatrix} \end{array}
$$

$$
P^2 = \begin{array}{c} \\ 1 \\ 2 \\ 3 \\ 4 \end{array} \begin{array}{cccc} 1 & 2 & 3 & 4 \\ \begin{bmatrix} 1 & x_1x_2 & x_1x_3 & x_1 \\ x_1x_2 & 1 & x_4 \vee x_2x_3 & x_2 \vee x_3x_4 \\ x_1x_3 & x_4 \vee x_2x_3 & 1 & x_2x_4 \vee x_3 \\ x_1 & x_2 \vee x_3x_4 & x_2x_4 \vee x_3 & 1 \end{bmatrix} \end{array} .
$$

Thus P^2 has entries coorresponding to paths of length 2, such as the x_3x_4 entry in the 2, 4-entry. Forming P^3, we obtain

$$
P \times P^2 = P^3 = \begin{array}{c} \\ 1 \\ 2 \\ 3 \\ 4 \end{array} \begin{array}{cccc} 1 & 2 & 3 & 4 \\ \begin{bmatrix} 1 & x_1(x_2 \vee x_3x_4) & x_1x_3 \vee x_1(x_2x_4 \vee x_3) & x_1 \\ x_1x_2 \vee x_1x_3x_4 & 1 & x_4 \vee x_2x_3 & x_2 \vee x_3x_4 \\ x_1x_2x_4 \vee x_1x_3 & x_4 \vee x_2x_3 & 1 & x_4(x_2 \vee x_3x_4) \vee x_2x_4 \vee x_3 \\ x_1 & x_2 \vee x_3x_4 & x_1x_3 \vee x_2(x_4 \vee x_2x_3) \vee x_3 & 1 \end{bmatrix} \end{array} .
$$

$$
\text{Therefore } P^3 = \begin{array}{c} \\ 1 \\ 2 \\ 3 \\ 4 \end{array} \begin{array}{cccc} 1 & 2 & 3 & 4 \\ \begin{bmatrix} 1 & x_1(x_2 \vee x_3x_4) & x_1(x_3 \vee x_2x_4) & x_1 \\ x_1(x_2 \vee x_3x_4) & 1 & x_4 \vee x_2x_3 & x_2 \vee x_3x_4 \\ x_1(x_3 \vee x_2x_4) & x_4 \vee x_2x_3 & 1 & x_3 \vee x_2x_4 \\ x_1 & x_2 \vee x_3x_4 & x_3 \vee x_2x_4 & 1 \end{bmatrix} \end{array} .
$$

Since the network has four nodes, we know that $P^3 = F$, and this is verified by checking P^3 with F of Figure 5.6.1.

5.7 NODE REMOVAL AND NODE INSERTION IN CONNECTION MATRICES

In the analysis of bilateral switching networks we assume that a network is given and we wish to determine the Boolean transmission functions between certain pairs of nodes, namely, the input-output terminals. Given the network, the primitive connection matrix P for the network can be obtained directly from the network. Both Theorems 5.6.2 and 5.6.3 give methods to obtain the switching functions between pairs of nodes. Calculating determinants by Theorem 5.6.2 may be rather laborious if we require the switching functions for many pairs of nodes; similarly, computing P^q gives the switching functions between every pair of nodes, of which many may not be input-output terminal pairs. We now describe a process of *node removal* by which nodes may be removed from a connection matrix C. (C may be either primitive or some other connection matrix of the network.) Suppose we wish to remove node k from the matrix representation C, that is, we wish to remove row and column k, but we still want the switching functions between other pairs of nodes to remain unchanged. This is accomplished as follows: to each entry c_{ij} of C where $i, j \neq k$ and $i \neq j$ we add the term $c_{ik} \cdot c_{kj}$, forming a c_{ij}' as $c_{ij}' = c_{ij} \lor c_{ik} \cdot c_{kj}$. After completing this for each c_{ij}, we delete row and column k of C, giving us a new connection matrix C_k for the network. That C_k is a connection matrix follows from the fact that term $c_{ik} \cdot c_{kj}$ gives any possible connections between nodes i and j which pass through node k. With successive node removals until only nodes i and j remain, we obtain the function between nodes i and j.

Thus, for the network of Figure 5.6.2, if we desire the function between nodes 1 and 2 we can use any one of the following methods: form the appropriate determinant of C; form C^2; or remove node 3 from C. The node removal process is illustrated below. The reader should check this result with the determinant and C^2 method of forming f_{12}.

$$
C = \begin{array}{cc}
 & \begin{array}{ccc} 1 & \qquad 2 & \qquad 3 \end{array} \\
\begin{array}{c} 1 \\ 2 \\ 3 \end{array} &
\left[\begin{array}{ccc}
1 & \bar{x}_3(x_1 \lor x_2) & \bar{x}_2 \\
\bar{x}_3(x_1 \lor x_2) & 1 & x_3 x_4 \\
\bar{x}_2 & x_3 x_4 & 1
\end{array} \right]
\end{array}
$$

$$
C_3 = \begin{array}{cc}
 & \begin{array}{cc} 1 & \qquad\qquad 2 \end{array} \\
\begin{array}{c} 1 \\ 2 \end{array} &
\left[\begin{array}{cc}
1 & \bar{x}_3(x_1 \lor x_2) \lor \bar{x}_2 x_3 x_4 \\
\bar{x}_3(x_1 \lor x_2) \lor \bar{x}_2 x_3 x_4 & 1
\end{array} \right]
\end{array}.
$$

Thus $f_{12} = \bar{x}_3(x_1 \lor x_2) \lor \bar{x}_2 x_3 x_4$. Let us consider the network of Figure 5.7.1 in which nodes 1, 2, 3, and 4 are terminal nodes and we desire the

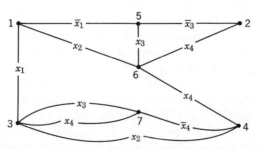

Figure 5.7.1   A network having terminal nodes 1, 2, 3, and 4.

switching functions between all pairs of terminal nodes, such as represented in the 4 × 4 output matrix. We illustrate the process of node removal from the primitive connection matrix P, where P_7 designates the matrix obtained by removing node 7 from P, $P_{7,6}$ designates node 6 removal from P_7, etc. The entries are simplified as we proceed.

$$
P = \begin{array}{c|ccccccc}
 & 1 & 2 & 3 & 4 & 5 & 6 & 7 \\
\hline
1 & 1 & 0 & x_1 & 0 & \bar{x}_1 & x_2 & 0 \\
2 & 0 & 1 & 0 & 0 & \bar{x}_3 & x_4 & 0 \\
3 & x_1 & 0 & 1 & x_2 & 0 & 0 & x_3 \vee x_4 \\
4 & 0 & 0 & x_2 & 1 & 0 & x_4 & \bar{x}_4 \\
5 & \bar{x}_1 & \bar{x}_3 & 0 & 0 & 1 & x_3 & 0 \\
6 & x_2 & x_4 & 0 & x_4 & x_3 & 1 & 0 \\
7 & 0 & 0 & x_3 \vee x_4 & \bar{x}_4 & 0 & 0 & 1
\end{array}
$$

$$
P_7 = \begin{array}{c|cccccc}
 & 1 & 2 & 3 & 4 & 5 & 6 \\
\hline
1 & 1 & 0 & x_1 & 0 & \bar{x}_1 & x_2 \\
2 & 0 & 1 & 0 & 0 & \bar{x}_3 & x_4 \\
3 & x_1 & 0 & 1 & x_2 \vee x_3\bar{x}_4 & 0 & 0 \\
4 & 0 & 0 & x_2 \vee x_3\bar{x}_4 & 1 & 0 & x_4 \\
5 & \bar{x}_1 & \bar{x}_3 & 0 & 0 & 1 & x_3 \\
6 & x_2 & x_4 & 0 & x_4 & x_3 & 1
\end{array}
$$

$$
P_{7,6} = \begin{array}{c|ccccc}
 & 1 & 2 & 3 & 4 & 5 \\
\hline
1 & 1 & x_2x_4 & x_1 & x_2x_4 & \bar{x}_1 \vee x_2x_3 \\
2 & x_2x_4 & 1 & 0 & x_4 & \bar{x}_3 \vee x_4 \\
3 & x_1 & 0 & 1 & x_2 \vee x_3\bar{x}_4 & 0 \\
4 & x_2x_4 & x_4 & x_2 \vee x_3\bar{x}_4 & 1 & x_3x_4 \\
5 & \bar{x}_1 \vee x_2x_3 & \bar{x}_3 \vee x_4 & 0 & x_3x_4 & 1
\end{array}
$$

$$
P_{7,6,5} = \begin{array}{c|cccc}
 & 1 & 2 & 3 & 4 \\
\hline
1 & 1 & x_2x_4 \vee \bar{x}_1(\bar{x}_3 \vee x_4) & x_1 & x_2x_4 \vee \bar{x}_1x_3x_4 \\
2 & x_2x_4 \vee \bar{x}_1(\bar{x}_3 \vee x_4) & 1 & 0 & x_4 \\
3 & x_1 & 0 & 1 & x_2 \vee x_3\bar{x}_4 \\
4 & x_2x_4 \vee \bar{x}_1x_3x_4 & x_4 & x_2 \vee x_3\bar{x}_4 & 1
\end{array}.
$$

Now $P_{7,6,5}$ is a connection matrix for the network, but it indeed may not be an output matrix. Thus, to obtain the switching functions between pairs of nodes 1, 2, 3, and 4, the matrix $P_{7,6,5}$ must be raised to powers until $P_{7,6,5}^q = P_{7,6,5}^{q+1}$. Forming $P_{7,6,5}^2$, we obtain

$$P_{7,6,5}^2 = \begin{array}{c} \\ 1 \\ 2 \\ 3 \\ 4 \end{array} \begin{array}{cccc} \quad 1 & \quad 2 & \quad 3 & \quad 4 \\ \left[\begin{array}{cccc} 1 & x_2 x_4 \vee \bar{x}_1(\bar{x}_3 \vee x_4) & x_1 \vee x_2 x_4 & x_1(x_2 \vee x_3 \bar{x}_4) \vee x_4(\bar{x}_1 \vee x_2) \\ x_2 x_4 \vee \bar{x}_1(\bar{x}_3 \vee x_4) & 1 & x_2 x_4 & x_4 \\ x_1 \vee x_2 x_4 & x_2 x_4 & 1 & x_2 \vee x_3 \bar{x}_4 \\ x_1(x_2 \vee x_3 \bar{x}_4) \vee x_4(\bar{x}_1 \vee x_2) & x_4 & x_2 \vee x_3 \bar{x}_4 & 1 \end{array} \right] \end{array}$$

As can be checked by the reader, $P_{7,6,5}^3 = P_{7,6,5}^2$, so that $P_{7,6,5}^2$ is the desired output matrix for the given network.

The following theorem indicates when a switching matrix is an output matrix.

Theorem 5.7.1 A switching matrix C is an output matrix of some bilateral switching network if and only if $C^2 = C$.

PROOF. If $C^2 = C$ and C is an $r \times r$ matrix, by Theorem 5.6.3, $C^{r-1} = C$ and it follows that C is an output matrix. Conversely, if C is an output matrix, by the discussion following Theorem 5.6.3, there is an $r \times r$ connection matrix C_1 such that $C_1^{r-1} = C$. Thus $C^2 = C_1^{2(r-1)}$, but by Theorem 5.6.3, $C_1^{2(r-1)} = C_1^{r-1}$ so that $C^2 = C$.

For synthesis of bilateral switching networks we are given certain input-terminal to output-terminal switching functions and we desire to obtain a network having these terminal characteristics. We consider the case in which the given switching functions are complete and show how switching matrices can be used for synthesis. For synthesis using matrices we start with an output matrix describing the input-output terminal functions, and wish to obtain a connection matrix with the same terminal characteristics as the output matrix, but having additional rows and columns so that the detailed structure of the bilateral switching network is readily determined by the connection matrix, such as is the case for a primitive connection matrix. A method of *node insertion*, rather like an inverse to node removal, is now described.

Given a set of functions for the input-output terminal behavior, a necessary and sufficient condition that these functions are consistent is that whenever $f_{ij} = f_{jk} = 1$, then $f_{ik} = 1$. The physical interpretation of this condition should be obvious. We illustrate node insertion by a simple two-terminal example. Suppose we desire a two-terminal network for $f_{12} = x_1 x_2 \vee x_1 x_3 \vee \bar{x}_1 \bar{x}_2 \bar{x}_3 \vee \bar{x}_1 \bar{x}_3 x_4$.

$$F = \begin{array}{c} \\ 1 \\ 2 \end{array} \begin{array}{cc} \quad\quad 1 & \quad\quad 2 \\ \left[\begin{array}{cc} 1 & x_1 x_2 \vee x_1 x_3 \vee \bar{x}_1 \bar{x}_2 \bar{x}_3 \vee \bar{x}_1 \bar{x}_3 x_4 \\ x_1 x_2 \vee x_1 x_3 \vee \bar{x}_1 \bar{x}_2 \bar{x}_3 \vee \bar{x}_1 \bar{x}_3 x_4 & 1 \end{array} \right] \end{array}.$$

We can factor this to obtain

$$
F = \begin{bmatrix}
\overset{1}{1} & \overset{2}{x_1(x_2 \vee x_3) \vee \bar{x}_1\bar{x}_3(\bar{x}_2 \vee x_4)} \\
x_1(x_2 \vee x_3) \vee \bar{x}_1\bar{x}_3(\bar{x}_2 \vee x_4) & 1
\end{bmatrix}.
$$

For the term $x_1(x_2 \vee x_3)$ we can insert a node 3 so that node 1 is connected to node 3 by x_1 and node 3 is connected to node 2 by $x_2 \vee x_3$. Thus we obtain the matrix

$$
C = \begin{array}{c} 1 \\ 2 \\ 3 \end{array}
\begin{bmatrix}
\overset{1}{1} & \overset{2}{\bar{x}_1\bar{x}_3(\bar{x}_2 \vee x_4)} & \overset{3}{x_1} \\
\bar{x}_1\bar{x}_3(\bar{x}_2 \vee x_4) & 1 & x_2 \vee x_3 \\
x_1 & x_2 \vee x_3 & 1
\end{bmatrix}
$$

Note that the term $\bar{x}_1\bar{x}_3(\bar{x}_2 \vee x_4)$ must still be part of the 1,2-entry so that the terminal conditions are not changed. Thus in the sense of input-output terminal behavior matrices C and F are "equivalent." Another node 4 can be inserted so that $\bar{x}_1\bar{x}_3$ connects nodes 1 and 4, and $\bar{x}_2 \vee x_4$ connects nodes 4 and 2. This gives another connection matrix C' where

$$
C' = \begin{array}{c} 1 \\ 2 \\ 3 \\ 4 \end{array}
\begin{bmatrix}
\overset{1}{1} & \overset{2}{0} & \overset{3}{x_1} & \overset{4}{\bar{x}_1\bar{x}_3} \\
0 & 1 & x_2 \vee x_3 & \bar{x}_2 \vee x_4 \\
x_1 & x_2 \vee x_3 & 1 & 0 \\
\bar{x}_1\bar{x}_3 & \bar{x}_2 \vee x_4 & 0 & 1
\end{bmatrix}.
$$

A two-terminal network realizing f_{12} is now evident from C' and is shown in Figure 5.7.2.

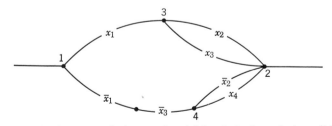

Figure 5.7.2 A two-terminal network satisfying desired terminal conditions.

One of the important manipulations in the design of a switching network by node insertion is the possibility of adding or removing "redundant" elements as the design proceeds so as to obtain an economical network realization. To illustrate redundancy consider the following connection matrix.

$$C = \begin{array}{c} \\ 1 \\ 2 \\ 3 \end{array} \begin{array}{ccc} 1 & 2 & 3 \\ \begin{bmatrix} 1 & x_1 \vee \textcircled{x_2} & x_2 \\ x_1 \vee \textcircled{x_2} & 1 & x_2 \\ x_2 & x_2 & 1 \end{bmatrix} \end{array}.$$

The circled term x_2 in the 1,2-entry and the 2,1-entry may be removed (that is, it is redundant) since there is a connection from nodes 1 to 3 by x_2 and from nodes 3 to 2 by x_2; this supplies the desired connection x_2 from node 1 to node 2 by way of node 3. In general, a term e_{ij} of entry ij is *redundant*, and can be removed if there are terms e_{ik} and e_{kj} such that $e_{ik} \cdot e_{kj} \supseteq e_{ij}$. At certain steps in node insertion it may be advantageous to add redundant terms rather than remove them. We illustrate this by the following two-terminal synthesis problem.

$$F = \begin{array}{c} \\ 1 \\ 2 \end{array} \begin{array}{cc} 1 & 2 \\ \begin{bmatrix} 1 & x_1(x_2x_3 \vee x_4) \vee x_2x_4 \vee x_3x_4 \\ x_1(x_2x_3 \vee x_4) \vee x_2x_4 \vee x_3x_4 & 1 \end{bmatrix} \end{array}.$$

Node 3 may be inserted to give

$$C = \begin{array}{c} \\ 1 \\ 2 \\ 3 \end{array} \begin{array}{ccc} 1 & 2 & 3 \\ \begin{bmatrix} 1 & x_2x_4 \vee x_3x_4 & x_1 \\ x_2x_4 \vee x_3x_4 & 1 & x_2x_3 \vee x_4 \\ x_1 & x_2x_3 \vee x_4 & 1 \end{bmatrix} \end{array}.$$

Now a redundant term x_2x_4 can be added to the 1, 3-entry since $x_2x_4 \cdot x_4 = x_2x_4$, where x_2x_4 is a connection from node 1 to node 2 and x_4 is a connection from node 2 to node 3. This gives us

$$\begin{array}{c} \\ 1 \\ 2 \\ 3 \end{array} \begin{array}{ccc} 1 & 2 & 3 \\ \begin{bmatrix} 1 & x_2x_4 \vee x_3x_4 & x_1 \vee x_2x_4 \\ x_2x_4 \vee x_3x_4 & 1 & x_2x_3 \vee x_4 \\ x_1 \vee x_2x_4 & x_2x_3 \vee x_4 & 1 \end{bmatrix} \end{array}.$$

Now since there is a connection x_2x_4 from node 1 to node 2 through node 3 (1 to 3 to 2) the term x_2x_4 is redundant in the 1, 2-entry and can be removed to give

$$
\begin{array}{c c c c}
 & 1 & 2 & 3 \\
1 & \begin{bmatrix} 1 & x_3 x_4 & x_1 \lor x_2 x_4 \\ x_3 x_4 & 1 & x_2 x_3 \lor x_4 \\ x_1 \lor x_2 x_4 & x_2 x_3 \lor x_4 & 1 \end{bmatrix}
\end{array}.
$$

Inserting a node 4, making a connection of x_4 from node 1 to node 4, will now allow us to use this x_4 path to create $x_3 x_4$ from node 1 to node 2 by having a direct connection of x_3 from node 4 to node 2, and also use the x_4 connection to supply the $x_2 x_4$ path from node 1 to node 3. This introduces a path $x_2 x_3$ between nodes 2 and 3 through node 4, but since this is a desired path between nodes 2 and 3 the terminal conditions are not changed. In fact, $x_2 x_3$ now becomes a redundant term in the 2, 3-entry, giving a connection matrix

$$
\begin{array}{c c c c c}
 & 1 & 2 & 3 & 4 \\
1 & \begin{bmatrix} 1 & 0 & x_1 & x_4 \\ 0 & 1 & x_4 & x_3 \\ x_1 & x_4 & 1 & x_2 \\ x_4 & x_3 & x_2 & 1 \end{bmatrix}
\end{array}.
$$

This matrix is also a primitive connection matrix. The resulting network is shown in Figure 5.7.3.

These examples illustrate that by successive node insertions and judicious use of redundancies, economical bridge networks as well as series-parallel networks may be obtained by node insertion.

The network we obtain by the node insertion procedure depends on the connections made to the inserted node and also on the various possible uses of redundancies at each step in the process. Indeed, many different networks may be obtained from any given output matrix simply by using node insertions and redundancies in different manners.

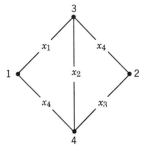

Figure 5.7.3 A bridge network-synthesis by node insertion.

In addition, the node insertion process does not specify an algorithm which necessarily arrives at a minimum element network. The exact network obtained is quite dependent on the exact node insertions made.

Thus, in the preceding example consider the output matrix F expressed as

$$F = \begin{array}{c} \\ 1 \\ 2 \end{array} \begin{bmatrix} \overset{1}{1} & \overset{2}{x_4(x_1 \vee x_2 \vee x_3) \vee x_1 x_2 x_3} \\ x_4(x_1 \vee x_2 \vee x_3) \vee x_1 x_2 x_3 & 1 \end{bmatrix}.$$

We can obtain another network for F by now inserting a third node with a 1, 3-entry of x_4 as

$$C = \begin{array}{c} 1 \\ 2 \\ 3 \end{array} \begin{bmatrix} \overset{1}{1} & \overset{2}{x_1 x_2 x_3} & \overset{3}{x_4} \\ x_1 x_2 x_3 & 1 & x_1 \vee x_2 \vee x_3 \\ x_4 & x_1 \vee x_2 \vee x_3 & 1 \end{bmatrix}.$$

No simplification can now be obtained by subsequent node insertions or use of redundancies. The resulting network for C is shown in Figure 5.7.4.

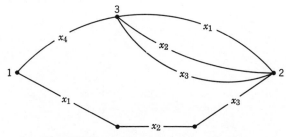

Figure 5.7.4   A second network realization.

This network requires seven elements, whereas the network obtained in Figure 5.7.3 requires only five elements, thus illustrating the different network complexity arising from different steps of node insertion.

Finally, we illustrate node insertion on a three-terminal problem. Design a bilateral switching network with terminals 1, 2, and 3 having transmission functions

$$\begin{cases} f_{12} = \bar{x}_1 \bar{x}_2 \vee x_1 x_3 \\ f_{13} = \bar{x}_3(x_2 \vee x_1 x_4) \\ f_{23} = 0 \end{cases}$$

The output matrix is thus

$$F = \begin{array}{c} 1 \\ 2 \\ 3 \end{array} \begin{bmatrix} \overset{1}{1} & \overset{2}{\bar{x}_1 \bar{x}_2 \vee x_1 x_3} & \overset{3}{\bar{x}_3(x_2 \vee x_1 x_4)} \\ \bar{x}_1 \bar{x}_2 \vee x_1 x_3 & 1 & 0 \\ \bar{x}_3(x_2 \vee x_1 x_4) & 0 & 1 \end{bmatrix}.$$

A fourth node can be inserted so that x_3 connects nodes 3 and 4 and $x_2 \lor x_1 x_4$ connects nodes 1 and 4. This gives

$$
C = \begin{array}{c} \\ 1 \\ 2 \\ 3 \\ 4 \end{array}
\begin{array}{cccc}
1 & 2 & 3 & 4 \\
\left[\begin{array}{cccc}
1 & \bar{x}_1 \bar{x}_2 \lor x_1 x_3 & 0 & x_2 \lor x_1 x_4 \\
\bar{x}_1 \bar{x}_2 \lor x_1 x_3 & 1 & 0 & 0 \\
0 & 0 & 1 & \bar{x}_3 \\
x_2 \lor x_1 x_4 & 0 & \bar{x}_3 & 1
\end{array} \right]
\end{array} .
$$

Now if we wish to eliminate term $x_1 x_3$ from the 1, 2-entry and $x_1 x_4$ from the 1, 4-entry of C, since we have a common element x_1 in both these terms, we may be able to use a single relay contact to realize x_1 in both these terms by inserting a fifth node, as shown in the following:

$$
\begin{array}{c} \\ 1 \\ 2 \\ 3 \\ 4 \\ 5 \end{array}
\begin{array}{ccccc}
1 & 2 & 3 & 4 & 5 \\
\left[\begin{array}{ccccc}
1 & \bar{x}_1 \bar{x}_2 & 0 & x_2 & x_1 \\
\bar{x}_1 \bar{x}_2 & 1 & 0 & 0 & x_3 \\
0 & 0 & 1 & \bar{x}_3 & 0 \\
x_2 & 0 & \bar{x}_3 & 1 & x_4 \\
x_1 & x_3 & 0 & x_4 & 1
\end{array} \right]
\end{array}
$$

This connection matrix describes the network shown in Figure 5.7.5.

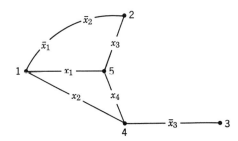

Figure 5.7.5 A multiterminal network realization.

The node insertion procedure has the distinct advantages that both bridge and series-parallel networks are easily attained and also that multiterminal networks may be readily realized by node insertion.

5.8 CRYOTRON LOGICAL NETWORKS

The cryotron is a superconductive switching element which has logical properties similar to a normally closed relay contact. In this section we illustrate how switching techniques for relay contact circuits may be readily applied and extended to cryotrons. Thin film cryotrons show promise as relatively inexpensive, small, and high-speed switching devices. Figure 5.8.1 depicts a crossed film cryotron (also called an inhibitor) that has a bilateral switching characteristic. If wire A is a thin film of lead,

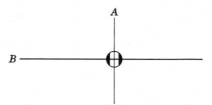

Figure 5.8.1   A cryotron inhibitor.

there is a thin film of insulation isolating wire A from wire B, and if wire B is also a thin film of lead except for a small segment of tin at the cross-over point, then with appropriate dimensions of the films and when cooled to near absolute zero, the following switching characteristic can be obtained. In the absence of sufficient current in wire A, the tin insert is superconductive (zero resistance); if, however, the current in wire A exceeds a certain critical value, the tin segment of wire B becomes resistive.

To represent switching functions with cryotrons, we represent each binary variable by a pair of wires connected to a single current source; we allow one of the pair to be superconducting and the other to be resistive; then exactly one path of zero resistance is available to the current source and all the current flows in the zero resistance path. For a variable x_i we label by a 0 the wire of the pair which contains current when $x_i = 0$, and we label the other wire of the pair with a 1 since it carries current when $x_i = 1$. With this representation for variables, we can realize any complete switching function f with a three-terminal network. This network has one input terminal connected to a current source and a pair of output terminals. The current of the input source is directed to one output terminal labeled f when $f = 1$ and it is directed to the other labeled $\bar{f}$ when $f = 0$. This is accomplished as follows. When $f = 1$, there is a superconducting path from the input terminal to the f output terminal (and no simultaneous superconducting path in the $\bar{f}$ side), and conversely for $\bar{f} = 1$. Such a network is called a *complementary output network*.

One method of realizing a complementary output network is by obtaining a normal form representation (that is, a cover) both for f and $\bar{f}$,

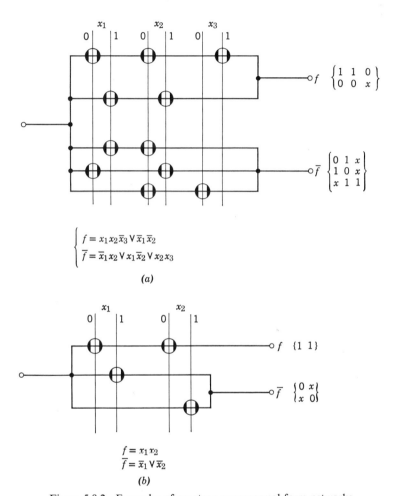

$$\begin{cases} f = x_1 x_2 \bar{x}_3 \vee \bar{x}_1 \bar{x}_2 \\ \bar{f} = \bar{x}_1 x_2 \vee x_1 \bar{x}_2 \vee x_2 x_3 \end{cases}$$

(a)

$$f = x_1 x_2$$
$$\bar{f} = \bar{x}_1 \vee \bar{x}_2$$

(b)

Figure 5.8.2 Examples of cryotron supernormal form networks.

and realizing f and $\bar{f}$ by two parallel sets of wires. Two such realizations called *supernormal form networks* are shown in Figure 5.8.2.

Note that each horizontal wire corresponds to a cube of the cover. For example, in Figure 5.8.2a the top wire corresponds to cube 110, and it is superconducting only when $x_1 = 1$, $x_2 = 1$, and $x_3 = 0$. From covers of both f and $\bar{f}$ the network structure is immediate. One horizontal wire is required for each cube, and cryotrons are placed on crossings of the respective variable wires according to the following rules.

1. If a 0 appears in the x_i coordinate of the cube, then a cryotron is placed at the crossing of the 1-wire of x_i.
2. If a 1 appears in the x_i coordinate of the cube, then a cryotron is placed at the crossing of the 0-wire of x_i.
3. If an x appears in the x_i coordinate, then no cryotron is placed on the x_i wire crossings.

It is evident that using minimum covers for f and $\bar{f}$ gives a supernormal form network that requires a minimum number of horizontal lines and a minimum number of cryotrons of any possible supernormal form network for f. It may be advantageous, however, to have only one superconducting horizontal line for any possible input. Note that both $\bar{f}$ lines of Figure 5.8.2b are superconducting for the condition that $x_1 = x_2 = 0$. If only one line is superconducting, the switching speed of the network may be faster since the inductance is a function of the length of line and the switching time depends on some L/R value, where R is the effective resistance of the cryotrons in the line. Obviously, we can obtain supernormal form networks having only one horizontal line superconducting at one time by using covers for f and $\bar{f}$ in which each cube of the cover is disjoint from any other cube of the cover. The minimum covers may be made disjoint by simply replacing appropriate x's with 0's or 1's, as required. Thus a supernormal form network still having a minimum number of lines is attained. Examples (a) and (b) of Figure 5.8.2 are modified for disjointness and shown in Figure 5.8.3a and b respectively.

If a multiple output cryotron network is desired for $f_1, f_2, \ldots, f_m$ where $f_i \cdot f_j \equiv 0$ for $i \neq j$ and $1 \leq i, j \leq m$, and $f_1 \lor f_2 \lor \cdots \lor f_m \equiv 1$, it should be evident that the supernormal form network technique can be generalized to construct such a network.

Since the $f, \bar{f}$ outputs of a cryotron network can act as an input to other cryotron networks, the techniques of decomposition discussed in Section 4.6 can be applied, as in gate-type networks, to realize the required output using some form of decomposition.

For example, if we wish to realize the function

$$\begin{cases} f = x_1 \oplus x_2 \oplus x_3 \\ \bar{f} = \overline{x_1 \oplus x_2 \oplus x_3} \end{cases}$$

using a supernormal form network with x_1, x_2, and x_3 as inputs, it would require 24 cryotrons, as can be checked by the reader. However, f and $\bar{f}$

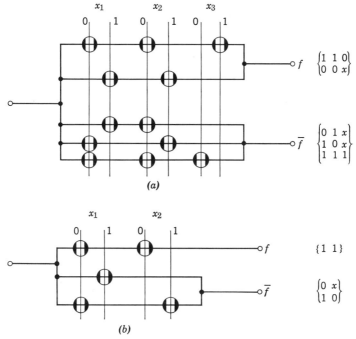

(a)

(b)

Figure 5.8.3   Supernormal form networks with disjoint superconducting lines.

can be decomposed as

$$\begin{cases} f = \bar{g}x_3 \lor g\bar{x}_3 \\ \bar{f} = gx_3 \lor \bar{g}\bar{x}_3 \end{cases},$$

where

$$\begin{cases} g = x_1x_2 \lor \bar{x}_1\bar{x}_2 = \overline{x_1 \oplus x_2} \\ \bar{g} = x_1\bar{x}_2 \lor \bar{x}_1x_2 = x_1 \oplus x_2 \end{cases}.$$

Realizing g as a network with inputs x_1 and x_2, followed by realizing f with inputs g and x_3, gives the network shown in Figure 5.8.4 which requires only 16 cryotrons.

The relay tree network and symmetric network techniques of Sections 5.2 and 5.4 may also be applied directly to obtain complementary output cryotron networks and multiple output cryotron networks. A complete cryotron tree for three variables is shown in Figure 5.8.5.

Note that the complete cryotron tree simply replaces each transfer contact of the complete relay tree with a transfer-type network using cryotrons. Thus, for simplicity, we shall represent the cryotron networks exactly like the relay contact networks.

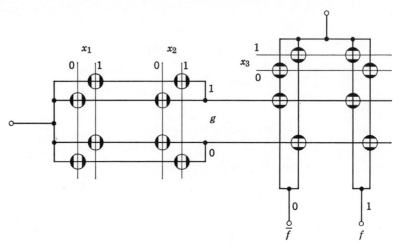

Figure 5.8.4   A cryotron network using decomposition.

As an example of a multiple output network designed from a complete cryotron tree, we consider the multiple output example.

$$\begin{cases} f_1 = \bar{x}_1\bar{x}_2 \lor x_2\bar{x}_3x_4, \\ f_2 = x_2x_3 \lor \bar{x}_1x_2\bar{x}_4, \\ f_3 = x_1\bar{x}_2 \lor x_1\bar{x}_3\bar{x}_4. \end{cases}$$

Here we have $f_1 \lor f_2 \lor f_3 \equiv 1$, and $f_i \cdot f_j \equiv 0$ for $i \neq j$. Starting with the standard complete tree on x_1, x_2, x_3, x_4 we label the outputs with the respective associated functions for the outputs, as shown in Figure 5.8.6. We can imagine all output terminals labeled f_i to be connected to a single output terminal for f_i.

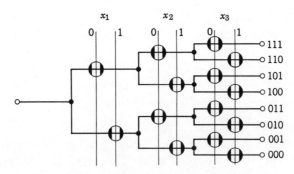

Figure 5.8.5   Complete cryotron tree for $n = 3$.

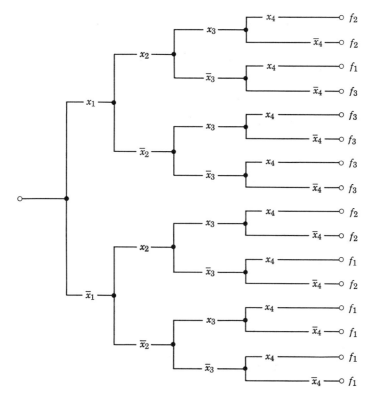

Figure 5.8.6 Multiple output cryotron network using complete cryotron tree.

Given the ordering of variables in the complete tree and all its subtrees, the following two rules can be used to obtain a simplified network.

I. If two nodes of the network can be connected by a short circuit without affecting the output response for any input value, this connection can be made and all paths to the right of one of these nodes may be removed.

II. If two such nodes are outputs of a transfer, that transfer may be removed and replaced with a short circuit.

Rule I can be seen to hold as follows. Since the output response is unchanged, the paths to the right of each of the nodes in the tree must be identical since the variables of the complete tree are ordered. Thus the paths to the right of one of the nodes can be eliminated—these paths being supplied to the right of the node to which the short circuit was applied. For Rule II, when the outputs of a transfer are interconnected, they form a parallel circuit $\begin{array}{c} x \\ \overline{x} \end{array}$. This subcircuit realizes the

function $x \vee \overline{x}$, which is identically 1 (realized by a short circuit), and thus Rule II is immediate. Using these rules on Figure 5.8.6, we obtain the network shown in Figure 5.8.7.

Using a different permutation of input variables or some folded tree may produce a simpler network, however, therefore the problem arises on how to determine the best tree to start with. The method used to design

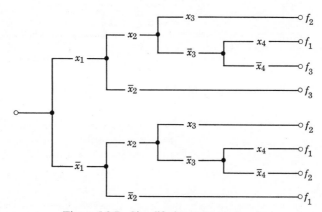

Figure 5.8.7 Simplified cryotron network.

simplified partial relay trees may be extended to be of some value here. We demonstrate this approach by considering the foregoing example and try to obtain a more suitable permutation of variables. First, we represent each function by a minimum cover, giving

$$
\begin{array}{cccc}
 & x_1 & x_2 & x_3 & x_4 \\
f_1 \left\{ \begin{array}{cccc} 0 & 0 & x & x \\ x & 1 & 0 & 1 \end{array} \right. \\
f_2 \left\{ \begin{array}{cccc} x & 1 & 1 & x \\ 0 & 1 & x & 0 \end{array} \right. \\
f_3 \left\{ \begin{array}{cccc} 1 & 0 & x & x \\ 1 & x & 0 & 0 \end{array} \right.
\end{array}
$$

Now the left-most transfer of the tree corresponds to some variable, and we try to pick one that has no x's in its corresponding column so that we can partition the covers on this variable. In this case no column has all

0's and 1's, but variable x_2 can be made to by changing the last cube $1\,x\,0\,0$ to $1\,1\,0\,0$, noting that $1\,0\,0\,0$ is also covered by cube $1\,0\,x\,x$ of f_3. Thus x_2 is a good choice for the first variable, and we partition on x_2, keeping track of the output associated with each cube as we proceed.

	x_2	x_1	x_3	x_4
f_1	0	0	x	x
f_3	0	1	x	x
f_1	1	x	0	1
f_2	1	x	1	x
f_2	1	0	x	0
f_3	1	1	0	0

Now for subtrees on the x_2 and $\bar{x}_2$ sides we must make further choices of the next variable. For $x_2 = 0$, using x_1 as the next variable is best because both the cubes $0\,x\,x$ and $1\,x\,x$ can then give outputs to f_1 and f_3, respectively without using variables x_3 or x_4 in the subtrees. Similarly, if x_3 is used as the next variable on the $x_2 = 1$ subtree, cube $x\,1\,x$ gives directly an output for f_2, and cube $0\,x\,0$ can be changed to $0\,0\,0$ since $0\,1\,0 \subseteq x\,1\,x$. The partial network realized up to this point is shown in the accompanying diagram.

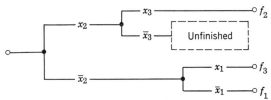

The unfinished part of the design corresponds to the cubes:

	x_2	x_3	x_1	x_4
f_1	1	0	x	1
f_2	1	0	0	0
f_3	1	0	1	0

Now column x_4 has no x's, and $x_4 = 1$ gives f_1, and $\bar{x}_4$ followed by an x_1 transfer gives the completed network. Thus the final network obtained by this iterative partitioning is shown in Figure 5.8.8, and requires only 10 cryotrons as compared with the 14 cryotrons required in Figure 5.8.7.

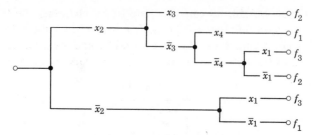

Figure 5.8.8 Simplified multiple output cryotron network obtained by successive partitioning.

Although this partitioning technique is helpful in determining a good choice for ordering the variable at each step, various possibilities may still have to be investigated to insure a best possible realization from a complete tree. The next example illustrates this difficulty. Suppose we desire a complementary output network for

$$
f \begin{cases} \begin{matrix} x_1 & x_2 & x_3 & x_4 \\ x & 0 & 0 & 0 \\ 0 & x & 1 & 0 \\ 1 & 1 & 0 & x \end{matrix} \end{cases}
$$

$$
\bar{f} \begin{cases} \begin{matrix} 0 & 1 & 0 & x \\ x & 0 & x & 1 \\ 1 & x & 1 & x \\ x & x & 1 & 1 \end{matrix} \end{cases}
$$

Each of these covers is a minimum cover, as can be verified by the reader. Changing cube $x\,0\,x\,1$ to $x\,0\,0\,1$, since $x\,0\,1\,1$ is also covered by $x\,x\,1\,1$ of $\bar{f}$, allows us to partition the covers on x_3, giving

	x_3	x_1	x_2	x_4
f	0	x	0	0
f	0	1	1	x
$\bar{f}$	0	0	1	x
$\bar{f}$	0	x	0	1
f	1	0	x	0
$\bar{f}$	1	1	x	x
$\bar{f}$	1	x	x	1

Now for the subtree from $x_3 = 0$ we should partition on x_2. This gives

	x_3	x_2	x_1	x_4
f	0	0	x	0
$\bar{f}$	0	0	x	1
f	0	1	1	x
$\bar{f}$	0	1	0	x
f	1	x	0	0
$\bar{f}$	1	x	1	x
$\bar{f}$	1	x	x	1

Since column x_2 has x's in each entry of the $x_3 = 1$ part, variable x_2 is clearly not required in the subtrees for this part.

At this point in the partitioning it appears that in part $x_3 = 0$, $x_2 = 0$, the next variable should be x_4; in part $x_3 = 0$, $x_2 = 1$, variable x_1 should be next, and in part $x_3 = 1$, $x_2 = x$, it is arbitrary whether x_1 or x_4 is chosen as the next variable since either cube $1\ x$ can be changed to $1\ 0$ or cube $x\ 1$ can be changed to $0\ 1$. Figure 5.8.9 shows both possibilities, where the resulting cubes are shown on the right.

Now using Rule I of simplification it is clear that the network in Figure 5.8.9b is superior to that of Figure 5.8.9a since in (b) the nodes marked A and B can be shorted together, thus eliminating one x_4 transfer. No such simplification is possible for network a. The resulting network, after applying Rule I to nodes A and B of Figure 5.8.9b, is shown in Figure 5.8.10.

In both of these two examples the rearrangement of the order of variables on each subtree, obtained by the partitioning procedure, could be viewed as a simple permutation of the variables in a standard relay tree. Thus each variable may be arranged as one column of the network, giving a particularly straightforward structure to construct by using cryotrons. Often, partitioning iteratively gives a network in which the variables do not align in columns. This corresponds to some folded tree that has been simplified by Rules I and II. If folding is undesirable (note that it may require the input variables wires to cross each other), the partitioning technique may be restricted simply to a permutation of variables on a standard relay tree.

The design of complementary output networks and multiple output networks to realize symmetric functions will not be discussed again for

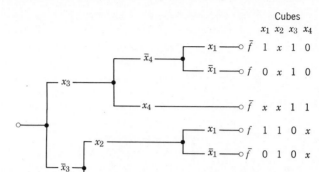

(a) Variable permutation x_3, x_2, x_4, x_1

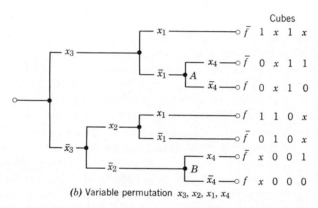

(b) Variable permutation x_3, x_2, x_1, x_4

Figure 5.8.9   Two realizations for a complementary output network.

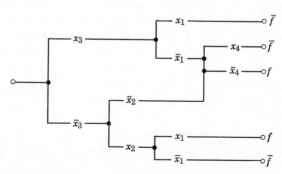

Figure 5.8.10   A simplification of Figure 5.8.9*b*.

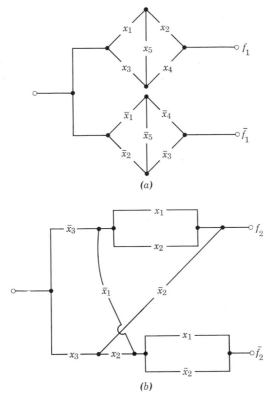

Figure 5.8.11 Two minimum cryotron complementary output networks.

cryogenic networks. From Section 5.4, and the description of how relay trees are applied to cryogenic networks, it is evident that the techniques for designing symmetric networks using cryotrons is similar to those for designing relay contact symmetric networks.

Finally, the structures of the two examples in Figure 5.8.11 illustrate that obtaining complementary output networks having a minimum number of cryotrons (or contacts for relay networks) may indeed be generally very difficult; and neither does the technique using trees or symmetric networks necessarily assure one of obtaining a network having a minimum number of cryotrons. That these networks are actually minimum will not be proved here.

5.9 SUMMARY

As can be seen by looking at the many references on bilateral switching networks, there are a large variety of techniques which treat special types of bilateral network structures. The relay tree and symmetric networks of Sections 5.2 and 5.4 are two of the most important such structures.

The approach of minimum covers and factoring discussed in Chapters 3 and 4 applies both to logical network and bilateral network design. For two-terminal networks, factoring a cover of a cubical complex often provides an acceptable series-parallel network. For multiple output networks where the output conditions are disjoint, the relay tree techniques of section 5.2 are helpful, but these methods are also restricted to networks with only one input terminal. Usually, if the symmetric network techniques can be applied to a problem, this approach gives a better design (being a bridge network) than can be obtained from the other methods. Methods have also been developed for interconnecting either symmetric networks, relay trees, or combinations of these, similar to those done in Figure 5.4.14, to yield non-series-parallel two-terminal or multiterminal networks. Nevertheless, not too much is known about general bridge network design. Boolean matrices are the most general approach to the design of bilateral switching networks, but the node insertion process does not supply a precise algorithm for obtaining good circuit designs. Rather, it depends somewhat on experience and skill to obtain a sequence of node insertions, with judicious use of redundancies, to achieve a reasonable design. All these design techniques, except for finding a minimum cover, are somewhat heuristic and are aimed at attaining a reasonably good network design rather than a design using a minimum number of contacts. Although exhaustive minimization algorithms can be described, it is unlikely that effective and precise minimization algorithms will be developed for bilateral networks, for bridge network structures seem to be inherently rather unmanageable. Usually, many considerations other than the number of contacts play an important role in design, however, and variations of the techniques discussed in this chapter often lead to satisfactory design.

Exercises

1. List all admissible sequences for complete relay trees with $n = 5$ in which no number is greater than 8.
2. Two essentially different complete relay trees for the admissible sequence 1, 4, 5, 5 were given in Figures 5.2.5 and 5.2.6.
    (a) Show that no other essentially different relay trees exist for the admissible sequence 1, 4, 5, 5.
    (b) Does more than one essentially different relay tree exist for the admissible sequence 1, 3, 5, 6?
3. Find a partial relay tree having a minimum number of transfer contacts for

the following output requirements:

$$x_1 \ x_2 \ x_3 \ x_4$$

x_1	x_2	x_3	x_4
0	0	1	0
0	1	0	1
0	1	1	0
0	1	1	1
1	0	0	0
1	1	0	0
1	1	0	1
1	1	1	1

4. From a complete relay tree, design a three output circuit, having as few contacts as possible, for the three functions:

$$\begin{cases} f_1 = x_1 \bar{x}_2 x_3 \vee x_1 x_2 x_3 \vee \bar{x}_1 x_2 x_3 \\ f_2 = x_1 x_2 \bar{x}_3 \vee \bar{x}_1 x_2 \bar{x}_3 \\ f_3 = x_1 \bar{x}_2 \bar{x}_3 \vee \bar{x}_1 \bar{x}_2 x_3 \vee \bar{x}_1 \bar{x}_2 \bar{x}_3 \end{cases}$$

5. Design symmetric networks, having as few contacts as possible, for the following totally symmetric functions:
   (a) $S_{0,2,4}(x_1, \bar{x}_2, x_3, x_4, x_5)$
   (b) $S_{0,1,3}(x_1, x_2, \bar{x}_3)$
   (c) $S_{1,3}(x_1, x_2, x_3)$
   (d) $S_2(x_1, x_2, x_3, x_4)$
6. Obtain relay contact networks having as few contacts as possible for the following functions, the duals of the functions, and the complements of the functions.
   (a) $f = x_1 x_2 \bar{x}_3 \vee x_1 \bar{x}_2 x_3$
   (b) $S_{0,2,3}(\bar{x}_1, x_2, x_3)$
7. Determine which of the following Boolean functions are totally symmetric. If totally symmetric, express in form $S_{a_1, \ldots, a_k}$, giving the variables of symmetry. If not totally symmetric, show why.
   (a) $f_1 = \bar{x}_1 x_2 \vee \bar{x}_1 \bar{x}_3 \vee x_1 x_2 \bar{x}_3$
   (b) f_2 defined by cover for $f_2^{-1}(1)$

$$x_1 \ x_2 \ x_3 \ x_4$$

$$\begin{Bmatrix} x & 1 & 0 & x \\ 1 & 0 & x & 0 \\ 1 & x & 0 & 1 \\ x & 1 & 1 & 0 \end{Bmatrix}$$

(c) f_3 equals 1 for the set of vertices:

$$
\begin{array}{cccccc}
x_1 & x_2 & x_3 & x_4 & x_5 & x_6
\end{array}
$$

$$
\left\{
\begin{bmatrix}
0 & 0 & 1 & 0 & 1 & 0 \\
0 & 1 & 0 & 0 & 1 & 0 \\
0 & 1 & 1 & 1 & 0 & 1 \\
1 & 0 & 1 & 0 & 0 & 0 \\
1 & 0 & 1 & 1 & 1 & 0 \\
1 & 1 & 0 & 0 & 1 & 1 \\
0 & 0 & 0 & 0 & 1 & 1 \\
0 & 0 & 0 & 0 & 0 & 0 \\
0 & 0 & 0 & 1 & 1 & 0 \\
1 & 0 & 0 & 0 & 1 & 0 \\
1 & 0 & 0 & 0 & 0 & 1 \\
1 & 1 & 0 & 0 & 0 & 0 \\
1 & 1 & 0 & 1 & 1 & 0 \\
1 & 1 & 1 & 0 & 1 & 0 \\
1 & 0 & 0 & 1 & 1 & 1 \\
1 & 0 & 0 & 1 & 0 & 0 \\
1 & 0 & 1 & 0 & 1 & 1
\end{bmatrix}
\right\}
$$

(d) f_4 equals 1 for the set of vertices:

$$
\begin{array}{cccc}
x_1 & x_2 & x_3 & x_4
\end{array}
$$

$$
\left\{
\begin{bmatrix}
1 & 0 & 1 & 1 \\
1 & 0 & 0 & 0 \\
1 & 1 & 1 & 0 \\
1 & 1 & 0 & 1 \\
0 & 1 & 0 & 0 \\
0 & 1 & 1 & 1 \\
0 & 0 & 0 & 1 \\
0 & 0 & 1 & 0
\end{bmatrix}
\right\}
$$

8. Prove the following properties of $p \times p$ switching matrices:
   $A = [a_{ij}], B = [b_{ij}], C = [c_{ij}].$
   (a) $A \vee (B \cdot C) = (A \vee B) \cdot (A \vee C)$
   (b) $A \cdot (B \vee C) = (A \cdot B) \vee (A \cdot C)$

(c) $A \subseteq B$ if and only if $A \cdot B = A$

(d) $A \times (B \cdot C) \subseteq (A \times B) \cdot (A \times C)$

9. For $p \times p$ switching matrices A and B prove in general that

(a) $A \times B \neq B \times A$,

(b) $A \times B = C$,

where C is not necessarily a switching matrix.

(c) $A \times A = A^2$ is a switching matrix.

10. Design relay contact networks, using node insertion, having the following terminal characteristics. Attempt to use as few contacts as possible.

(a) $f_{12} = \bar{x}_2\bar{x}_3 \vee \bar{x}_1\bar{x}_3 \vee \bar{x}_1\bar{x}_2x_3x_4 \vee x_1x_3x_4$

(b) $f_{12} = x_1x_4 \vee x_2x_3x_4 \vee x_1\bar{x}_2$

(c) $\begin{cases} f_{12} = x_1 \vee x_2x_3 \vee x_4 \\ f_{13} = \bar{x}_1 \vee x_2\bar{x}_3 \vee x_4 \\ f_{23} = x_4 \vee \bar{x}_1x_2x_3 \vee x_1x_2\bar{x}_3 \end{cases}$

(d) $f_{12} = x_2x_3 \vee \bar{x}_1x_2x_4 \vee x_1x_3x_4$

REFERENCE NOTATIONS

Many relay contact circuit design techniques for various special applications are presented in previous books on switching circuit design. For example, see [11] by Keister, Ritchie, and Washburn, and [5] by Caldwell. Also, the book by Roginskii [21] is entirely devoted to relay switching circuits and includes a bibliography of 137 references, many of them Russian.

Some references on design techniques based on relay trees are [4, 13–17, 20, 22, 25, 26, 29]. In [26] Shannon developed the basic approaches to admissible sequences for relay trees treated in Section 5.2 as well as the techniques for symmetric network design discussed in Section 5.4. Burks et al. in [4] provided a precise derivation of methods for obtaining admissible sequences. The method of Section 5.2 for ordering the variables for partial relay trees closely follows the work by Marcus [16, 17]. Lawler [12] and Levien [13] have recently proposed other techniques for obtaining orderings. The concept of planar networks and dual networks discussed in Section 5.3 is based on analogous graph theory concepts. These and related graph theory concepts can be further studied in Berge [2] and Seshu and Reed [24]. Section 5.5 on the detection of totally symmetric functions follows the work of McCluskey [18].

The Boolean matrix approach discussed in Sections 5.6 and 5.7 follows most closely the work of Hohn and Schissler [7], and Hohn [8]. Many works have appeared on Boolean matrices and related approaches to bridge network design [1, 7–10, 14, 19, 23].

A basic description of cryotron circuits is given by Buck in [3]. Sussenguth [28] discusses a programmed cryotron circuit design procedure which uses the complete tree circuit. Short [27] discusses some similar procedures, giving Rules I and II of Section 5.8, and also gives some bounds on the number of elements required in such circuits. The supernormal form cryotron circuits are described in [6] by Griesmer, Miller, and Roth where methods of using redundancy to eliminate cryotron circuit failures are discussed at some length.

REFERENCES

1. Aranovich, B. I., "The Use of Matrix Methods in Problems of the Structural Analysis of Relay Contact Networks," *Avtematika i Telemekhanika*. Vol. 10, No. 6, pp. 437–451, 1949.

2. Berge, C., *The Theory of Graphs and its Applications,* translated by Alison Doig, John Wiley and Sons, New York, 1958, Chapter 21.
3. Buck, D. A., "The Cryotron—A Superconductive Computer Component," *Proceedings of the IRE,* Vol. 44, No. 4, pp. 482–493, April 1956.
4. Burks, A. W., R. McNaughton, C. H. Pollmar, D. W. Warren, and J. B. Wright, "The Folded Tree," *Journal of the Franklin Institute,* Vol. 260, No. 1, pp. 9–24, and No. 2, pp. 115–126, 1955.
5. Caldwell, S. H., *Switching Circuits and Logical Design,* John Wiley and Sons, New York, 1958.
6. Griesmer, J. H., R. E. Miller, and J. P. Roth, "The Design of Digital Circuits to Eliminate Catastrophic Failures," *Redundancy Techniques for Computing Systems,* Spartan Books, Washington, D.C., pp. 328–348, 1962.
7. Hohn, F. E. and R. L. Schissler, "Boolean Matrices and the Design of Combinational Relay Switching Circuits," *Bell System Technical Journal,* Vol. 34, pp. 177–202, January 1955.
8. Hohn, F. E., "A Matrix Method for the Design of Relay Circuits," *IRE Transactions on Circuit Theory,* Vol. CT-2, pp. 154–161, June 1955.
9. Hohn, F. E., S. Seshu, and D. D. Aufenkamp, "The Theory of Nets," *IRE Transactions on Electronic Computers,* Vol. EC-6, No. 3, pp. 154–161, September 1957.
10. Humphrey, W. S., Jr., *Switching Circuits with Computer Applications,* McGraw-Hill Book Co., New York, 1958, Chapters 7 and 8.
11. Keister, W., A. E. Ritchie, and S. H. Washburn, *The Design of Switching Circuits,* Van Nostrand Co., New York, 1951.
12. Lawler, E. L., "The Minimal Synthesis of Tree Structures," *Proceedings of the IEEE Fourth Annual Symposium on Switching Circuit Theory and Logical Design,* S-156, pp. 63–82, September 1963.
13. Levien, R. E., "Determining the Best Ordering of Variables in Cascade Switching Circuits," *Proceedings of the IEEE Fourth Annual Symposium on Switching Circuit Theory and Logical Design,* S-156, pp. 83–104, September 1963.
14. Lunts, A. G., "The Application of Boolean Matrix Algebra to the Analysis and Synthesis of Relay Contact Networks," *Doklady Akademii Nauk SSSR,* Vol. 70, pp. 421–423, 1950.
15. Lupanov, O. B., "On the Synthesis of Contact Networks," *Doklady Akademii Nauk SSSR,* Vol. 119, No. 1, pp. 23–26, March 1958.
16. Marcus, M. P., "Minimization of the Partially-Developed Transfer Tree, " *IRE Transactions on Electronic Computers,* Vol. EC-6, No. 2, pp. 92–95, 1957.
17. Marcus, M. P., *Switching Circuits for Engineers,* Prentice Hall, Englewood Cliffs, New Jersey, 1962.
18. McCluskey, E. J., Jr., "Detection of Group Invariance or Total Symmetry of a Boolean Function," *B.S.T.J.* Vol. 35, pp. 1445–1453, November 1956.
19. Miller, R. E., "Formal Analysis and Synthesis of Bilateral Switching Networks," *IRE Transactions on Electronic Computers,* Vol. EC-7, No. 3, pp. 231–244, September 1958.
20. Moore, E. F., "Minimal Complete Relay Decoding Networks," *IBM Journal of Research and Development,* Vol. 4, No. 5, pp. 525–531, November, 1960.
21. Roginskii, V. N., *The Synthesis of Relay Switching Circuits* (English translation), Van Nostrand Co., New York, 1963.
22. Scheinman, A. H., "The Numerical-Graphical Method in the Design of Multi-terminal Switching Circuits," *Transactions of the AIEE,* Pt. 1, pp. 515–519, November 1959.

23. Semon, W., "Matrix Theory of Switching Networks," Computation Laboratory, Thesis, Harvard University, Cambridge, Mass., 1954.

24. Seshu, S. and M. B. Reed, *Linear Graphs and Electrical Networks*, Addison-Wesley Publishing Co., Reading, Mass., 1961, Chapter 3.

25. Shannon, C. E., "A Symbolic Analysis of Relay and Switching Circuits," *Transactions of the AIEE*, Vol. 57, pp. 713–723, 1938.

26. Shannon, C. E., "The Synthesis of Two-Terminal Switching Circuits," *B.S.T.J.*, Vol. 28, pp. 59–98, 1949.

27. Short, Robert A., "The Design of Complementary-Output Networks," *IRE Transactions on Electronic Computers*, Vol. EC-11, No. 6, pp. 743–753, December 1962.

28. Sussenguth, E. H., "An Algorithm for Automatic Design of Logical Cryogenic Circuits," *IRE Transactions on Electronic Computers*, Vol. EC-10, No. 4, pp. 623–630, December 1961.

29. Washburn, S. H., "Relay Trees and Symmetric Circuits," *Transactions of the AIEE*, Vol. 63, Pt. 1, pp. 582–586, 1949.

Index